Salt Lake City, or the painstaking research of original source. The system does provide a low cost format for launching your search.

May I suggest that you start your personal search by turning to the section explaining, "How to Use the Reference Directories". As you can see, this is the heart of the book and information about your family should be recorded as soon as possible on the charts provided. If you proceed in a diligent manner, you will accumulate a great deal of valuable knowledge about your family before it becomes lost forever.

## ABOUT THE COVER

In doing research for this publication, I had an opportunity to visit Colonial Williamsburg in Virginia where the art of bookbinding is still being performed as it was in the early days of our nation. A bookbinder of the period not only printed and sewed all the pages together by hand but actually made and designed the cover as well. As a craftsman who was competing with others engaged in the same trade, the artistry and professionalism displayed in the cover design often became a testimonial to his craftsmanship. Accordingly, many of these early tradesman deleted the title of the book from the cover so as not to interfere with his original art work. The gold stamping which appears on the cover of this work is an original design based on art work discovered during our research. I would like to thank Kelly Ann Glinsky, the artist on our staff, as well as the Colonial Williamsburg Library for their efforts in creating this interesting cover.

Good Luck and God Bless.

Sincerely,

*Beatrice Bayley*

Beatrice Bayley

# THE

# BURROUGHS

# FAMILY

# HERITAGE

# BOOK

Published by

*Beatrice Bayley, Inc.*

*Beatrice Bayley, in christening dress, age 4, and her mother, Myrtle (Riker) Bayley in wedding gown. 1912 Brooklyn, New York.*

# INTRODUCTION

Thank you,

For purchasing this Family Heritage Book. I sincerely appreciate your interest in tracing family heritage. There are other persons with your family name who are also searching their family background and our response has been overwhelming. We have had wonderful letters from all types of people, some just say thanks, some are just getting started, some have found lost children and cousins, others have promptly added additional names to the directory, wives have started the heritage work for their husbands, there are those scheduling family reunions, and others sending and receiving birthday cards and correspondence. For example, Mrs. Villines of California writes, "Last month we received our copy of the Villines Heritage Book and have used the Villines Family Directory to contact a number of other Villines Families in our 'hunger' for further information on the family tree. The efforts are bearing fruit and just wanted you to know that your book has been useful to us."

Mrs. Bushnell of Idaho writes: "This brief letter of thanks to you for a good work very well done. Allow me to state you certainly had a very beautiful mother. The enclosed picture of you with her in 1912 is a rarity depicting how our women dressed in the old days. I appreciate your labor of love in behalf of many Bushnell Families."

Mr. Russell C. Coley of North Carolina states: "Just wanted you to know how pleased and how impressed I am with what you have put together. I'm sure that I will spend many hours pleasantly in search of those who are with me now and those who were before me. Thank you much."

I would like to say that I feel good when I hear people have used the book to expand their knowledge. Some letters are touching and heart moving, a friend in Bakersfield, California was reunited with his natural father because of the heritage book. These things are part of making life worth while.

The following is a general explanation of my information development methods. The individual Family Heritage Books are designed to act as a guide to the discovery and documentation of your personal heritage. The book is a general book on genealogy but with specific sections containing a national directory of a particular family, the means and forms for using this directory, plus an explanation of how to search for your ancestors.

I and my staff first analyzed the rarity of various family surnames using a laborious manual search of public telephone directories of major cities plus a report by H.E.W. called "Report of Distribution of Surnames in the Social Security Number File" BDP Pub. #034–75. After three months of manual work, we developed a computerized approach to searching national data banks of family surnames.

At a cost of over $10,000.00, a private report and procedure was developed producing a report of over 7,000 computer written pages. From these months of work we were in a position to scan the national data banks for the names and addresses of families of rare and distinct surnames. The data banks are composed of names and addresses from automotive registrations, telephone listings, and house to house canvassing for cross street directories.

Each time that we research the 70 million national data bank names on file, we spend over $11,000.00 for the file analysis plus a per item charge for the full names and addresses that we select. If a single family surname were selected it would cost that family $11,000.00. Since we invest in many family surnames at a time, we are able to get the cost down to a reasonable figure.

Once we have the research directories boiled down to individual surname directories, we then combine this information with the general chapters on historical background and the explanation sheets. This collection of historical and current information gives you the ability to continue the discovery and documentation of your own personal and family heritage.

It is my opinion that the information we have compiled, as well as the personal data which the recipient records, will make them exceptionally valuable to each and every family.

The need for a directory and book of this type became apparent to me in my own search for family ancestors, and caused the development of the Bayley System. The Bayley System of Genealogical Research is one of many ways to trace and record your current family members and your common family ancestors.

I and others have used this approach to trace current and past family members for a long time but only now, as the formal Bayley System, has it been organized into an economic and effective approach. The System has computerized the genealogical attack and placed at people's finger tips the guides and means to discover and document their personal history.

In the past, persons with relatively distinctive, unusual or rare surnames would check telephone directories in every city that they passed through and comments usually ran, "Oh, I see that there is a Bayley in that directory. I wonder if they are a relative?" Considering that there are thousands of telephone directories for both large and small communities, and many with unlisted numbers, the old approach is of only small value.

Our families own personal use of the Bayley System has traced the Bayley families origin back to John Bayley, Sr. who came over to the New World on the ship, "Angel Gabriel." John Bayley, Sr. was shipwrecked in 1635 off the coast of Maine and settled in New England. The Riker family line was traced back to Abraham Van Rychen who came to New Amsterdam in the early 17th century. The Morse family was traced back to the 1490's. All of the information that was collected was known by some one prior to our search. However, our approach enabled us to bring it together at our house for our knowledge and enjoyment.

It is a pleasure to know that so many people have received this much enjoyment from our book.

Through the use of my System, you will expand your knowledge of the origin and meaning of your name and roots of one side of your family. This system will not replace the hard work that must be done by professionals at the Library of Congress, The Latter-Day Saints Library at

# Contents

*Landing of the Pilgrims at Plymouth, December 11, 1620 (engraving)*

## How To Search For Family Ancestors

This chapter is a basic introduction on how to start and how to organize your attack on collecting and recording family history. It tells you how to tie in your local family knowledge and expand to a national search.

## History of Ethnic Origins and Activities

The motivating forces behind the movements of races, tribes, families, and nationalities of people is one of the keys to tracing the heritage of our forebearers. What our ancestors worked at, their religious beliefs, their means of transportation, and their habits and customs will tell us what sources of information to check and where to check them.

## The Meaning and Origin of Heraldry

The more noble, though sometimes villainous, ancestors have carried family crests and coats of arms through generations. Your direct lineage may carry Nobel Rights.

## The Origin of Names and Their Meaning

Be your name Royal or Common, Rich or Poor, IT HAS MEANING. Searching for the meaning of your name and your ancestors' surnames gives you significant clues to national origin and family activities.

## The Reference Books

All people—all migrations—all nationalities—all religious activities, etc. cannot be represented in this book. This chapter is designed to give you the major sources of reference for various states, nationalities, government records, religious documents, military reports, and family histories.

## The Directories and Family Charts

This is your activity area for the search, organization, and recording of results. This will give you the ability to structure the questions that you ask and then analyze your results. It will record forever the facts that you have collected and will make them available to your descendents and relatives for generations to come.

# 1600 — 1700

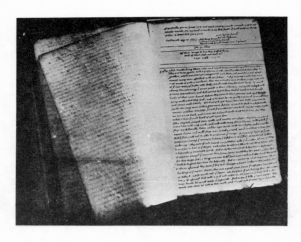

Log of the Mayflower recording events during its first trip to the New World.

Baptism of Virginia Dare, the first child born in the settlements.

Plymouth Rock, Plymouth Mass. This is where the pilgrims landed in December, 1620.

Landing slaves from Dutch man of war at Jamestown, Virginia

Emigrants from Connecticut to Eastern Ohio in 1805. The distance of 600 miles took 90 days for these ten people.

Emigrants descending the Ohio on a flatboat.

Chinese arriving in San Francisco undergo customs inspection, ca. 1877.

# How to Search for Family Ancestors

The interest in tracing family histories has long been a popular pastime. Anyone who has listened to parents or their grandparents reminisce about their great-grandparents arrival from Ireland or their great-grandfather's life in a lumber camp, knows the feeling of interest aroused by such stories. What were these people like, what kind of a life did these people lead, what were the times like? From there it is an easy step to relatives further back-where did they come from and why? One question leads to another until you find yourself hot on the trail of all your ancestors and the times they lived through.

When you begin your search for your family the most important thing to remember is BE SKEPTICAL! Don't believe everything you are told or every fact you find. Always try to have several sources for every fact. If these

*Wedding party, Albany, Minnesota, 1912.*

sources do not agree, make sure you note the source and the fact and hope that a third fact can be found at a later date to confirm one of them. You must keep detailed records of everything you find—and don't find. Sometimes what you don't find can be just as important in your search.

*Irish emigrants are leaving home but have the priest's blessing to speed their journey, ca. 1851.*

The tools you'll need are not expensive— a standard loose-leaf notebook and lots of paper. Write down everything. Also, from our charts in the back of this book, start filling in your family "tree" as you now know it. Include these in your notebook. When you go out tracking down members, take all of this information with you, for you never

*Lewis, Delaware, 1941, Churchyard.*

know when you'll come across a member you weren't after and need your lists.

*Immigrant party of Swedes, ca. 1860.*

Start with yourself on the family chart, then your parents, and then grandparents. Also, don't forget brothers, sisters, aunts, uncles, cousins, and in-laws. When you have gone as far as possible on your own, call one of your relatives and explain what you are

*Jewish refugees from Russia passing the Statue of Liberty, 1892.*

doing and ask for their help. Your grandmother may thoroughly enjoy telling you

about her grandfather from Ireland who lived with her for a few years. Or about the time your mother wore green on Saint Patrick's Day to her grandmothers and was very emphatically told that her grandfather had been an Orangeman. From this story you have learned a very important fact about your mother's family—that they were Protestant Irish.

*Leaving their Scottish homeland for America.*

Ask your relatives for the addresses of other members of the family who might help you out in your search. Take the time to compose a friendly letter to them asking for their memories about their grandparents and details on themselves and their immediate families. Be sure to enclose blank family charts for them to complete. And always enclose a stamped, self-addressed envelope for their use. This is a courtesy that should never be ignored. Remember, you are asking for their help and should show appreciation.

Another source of information is the

family photo album. Ask someone to sit down with you and go through it, telling you about each person in the pictures and writing names and dates for each photograph. You can ask for these pictures, but remember their value to your relative and consider having copies made by a reputable photographer. But watch your costs and have that clearly determined ahead of time.

*German immigrants headed for Salt Lake City, 1880. Meeting at Castle Garden, N.Y. before departure.*

You can also ask for old family documents, such as birth certificates, letters, diaries, family Bibles, death certificates, baptismal papers, marrage licenses, and citizenship papers. Other sources of information are school yearbooks, report cards, baby books, funeral memorial cards, health and hospital cards,

wills, deeds, newspaper clippings, and military records or medals. There is no end of information you can gather from your relatives in the family momentos they have kept through the years. And ask about silver and china passed down through the family or jewelry—our family has the engagement bracelet given to my great-grandmother in the original box, and labeled with the store in Belfast where it was purchased. I doubt if the store has any record of the sale, but it provides valuable proof of that portion of the family's origin. Don't overlook any such heirlooms from samplers to silver.

When you get all the information available from your relatives, then you have to start the hard part of digging into official records. Do you know when your great-grandparents came to this country? Can you check the boats that arrived around that time—are the passenger lists available? Did they come through Ellis Island? Did they become naturalized citizens? Can you get copies of their papers? All of these records are available at

*Arrival of the Mennonites from Russia 1873.*

local, state, or federal government record offices. For naturalization records and passenger lists, start with the National Archives in Washington, D.C. and the Immigration and Naturalization Service, Washington, D.C. 20536.

If you do not have the advantage of knowing a lot about when your family arrived in this country and have to trace it back from

*New England Tombstone, 1678.*

very little information, you can start with your parents' marriage certificate which will provide you with their birth dates and place of residence at the time they were married. From there you can check into census information for that state and country. The census is taken every ten years.

If you do not have the advantage of knowing as much about your family, you can start with census records. These are available in a variety of forms and places depending on when they were taken. From about 1600 through 1789, the colonial governors supervised censuses and they are not regular in time or information collected. In 1790 the first Federal census was begun. It was what one would expect from a first census—the information is not always complete, accurate, or available. There were no standard forms used and the census takers were not well paid, so use the information with great care.

Also, watch the spelling. These people were not careful to get the correct spelling and often spelled phonetically. (Have you ever read any of George Washington's letters? He would surely have flunked spelling today!)

However, the censuses from 1850 onward were more organized in the information required: names, dates, ages, and relationships of all the people at the same address. Use the census information with care and use several censuses. Since they are taken every ten

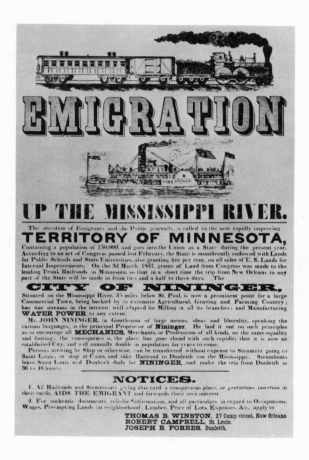

years, there is a possibility that you can verify or correct information from one to the other. And from this information you can start tracking down birth records and death certificates in the locale given on the census record.

A note of warning here. Often the boundaries have changed since the census was taken, especially from the early ones. This is where the local historical societies can be of assistance to you. Every town has one these days and if approached in a polite manner, they will probably be delighted to help you out. You can also check with the local government offices for assistance in the boundaries at specific time. But it is best to call ahead to verify the person you should see and try to determine a convenient time for that person. These county clerks are busy with current work and may not appreciate your turning up out of the blue demanding information.

The county courthouse is a good place to start for deeds if you know or suspect that your relatives owned land in the county, or were married there or had children there. You can check the local churches for baptismal certificates and marriages if their records are available. If a family Bible is available it should give you a clue as to the religion of the

*European migrants crossing the Atlantic to America, ca. 1890. Aboard the S.S. Westernland.*

family. Keep in mind that in the early years many towns had only one church and when people moved, they joined the church availa-

ble to them and so may have changed their religion every time they moved. You might also want to look over the cemeteries where your relatives were buried. You probably have heard of the fascinating epitaphs on the old gravestones which can be amusing as well as informative.

While you are poking through the local courthouse, don't neglect the civil and criminal records. Your great-great-grandfather might have been a smuggler and have a re-

*Norwegians after landing in Quebec await their transfer to trains to the Northwest of Canada, ca. 1900.*

cord. You may not like it, but you can still get information from it. Or you may find that Aunt Agatha was suspected of being a witch during the witch trials in Salem—and maybe she was cleared of the charges or left town.

There are several sources which may be able to help you such as the Daughters of the American Revolution, The Church of Jesus Christ of Latter-Day Saints (Mormons), and The National Genealogical Society in Washington, D.C.

There are some basic things you should always watch for while doing your searching that may lead you astray. The family Bible is

*A group of Italian arrivals ready to be processed at Ellis Island.*

an excellent source, but watch it—is the handwriting the same? When was this Bible published? Before or after the date of the entries? Did someone copy all the information at one time or fill in from memory or was

*Greek Immigrants at Ellis Island.*

the record completed as the events took place (reflected in variations in ink color and handwriting styles). Are you aware that the calendar was changed in 1752? Are you aware that several countries varied in their calendars and that religious calendars are

vastly different from secular calendar systems? Watch yourself with dates when you start going back in time. Check out what calendar was in use at that time in that country.

Are you aware of the styles of handwriting that were popular a hundred years ago? In many cases an "s" looked like an "f". Did you stop to consider that many records have been lost due to fires or floods? Some have been recreated, but not all.

Do not overlook the tax records, voter registration lists, and for later day research, automobile licenses and mortgage records. There are some banks that have decided to make available old records for family researchers.

*Naturalization Day: New citizens take the oath of allegiance. Court of the Eastern District of New York, 1924.*

This brings up another point in regard to the availability of information. Much of the recent records regarding immigration and naturalization are not open to the public from the early 1900's.

So good hunting. It can be a lot of work that will take years to complete and you may have to hire a specialist to help you out on different problems, but you will find it a very rewarding and amusing pastime.

# History of Ethnic Origins and Activities

America—The New World!

Through the ages man has moved—he has always been a restless animal seeking new territories and new opportunities. His reasons and needs are endless. Nature can force people to move with droughts, floods, ice ages, insect invasions (locusts), earthquakes, and volcanic eruptions. Man's own habits can force such movements, with overpopulation, land abuse, greed, oppression, and hate.

A person on the move can be known as either an emigrant or an immigrant. Both words describe a person who is leaving his native country or region to settle in another. The basic difference is that an immigrant is one who is moving to another region for PERMANENT residence.

When this person leaves his native region for a new one, he is often found to have settled into an area where others of his region have also relocated, or what is commonly called today, an ethnic neighborhood. The term ethnic pertains to characteristics common to a group. This can cover a pattern or accent of speech, a religion, a part of the country, cultural patterns, or racial characteristics.

The belief in the inherent superiority of one's own group is called ethnocentrism, and is usually accompanied by a feeling of contempt for the "ethnic" group. Every "ethnic" group in history has been both superior

*The Trail Makers ?*
*Glacier National Park, Montana*

and inferior at one time or another.

The general pattern of immigration has always been from north to the south and

*Golden Anniversary—three generations gather to celebrate.*

from the east to the west. The notable exception was the movement of peoples from Mongolia and China to the new world across the Bering Strait in prehistoric times. But from there, they conformed in their movement southward, with the Eskimos remaining in the north, the American Indians settling our own country, and further movement into the central and southernmost parts of the South American Continent. Even the Aztecs were late-comers in this, moving originally from our southwest into the Valley of Mexico to eventually take over the rule of most of Mexico. Another group who migrated to the east were the islanders of the Pacific Ocean. Although it is still being debated which area they came from, it is generally believed that they came from Southeast Asia and slowly spread over the Philippines, Malaysia, New Guinea, Australia, the Fiji Islands, Easter Island and Hawaii.

On the other side of the world, the same movement was taking place. As early as 3000-2000 B.C. the Hellenes, who spoke an indo-european language, migrated from the north into what is now known as Greece. They followed this up with an invasion of Italy around 2000 B.C. from the north. During approximately the same era, the Aryans entered India through northwestern passages. Further south around 1680-1580 B.C., the Hyksos invaded and ruled Egypt. These people were a nomadic population originally believed to have come from Asia. They also introduced the horse to Egypt.

Moving forward to 1225B.C., during the 19th Dynasty in Egypt, Moses led the Israelites "into the desert". This was followed with the Israelites and Philistines invading Canaan (Palestine).

A thousand years later, Dorians invaded Greece from the north and west. In another thousand years, Egypt is again overrun by foreign peoples.

Europe, Asia, and Africa (Egypt) are constantly shifting and changing; being invaded by new people, new blood lines, languages, and customs. Some of the motives were religion, empire building, new land, or the ever-present pressure of other peoples coming in and forcing the old out. Trying to trace your ancestors back to this time period is almost impossible due to the massive upheavals and lack of census material. Unless you descend from a pharaoh of Egypt, a Greek or Roman senator or general, or possibly Alexander the Great, you won't find records for individuals.

How did Europeans come to the new world? By accident! Although it is still being hotly debated between Italians and Nordic people, it is proven that the Vikings were the first European people to land in the Americas. Not only did they land, but they established colonies in New England, Nova Scotia, and as far west as Minnesota. At approximately 1000 A.D. Leif Ericsson, the Norse, landed and named his first settlement Vinland. Coming from Greenland, the new world was a wealth of timber, furs, and farm lands.

Many years later, Europeans were looking for new trade route to China by sea. In pursuit of this, Columbus landed in the Bahamas on October 12, 1492. He went on to also land at Cuba, and Santo Domingo. On his fourth voyage, he landed on the mainland of South America at Hondorus. Since he was in the service of Queen Isabella and King Ferdinand of Spain, this was all claimed by the Spanish crown and the first colonies were Spanish. Following hopes for a trade route by sea to China and India, they continued to explore and systematically conquered and converted the native Americans under the leadership of Cortez and numerous other conquistadors and priests. Although they never discovered their trade route, they did destroy many cultures and found great wealth—and tobacco and chocolate. The conquest of the new world is a prime example of ethnocentrism in action.

Back in Europe at this time, the "Spanish Inquisition" was in full power. The Moors were driven from Granada, and the Jews of Spain were evicted from the country. Keep in mind that the inquisition was in action over the entire continent and all people lived in fear of it, not only the Jewish people. In England, the country was turmoil and the War of the Roses and Brittany is joining with the French crown; Venice, Milan, Ferdinand of Aragon, Pope Alexander VI, and Emperor Maximilian have formed a coalition in protection against French invasion. Maximilian, Emperor of Germany, also expands into the Netherlands with his marriage, and the marriage of his son into Spanish royalty, brings a major portion of Europe under his rule.

*Alaskan, Mr. Ethlota, and his family, ca. 1904.*

Of major importance at this time is the Treaty of Tordesillas (1494) between Spain and Portugal which gave to Portugal all lands east of a line of demarcation 370 leagues west of the Azores while Spain retained all lands west of this line. The result of this was the possession of Brazil by Portugal.

During this same time that the Spanish and Portuguese were exploring in the southern areas, the English were looking in the

*Cotton Picking in Alabama, 19th Century.*

northern hemisphere. John Cabot, another Italian navigator, was in the service of England and was exploring the north coast of America from Labrador to possibly as far south as Delaware (1497-1498).

*Two young Polish peasant women ready to leave Ellis Island, ca. 1910.*

Moving ahead, we find that in 1501 and 1502, Amerigo Vespucci, an Italian in the service of Portugal, is exploring the eastern coast of South America. Eleven years later, Vasco Nunez de Balboa discovers the Pacific Ocean and Juan Ponce de Leon discovers Florida. All during this time Europe is in a state of constant warfare, alliance, and reorganization. England is also involved with the European wars as well as the English reformation, and internal strife with Scotland. Henry VIII is on the throne and forms the Royal Navy, and fathers both Mary I and Elizabeth I, and founds the Church of England, breaking with the Catholic Pope.

During the following years, we see the rise of Martin Luther (1520) and the Lutheran branch of religion, the rise of the Ottoman Empire (Turkish) and their conquest of Belgrade and Rhodes with continued campaigns against Hungry and Gustavus I, of Sweden, breaks with the pope and secularizes church estates, discontinues payments to the pope, makes bishops dependent on the king, and has the New Testament translated into Swedish. Martin Luther has been also translating the Bible into German, under the protection of Frederick of Saxony. We also find the beginning of the Protestant branch of religion in Germany with an anti-Lutheran resolution passed in 1529.

As you can see, Europe is in a time of great turmoil with divisions in religion, constant wars, and exploration in the new world. The need for money to finance all this was tremendous, and is reflected with the shipments of gold and trade goods from the new world home to the mother country. Francisco Pizarro extracts large amounts of gold and goods from the Incas in Peru and brings it under Spanish rule, executing the native ruler.

Ivan the Terrible is now added to the turmoil in his attempt to gain seaports for Russia. He is at war with Poland, the Tartars from the Crimea, and with Sweden. Peace is not seen until a treaty is signed in 1582 by Russia, Sweden, and Poland. And just to keep everyone on their toes, John Calvin heads a theocratic state at Geneva from 1541

through 1564. In England, "Bloody Mary" comes to the throne and restores Catholicism, and the persecution of the Protestants. However, with the reign of Elizabeth I Catholicism is revoked and the Anglican Church is restored. Sir Francis Drake is searching for new territory in the West Indies. The Thirty Years War is under way in Europe and is basically a war between Catholics and Protestants. Peace is not restored until 1629. In France, the Wars of Religion are in progress involving the persecution of the Huguenots and Catholics. This is finally settled in 1589 with the granting to the Protestants the same civil and political rights as the Catholics exercise. Tracing your ancestors through Europe at this time means knowing their religion and watching your boundaries, depending on which country or alliance was currently in power.

Who came to the new country to settle? Why did they come? They came to make their fortune, serve their ruler, escape persecution because of their religion.

The estimated population in the colonies in 1630 is 4,646 including 60 negro, from Virginia and New York. The population was located in Maine, New Hampshire, Plymouth, Massachusetts, New York and Virginia.

By 1680 the population had increased to 151,507 including 6,971 negroes. Keep in mind that Maine was included as part of Massachusetts from 1660 through 1760. There are no figures included for Vermont until 1770, so the population figures are included elsewhere. Pennsylvania is first included in the estimated population at 680 residents in 1680 and South Carolina in 1670 with a count of 200.

Georgia does not show up in the estimates until 1740 with an estimated population of

# Some Went West

The Drake Well, E. L. Drake to the right and Peter Wilson on the left, 1866, ca. Oil City, Pennsylvania.

Construction crew with woodburning balloon stack locomotive at a crossing of the Green River, west slope of the Cascades, 1885.

"We have it rich". Washing and mining gold, 1889.

Buffalo hunter moving in for the kill, ca. 1822–1888.

Cowboys around the chuckwagon, ca. 1890.

# Some Stayed East

1891, New York, Lower East Side. Interior of a pantmaker's workshop, a "sweat shop" at Ludlow Street. Kneepants were paid at .45 a dozen. Total income of the workman's family, all of whose members work from morning to night, $8 a week. A family of six and two boarders. How do they make it? Bread .15 a day, milk 2 quarters a day at .04 a quart, and one pound of meat for dinner .12.

Child labor in the Textile industry. Young doffer and spinner boys in Seaconnet Mill, Fall River, Mass. January, 1912.

Whaling: The whale fishery attacking a sperm whale and "cutting in".

Old time factory with overhead transmission belts. Waltham Watch Company, ca. 1900.

Factory for silk hats. All the work was done manually by women, ca. 1909.

2,021 and Kentucky and Tennessee are first entered in 1770 with 15,700 and 1,000 respectively. By 1770 the total estimated population is 2,148,076 with 459,822 negroes, with the highest concentrations in Virginia (187,605), South Carolina (75,178), North Carolina (69,600), Maryland (63,818), and New York (19,112). The remainder of the colonies show a few hundred to a few thousand.

With the population close to three million and the colonies now the United States of America, where had all these people come from? The distribution by nationality in 1790 is as follows: English-60.9%, Scotch-8.3%, Irish-Ulster-6.0%, Irish-Free State-3.7%, German-8.7%, Dutch-3.4%, French-1.7%, Swedish-0.7% and miscellaneous 6.6%.

Jumping forward to 1820, statistics show a total of 8,385 immigrants to the United

Baltic States, 30 from Italy, 1 from the countries of Bulgaria, Rumania and Turkey, and 174 from Southern Europe-Spain, Portugal, and Greece.

Italian immigration first peaked in 1882 with 32,159 persons coming to the U.S. The records show that immigration picked up in 1900 with 100,135 to 222,260 in 1921. Other years show a steady but less numerous flow of arrival.

Polish immigrants arrived in greatest numbers from 1921 (95,089) through 1924 (28,-806). The U.S.S.R. and Baltic populations showed steady movement from 1884 through 1924 to the U.S., with the greatest numbers arriving from 1902 (107,347) to 1914 (255,-660).

The German people show a steady high rate of immigration from 1846 (57,561) through 1914 (35,734). However, the great-

*Busy days on the Mississippi Landing at Nashville, Tennessee. Large stores of wire, wood, and other products laid for shipment, late 1870's.*

States with approximately 2,410 from Great Britain, 3,614 from Ireland, 23 from Scandinavia (Norway, Sweden, Denmark, and Ireland), 452 from Netherlands, Belgium, Luxembourg, Switzerland and France, and 968 from Germany-Austria. In addition, there were 5 from Poland, 14 from U.S.S.R. and

est numbers came in 1852–1854 (150,000–200,000), 1866 to 1873 (115,000–149,000), 1881–1892 (210,485–119,168). There are only 32 years, between 1820 and 1957, in which German immigration fell below a five digit figure.

The Scandinavian populations—Norway,

Sweden, Denmark, and Ireland—did their greatest movement between the years of 1880 and 1914 with another rise in 1921 through 1924. During the first immigration, the count did not fall below 19,000 and reached a height of 105,326 in 1882.

The great day of the Irish immigrant was 1847 through 1854 averaging 150,000 per year. Up until 1930 the Irish have moved to the U.S. in steady numbers, not falling below five digits.

Of course, the English (Great Britain) have always regarded the U.S. as part of their country, and the immigration records indicate a constant flow of citizens to the new country. The only three years that the numbers dropped sharply were 1933 (979) and 1942 (907), and 1943(974)—the war years when all immigration dropped off from all countries.

But what of the rest of the world? We all know that the Irish built the railroad going west and the Japanese and Chinese built it going east from the Pacific. When did they arrive? And what about people from Turkey, Africa, Australia, and Mexico? Everyone knows of the European movement, but the rush to the "New World" came from all over the world. Did you realize that in the year of 1881 there were approximately 127,577 Asians and Turks admitted to this country? Thirty-three Africans? 1,802 from Canada and Mexico? 1,188 from Australia and New Zealand?

In 1882 there were 39,579 Chinese admitted while only 5 Japanese came? The records show that Chinese immigration was fairly steady at two to six thousand arrivals per year with a drastic drop in the 1930's and early fourties and again in the early 1950's.

The only period that the Japanese really came in numbers were the years from 1899 through 1924, with another rise in the 1950's.

The Turkish immigration records were not kept until 1869, but do not reflect any massive movements. The greatest numbers—and these are low compared to other nationalities —were between 1910 (15,212) and 1914 (21,716). The years between 1895 and 1924 show four to six thousand averages each year with the peak of 1910–1914, while other years show only a few hundred, if that. In 1950 only 13 immigrated.

With so much focus on the African heritage of our country today, what do the figures show? Basically only a few hundred a year have come to this country. In 1900 approximately 30 Africans were admitted while 1907 (1,486) through 1914 (1,539) there was a larger movement. Again in 1921, 1,301 came and then very low numbers until 1946 it has risen back into the four figure counts again. But keep in mind that an approximate total of 575,420 African people had been resident in the U.S. by 1780, with the first 60 arriving in 1630. Although they were slaves until the civil war, they can be proud of the role they played in developing a new world.

And what of our southern neighbors— Mexico? They settled much of the southwest and California. Mexicans have always come across the border in high numbers to find work and land of their own. Although records are not consistantly available, they show that from 1909 onward, Mexicans have been immigrating at the rate of 16 to 60 thousand per year. There was a drop 1931–1952 but it has risen again to the 30 and 40 thousand per year figure in 1953–1957.

Everyone of these people can be considered a member of an ethnic group and each had to gain acceptance in a new country. Each has undergone the changes and adjustments to their new culture. And each has made its' contribution to the building of a great country. America was built by people who had the courage to leave their familiar surroundings and start over in a new world where they often could not even speak the language. When you trace your great-grandfather down to find he was an immigrant who started in this country by working in the mines or lumber camps while he saved his money and learned the language, be proud of his courage. Or if he worked on the Union-Pacific railroad, remember the Indians he fought and the bitter-harsh weather he endured to cross our continent with rails.

# Moving In

*Oklahoma land rush on September 16, 1893.*

*Three related Oklahoma drought-refugee families in Lordsville, near New Mexico, May 3, 1937.*

# Moving Out

# The Meaning and Origin of Heraldry

*Medieval Crusader*

Throughout history, man has adopted symbols and objects of luck to represent him. This has changed and adapted with the specific times and necessities. It is believed that the Achievement of Arms came as a result of necessity created by man's nature to conquer.

As civilization developed better weapons with which to do battle, he also had to develop better protection for himself. This resulted in wearing padded suits, chain mail, and finally solid armour and helmets. It finally ended up with the fighters body and face being completely covered, so that by the 13th century, with the development of armour, men had to have a means of identification on the battlefield.

The Crusades of the 12th and 13th centuries made this imperative with the soldiers of the entire "civilized" world at war and mingling on the same battlefield.

Although symbols and devices were used commonly at this time, organization was not begun until around 1417 when Henvy V sent a writ to the sheriffs of several counties of England stating penalties were to be imposed on any persons coming on the expedition to France that year who wore arms to which they were not entitled, except those who had worn them at the Battle of Agincourt.

At this time, many assumed the Achievement of Arms without the right to them and there was no organization or system. So in 1483-4, Richard the III granted a Charter of Incorporation to the Officers of Arms —better known as the College of Arms. The Heralds have jurisdiction over any disputes and rights in the Achievement of Arms. The Heralds determined what arms were being borne and who was entitled to them. Their records contain thousands of "pedigrees" and are a good source for genealogists, as well as a record of Arms. Since that time, Arms are granted by the Crown on the authority of the College of Heralds. Today it is considered unethical and in some countries illegal to appropriate an existing Achievement of Arms. To use an existing "Coat of Arms" you must be able to prove descent from the family by the laws of inheritance, generally through the male line of descent.

*Shakespeare*

However, in Ireland, all people with the same last name are entitled to use the same "Coat of Arms".

Before going any further into this; let's clarify our terms. A "Coat of Arms" is actually only a surcoat worn over the armour with the Arms embroidered on it.

The "Achievement of Arms" includes the shield of arms and all of the accessories that go with it. Hereafter, let's refer to the "Arms" for brevity and clarification. This is a very complicated and detailed system—especially when it began as identification on the field of battle! I will review each part:

*The coat of arms of the Trevelyan family. Shield, Helmet Crest*

An Achievement of Arms consists of the following:

    Crest
    Wreath
    Mantle
    Helmet
    Shield
    Motto

**Blazon** — this is a verbal description of Arms. The terms are basically old Norman and French but pronounced in English. Of course, you will recognize your high school latin coming through.

**Shield** — this is the most important component—without it there is nothing else. It is also known as the escutcheon. The shield consists of two basic parts, the field—the surface or background, and the charges—patterns and/or symbols drawn on the field. There is much more detail on this to come.

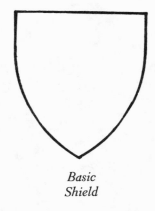

*Basic Shield*

**Helmet** — or helm, was the portion of armour which protected the head and eventually covered the face. The depiction of the helmet on the shield indicated the rank of the bearer of Arms: sovereign, peer, knight, or gentleman.

**Mantle** — also called lambrequin, was a piece of fabric attached to the helmet to protect the wearer from the heat of the sun. There are basically two styles, a whole mantle or a "much divided" or seaweed mantle which supposedly indicated struggle and hand-to-hand combat. This covers the essentials of the normal achievement.

**Crest** — this is the figure of symbol attached to the top of the helmet to aid in identifica-

tion. It is generally taken from the shield and was made of light-weight wood or leather. It always accompanies Arms—never is a crest used by itself.

**Wreath** — or torse, was a twisted cloth or silk placed at the base of the crest to conceal the joint of the crest to the helmet. It came to be a standard of six twists alternating the color and metal of the shield.

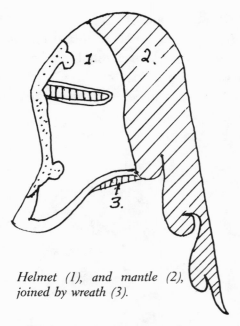

*Helmet (1), and mantle (2), joined by wreath (3).*

**Motto** — this is a saying, war cry, hope, etc. shown on a "ribbon" below the shield or, as is usual in Scottish heraldry, shown above the shield. It is not an essential part of the Achievement.

**Insignia of Office** — such as a baton or wand which denotes a high office is displayed from behind the shield, coming to view outside of the actual shield boundary.

**Insignia of an Order of Knighthood** — any grade of an order of knighthood was entitled to display an insignia with his amoral achievement. It could take the form of a circlet of some description around the outer edge of the shield or could merely be a badge suspended below it.

**Coronet** — this denotes a peer of the realm. The coronet rests above the shield and supports the helmet.

**Robe of Estate** — this also denotes a peer and was used as a background to the Arms. It is scarlet with taffeta lining. The degree of rank is shown by "guards" or bands of fur.

**Pavilion** — not to be confused with the above, this is a tent-like background peculiar to continental heraldry.

**Compartment** — this is the base for the supporters, usually in the form of ground or possibly the "ribbon" motto. It is believed to have originated in Scotland and possibly represented the territories or lands held by the owner of Arms.

**Marshalling** — the combining of two shields of Arms inherited by one man. The modern

*Shield, Helmet Crest*

*The Royal Arms*

*Note the use of motto, supporters, compartment and crest.*

**Supporters** — these are exactly what they sound like—usually in the form of people or beasts at the base of the shield supporting it. These are shown by peers, government units, and corporate bodies. They were originally called bearers in Scotland.

usage can denote sovereignty and dominion, alliance, descent, or mere pretension.

Now that you understand the basic components of the Achievement of Arms to their fullest, let's return to the shield. This is the

# COLOURS

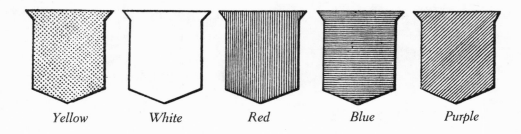

Yellow    White    Red    Blue    Purple

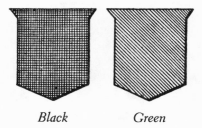

Black    Green

The tinctures are the "metals", "colors", and "furs" used on the field. These are used to create the design or insignia on the shield. There are two metals: gold (or) depicted in yellow, and silver (argent) which is shown as white. There are five colors: red (gules), blue (azure), green (vert), purple (purpure), and black (sable). And finally there are two furs: an ermine pattern in black and white (and occasional gold and black) and a vair pattern which is an alternate blue and white (or occasional silver and blue). The vair was a kind of squirrel that was a blue/gray color on top with a white underside. This fur was very popular as a lining of cloaks.

most important item and contains a great deal of detail and information. As you may know, the shapes of shields has varied through the years, much as fashion varies today, and this is not important in reading the meaning of the shield although it may assist in dating it.

The field or actual shield surface is divided into four basic sections. For this pretend you are holding the shield up in front of yourself as if for protection—dexter or right side, sinister or left, chief or top, and base or bottom. There is also the fess point or center. These are known as the points of the shield.

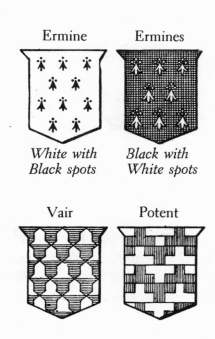

Ermine    Ermines

White with Black spots    Black with White spots

Vair    Potent

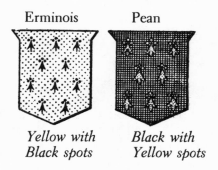

Erminois    Pean

Yellow with Black spots    Black with Yellow spots

**FUR**

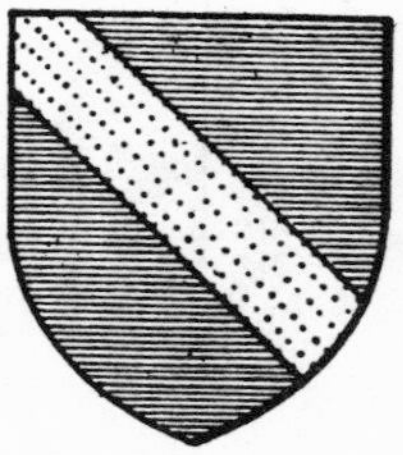

*Bend*

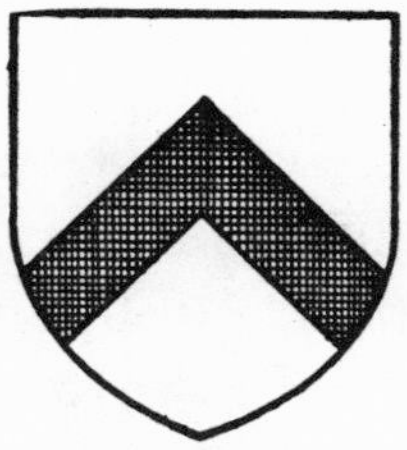

*Chevron*

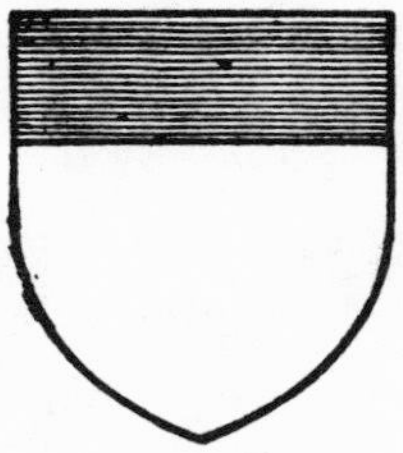

*Chief*

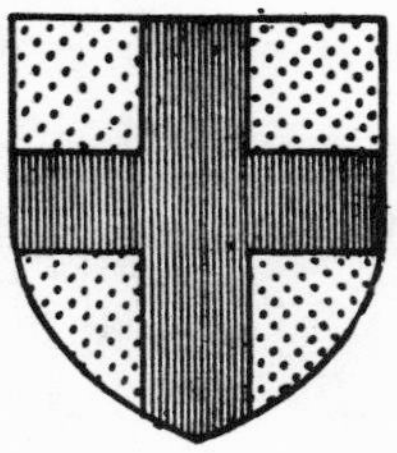

*Cross*

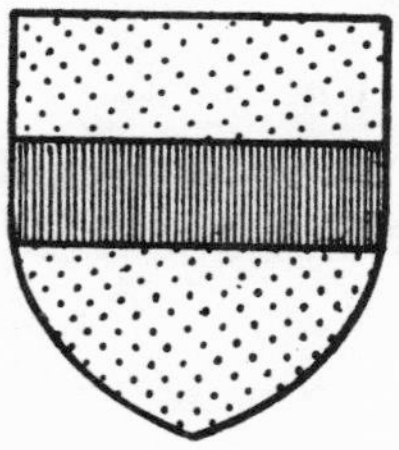

*Fess*

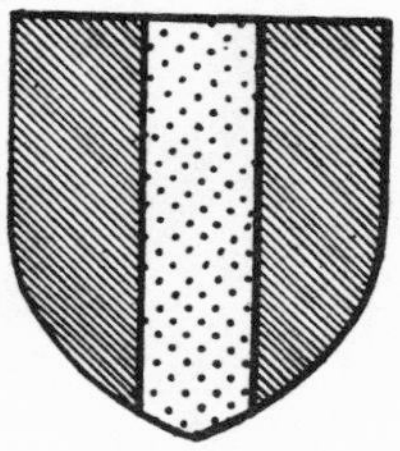

*Pale*

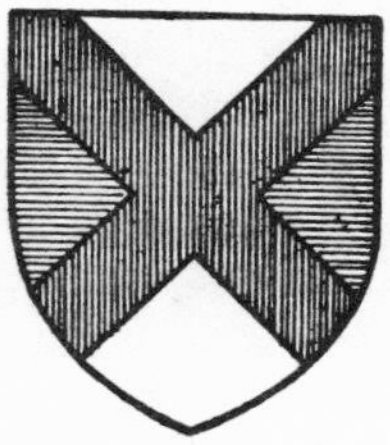

*Saltire*

There are two additional colors rarely used and said to be marks of disgrace due to "abatement of honor": reddish purple (murray or sanguine) and orange-tawny (tenne).

As contrast and definition of design was important on the field of battle, a standing rule is that metal is always displayed on color and color always on metal. For example, blue on gold, not blue on green, as it would lose the sharpness of the design. There are, of course, exceptions to this rule, but very few.

Now, there are also charges on the field. These are the designs such as animals, flowers, crosses, anything animate or inanimate, the most popular being the lion, the rose, and the lilly.

Then there are the ordinaries: the honorable ordinaries and the sub-ordinaries. These are geometrical figures used as charges on the field. There are seven honorable ordinaries: the bend, the chevron, the chief, the cross, the fess, the pale, and the saltire. There are fourteen sub-ordinaries: the annulet, the billet, the bordure, the canton, the flaunch, the fret, the gyron, the inescutcheon, the label, the lozenge, the orle, the pile, the roundel, and the tressure.

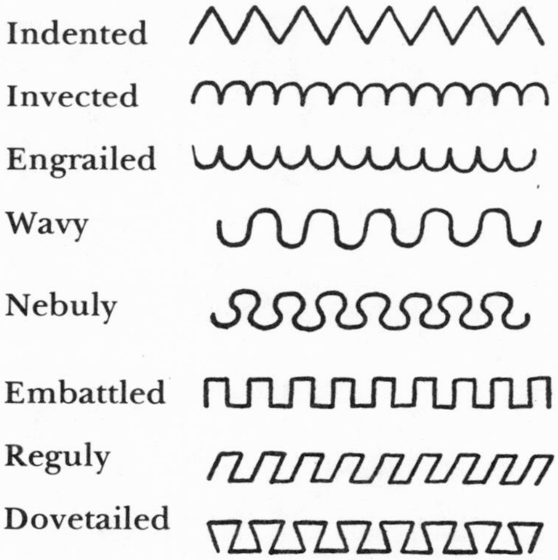
Indented
Invected
Engrailed
Wavy
Nebuly
Embattled
Reguly
Dovetailed

*Partition Lines*

The partition lines are used to partition the field and to border the honorable ordinaries and sub-ordinaries. There are eight basic styles: Indented, Invected, Engrailed, Wavy,

Nebuly, Embattled, Reguly, Dovetailed.

The ordinaries and partitions were originally additional pieces that were added onto the shield to strengthen it. These would be painted to enhance the decoration on the field and eventually became a traditional component of the shield and of charges.

As you can realize, heraldry is a complicated and detailed system. Should you decide to create your own shield review the information I've provided and go slowly. However, if you have an Achievement of Arms in your family, the best advice I can give you is to send a good copy of it to The College of Arms, Queen Victoria Street, London, E.C.4, England. What I have described to you is the English system with some Scottish and Irish variations. The French were as detailed and systematic as the English. Germany also has its heraldry, and most European countries have their heraldic organizations to lesser or greater degrees.

If you've always wondered about a "Coat of Arms", now you have the information to track yours down or to create your own.

# Origin of Names

The record of humankind indicates a desire to make order from chaos. The desire to arrange things into a meaningful order was, is, and will be. It is now known that infants are constantly filtering and ordering stimuli from the home. Shapes, odors, touches all bring to the child a sense of place and meaning, comfort or discomfort, happiness or unhappiness. Soon sounds and combinations of sounds permit the babe to identify, that is, to name persons, places, and things. This common, wonderous phenomenon of speech so deeply imbedded in our genetic being may be the origin of what we call genealogy. There are only three ways to arrange knowledge, things, people-anything. The arrangement can be by category-a taxonomy of things. The science of biology uses this arrangement and it is known to all who suffered through the subject in the **tenth grade.**

The second arrangement is by place. This method is most commonly found in geography, another subject that gave many indigestion of mind. The third and final configuration available to us is to arrange people, places, things and events by time. Those who died by inches in Miss Jones' American History class will remember this-fondly one would hope.

In a way genealogy is a combination of all of the foregoing, but with one crucial difference. Genealogy is about you. It is about what you are called now, what you were called then, where you acquired your name, to where you and yours will carry it.

To pursue knowledge of our past is a wholly human and noble gesture. *Homo Sapien*—know man is what we all are. To aid in this quest you will need a map, a guidebook to direct your efforts. The journey to a knowledge of ourselves can have convenient roadsigns to aid, but to the unwary a misread roadsign will lead to the wrong destination. So, let us chart our course and take the first tentative steps to realize the splendid sentiments of Alexander Pope when he reminded us:

Know then thyself,
Presume not God to scan;
The proper study of mankind is man.

People, places, and things were always called something. Surprising as it may be, places and things had *names* before people. Thus Rome was Rome and could be identified before, indeed, long before Enrique Caruso could be known as the greatest star of the operatic galaxy. For if one looked at the origin and meaning of the name Caruso one would find that it meant a person with what we call a crew cut for hair, a laborer in the sulphur pits. Certainly the stage of the Metropolitan Opera is a long way from the sulphur pits of Rome; and a glance at Caruso's coiffure would deny his affection for a close cropped head. Still the meaning and derivation of the name is unchallengable. We refer to a man as another Caruso, we mean a great or potentially great singer. When Caesar referred to Caruso, yes, he was referring to his sulphur pit workers.

The point is simply that current usages of some names can be and often are completely misleading as to original meaning or intent.

If places had names before people, so too did things. Temples, Cathedral, pyramids, chariots, clerical garments the stuff of history all had names before people.

Economic and political reasons conspired to the origin of names for common people just as they did for the nobility. If the internal revenue service knows you better by your social security number than by your surname, middle and first name, you know the reason why. They have to be able to distinguish the John Smith who makes fifty thousand dollars a year from the John Smith who makes five thousand dollars.

So too, the lords of old. They had to tell one Robert from another; one Tom from another. It became a common practice for economic reasons after the Crusades for the clerks of the lords to attach bynames for descriptive reasons to the vassals of the Lords. This was done often by simply adding a preposition to a location where the vassals lived. Thus a Robert would for reasons of tax and identification become a Robert Underwood. This would distinguish him from Robert Attehill (at the hill).

Other procedures involved ridicule on descriptive words. These were applied to nobility and commoners alike. Charles the Fat, and Louis the Bald, kings of yore, are examples of unspared nobility. Nicknames, descriptive names are the forerunners of surnames but were not surnames in the hereditary sense as we know them.

John Tallman could become John Small if for some reason the son were considerably shorter than father. Such a situation is hardly a genealogists delight. For it says that at some point all of us regardless of the quality of the search will reach a point where we can go no father back to our origins. But our search can take us to a place and time in our origin.

The first group of Europeans to adopt hereditary surnames were the Venetions. This happened during the eleventh century; in France surnames were taken in the thirteenth century; England the fourteenth; Germany the fifteenth, and in recent times the practice found expression in the Scandinavian countries and in the more remote regions of countries already cited.

Again, a principal reason for taking a name was economic. Landed gentry wished to insure the continuity of the estate, the inheritance. The name of the land went to son; the son acquired not only the land but also a last name.

Moving to the lower classes, the guild system, a forerunner of the trade union system led to the gradual development and acceptance of last names by occupation. The guilds were tightly controlled and sons often, indeed usually followed the father's craft. The acquisition of the craft as well as the indentity gave pride, control and a form of economic insurance to the bearer. However, if a family had many sons, it was possible that not all sons could follow in the father's craft.

When a son left the home, pursued another occupation but retained the last name of the father, that is the *inheritance* of a name. The boy may be a butcher, a baker or a candlestick maker, but if he kept the name,

Smith, that is where genealogy begins. Probably all Smiths' of the world are descendants of the mighty village Smith at some time in antiquity. But in reality most are descendants of one son or another who took the father's occupation name, never practiced Smithing, and passed the name on to heirs regardless of occupation.

This phenonenon is not restricted to the Angle Saxons alone. Helmut Schmidt is the Chancellor of West Germany. His heirs will be known as Schmidts, while his forebearers were the moulders of iron.

Gabriel Faur was one of France's greatest composers of symphonic music; Jacques Lefebure, one of her greatest historians. Alas, they are Smith's, too.

The same is true for Slavic: *Kovac;* The Danish *Smed;* the Italian *Ferraro;* the Russian *Kuznetzov*, the Polish *Kowal.* Smith's all.

If your last name begins with an occupation of some sort, you know that some where at some time some one did that. But in all liklihood your search will find grandfathers and great and great great grandfathers who engaged in a range of pursuits to boggle the imagination.

Many common names were derived from the variety of animals in the world and characteristics human's attributed to them. Thus, "cunning as a fox;" "brave as a lion" and so forth.

"Good morning, Mr. Fox."
"Hello Mr. Lion."

One would wish to offer unequivocally to all the Lions, (Lyons), *Fox's, Owls, Wolf's, Bulls* of the world that, yes, your forebearers did possess these characteristics. They were brave, cunning, quick shrewd, tenacious.

They may have been, but your name is no guarantee.

Names were derived from and given to people according to animal like characteristics. But the majority of names of that variety come from signs, signs that identified landmarts, inns, and ecclesiastical buildings.

Thus, Mr. Lion could have been very brave and named for the "golden warrior" of the African Plain. One would like to think so. Or he could have been a farmer who ploughed at the sign of the Lion. This sign would be placed in front of an Inn as an identifying landmark in days before the ready availability of Exxon road maps.

Mr. Cross may have been a pious Christian. Then again he may have been a mighty sinner who resided near "the sign of the cross." We do not know. Nor do you; but the chase and quest may tell.

The fame of Major Major Major in *Catch 22* offers another insight into a possible origin of your name. A title, a first name, and a last name all the same. Confusing, perhaps, but a true source of the origin of a name, regardless of characteristics, place of residence, or occupation.

The fathers first name is George. The son's name is George's George. The son keeps his George and names his son Henry. Thus the common name and occurrance of two first names for a first name and last name. The Germans often followed this tradition; most people, however, merely added the suffix "son" to the first name. This explains the large numbers of names ending in "son"—Johnson, Peterson, Robertson, Jackson and so on. Our European brothers were no different. The Scandinavian—sen; the Polish—wicz, the Spanish—ez all mean son, son of.

The Irish *Mac*, Norman *Fitz* and Welsh

*Ap* are prefixes denoting "son of." MacMillan is the Irish for son of Millan' Fitzhugh, son of Hugh. Finally there are the pet names and the diminutives of first names as a source of subsequent surnames. The son of Richard would be called Dick. His son would be called Dickson. So it is also with Thomas and Thomson or Tomson, Clement and Clemson.

Extraction, nationality and variations all will have an effect on the spelling, meaning and origin of a name. Boundry lines of Europe changed considerably since the death of Charlemagne in 843. Wars moved armies, soldiers co-mingled with the inhabitants of the lands to which they moved. Some stayed, some moved because of social, or economic upheaval. Some were slaves carried to the United States. Others emigrated and had emmigration officials alter, barbarize or simply give a name to the emigre. Your name will give you a clue to your origins, but be wary of false clues. You may assume certain things about yourself as a result of your name, but only a thorough search will confirm or deny the accuracy of your assumptions.

Can a name be an asset or a liability? There is much discussion on the subject, but very little evidence one way or another.

Two Johnson's were Presidents of the United States. The name is common enough. Millions of other Johnsons were never considered or considered themselves as candidates for the presidency of the United States.

Perhaps a classic example of a name that by meaning is unflattering, but did not seem to affect the fortunes of some of its bearers would serve as a case in point.

Kennedy is derivative from two sources. It means one with a grotesque skull or helmut headed. There is no agreement as to whether or not helmut headed meant descendant of a warrior or was simply a way of ridicule to describe those with abnormal heads. (skulls).

Certainly if John F. Kennedy were publicized as John Misshapen Head when he was running for the presidency, his name would have been a liability. But he was known simply as John F. Kennedy. Genealogy can and will give proof to the American dream of equality of opportunity and ambition. Regardless of the positive or negative aspects of your surname, the things that matter are the things you do yourself.

You may find rouges and angels, saints and sinners during the search. The one thing you won't find is dullness. Oops, apologies to all the Dillings and Dillingers. Your name may say you are descendant from dull ones, but we all know better.

# Noble Families (a few)

Every continent or populated island contains tribal or national leaders. We have represented here some of the more relevant aristocratic families. The following family names are associated to the ruling class by birth or marriage. Many Noble family names are represented in more than one country. These represent marriages between families or the conquering of one country by another.

# England

Athelstan, Augustus, Beauchamp, Beau fort, Beaufort, Berengar, Boleyn, Bolingbroke, Brandon, Canute, Cavendish, Clifford, de Bohun, de Boulogne, de Burgh, de Coucy, de Holand, de Montfort, de Normandy, Dowding, Dudley, Egbert, Ethelbald, Ethelbert, Ethelred, Ethelwolf, Ferrers, Gray, Grey, Hardi canute, Hepburn, Howard, Hyde, Ironside, Jones, Lyon, Marshal, Mortimer, Neville, Ogilvy, Parr, Plantagenet, Pole, Scott, Seymour, Seymoure, Stanley, Stein, Stewart, Stuart, Sweyn, Swynford, Tudor, Visconti, Waldegrave, William, Woodville, Worsley.

## France

Amadeus, Bonaparte, Bourbon, Capet, Carolingian, Charlemagne, Conde, d'Angouleme, de Joinville, de La Roche, de Lorraine, de Medicis, de Montpensier, de Poitiers, d'Estouteville, de Vallabriga, de Vendome, Gaston, Godoy, Habsburg, Leszczynska, Martel, Merovingian, Pascual, Penthievre, Philibert, Rubertian, Valois, Visconti, Xavier.

## Germany

Adamowic, Ascanian, Bathory, Billung, Brunonian, Carolingian, Charlemagne, Chotek, de Ligne, de Medici, d'Este, Habsburg, Hesse, Hohenberg, Hohenstaufen, Hohenzollenn, Kaltenbrunner, Laufenburg, Leopoldina, Lorraine, Ludovica, Luidolfings, Luitpold, Martel, Merovingian, Orth, Petznek, Salian, Salvator, Saxon, Schillingsfurst, Sforza, Swabian, Syringus, Tomanek, Toselli, von Arenberg, von Hohenlohe, von Moran, von Nordheim, von Rheinfelden, von Salm, von Supplinburg, Welf, Welser, Wettin, Wisniowecki, Wittelsbach, Wolfling, Wurttemberg, Zahringen.

## Ireland
## (A King In Every County)

Aed Findliath, Ailech, Burke, Butler, Cenel n Eogain, Clann Cholmain, Conall Enda, Conn, Cormac MacArt, de Brugh, de Clare, De Courci, De Lacy, Domnall Ua Lochlainn, Eogan, Fitzgerald, Garret, Kavanaugh, Luineach, MacMurrough, Mac Murrough, Mac William, Mael Muaid, Maelsechlainn, Mathgamain, More, Murchad, Nial Glundub, Niall, O'Brien, O'Connor, O'Donnell, O'Melaghlin, O'Neill, Ruadri Ua Conchubair (Rory O'Connor), Talbot, Todelbach, Toirdelbach Ua Conchubair, Vlaid.

## Italy

Aistulf, Albizzi, Augustulus, Authari, Bentivaglio, Borgia, Buglioni, de Beauharnais, della Scala, de Medici, Este, Fagginola, Farnese, Florence, Galleazzo, Gonzaga, Guiscard, Ivrea, Ladislas, Luitprand, Manin, Odoacer, Palaeologus, Petrucci, Sforza, Theodoric, Theophylact, Valois, Visconti.

## Portugal

Aviz, Braganza, de Boulogne, de Castro, de Guzman, de Leon, de Savoie, de Trastamara, Dias, Diniz, Goncalves, Henriques, Nemours, Teles.

## Russia

Alekseevich, Apraksina, Basilli, Dolgorukaya, Dolgoruki, Donskoi, Fedorovna, Godunov,

Gorbataya, Gruszecka, Ivanovna, Kalita, Karnovich, Krasinski, Leopoldovna, Lopukhina, Lyapunov, Mikhailovich, Miloslavskaya, Momonov, Monomakhi, Naryshkina, Nevski, Palaeologus, Porphyrogenitus, Pozharski, Romanov, Salty Kova, Shestova, Shuiski, Skavronskaya, Trubetskoi, Tzimisces, Yurievich, Zarutski.

## Scotland

Canmore, de Balliol, de Bruce, Douglas, Hamilton, Hepburn, Mac Alpine, Macbeth, Mac Donald, Strathclyde, Stuart.

## Spain

*(Visigoth)* Alaric, Athanagild, Leovigild, Reccared, Recesswinth, Roderic, Sisenand, Swintila, Wamba, Witiza. *(Moorish)* Hakam, Hammuda, Omayyad, Rahman. *(More Recent)* Asturias, Barcelona, Bereguer, Bourbon, Charlemagne, de Asis, de Bar, de Borbon, de Pavla, di Caserta, Farnese, Garces, Gonzalez, Trastamaran.

# Prefixes and Suffixes

at      ie. Attwell-at the well

bi, by      beside
ie. Byfleet-by the fleet,
Byduk-by the dike

botle, bottle      abode or house
ie. Bolton-an enclosure with
a house

burg, buruh,
burh, bury,
burgh, bor-
ough      Usually defines the defensi-
ble places such as an early
earthwork and later a fortified town
ie. Pittsburg- the fortified
town of Pitt Fort Pitt

by, baer,
boer,
byr, bo, bua      to dwell in (as a building or
farmstead later denoted a
village or town)
ie. Skidby-a log hut (as a
dwelling)

carrick, craig,
crick, crau      a rock or craig
ie. Ascric-ash ridge

chester, ces-
ter, caster,
ceaster      indicate sites of Roman occupation
ie. Westchester- a western
site

combe, cum      a hollow in a hillside
ie. Winchcombe-woods in
the corner (wincel) of the
land

dell, dale,
thal      a valley
ie. longsdale-a long valley

den, dene,
denu      denoted woodlands suitable
for the pasturage of goats or
swine
ie. hazeldon-hazel trees in
the woods

dic, dyke,
ditch      a ditch
ie. Ditchford-dicford

Don, Dun      A hill, height, or fort or
earthwork
ie. Dundrum-the fort on
the hill Dunbar-the hill of
Saint Bar

dorp, dorf,
tref, treb,
trev,
tre      township or hamlet
ie. Langthorpe (lambetors-
lamb) a township with
lambs

et      ie. Ettun-at the tun farm-
house

field, mat,
maes, magh,
mag      a home by the field
ie. Masham

| | | | |
|---|---|---|---|
| ford, fjord, fuhrt, forde | a crossing but in old norse, an arm of the sea<br>ie. Kingsford-the king's crossing Orford-the shore of the fiord | ley, loo, lea, leigh | fallow or untilled land or pasture an open place in the woods, woodland pasture<br>ie. Leighton-pasture by the homestead |
| gale, gill | denotes ravine or narrow lane or hollow in a hill<br>ie. Fingal-woodpecker's (fin) hollow | or | the shore of the river or sea |
| | | ridge, hrycg, rudge, rigge | a back or ridge<br>ie. ardridge-a high ridge |
| garth, acre | small enclosures such as a small field, yard<br>ie. Applegarth-an enclosed area of apples Sandiacre-an acre which is sandy | sculf, shelf, shel, skel | a shelf or lodge<br>ie. shelford-a shallow ford |
| | | thwaite | to chop, clearings or a place cleared of woods<br>ie. Thornythwaite-a place cleared of thorns |
| hall, healh | originally thought to be a stone house, but now defined as a slope (healh), steep hill, bank<br>ie. Westhill-the Western slope | ton, tun | signifies a farmstead, commonly preceded by a descriptive term<br>ie. Hampton-a high farmstead Dalton-a farmstead in a dale |
| ham, heim, hen, home | is usually combined with the name of the original settler<br>ie. Buckingham | weald, wall | a homestead by the wall<br>ie. Walton |
| hop | a small bay or inlet, haven also a pool in a moor or marsh<br>ie. Hopston-the pool or bay by the farmstead | wick, wich | a dwelling place; a bay<br>ie. Hardwick-the abode of the herd Sandwich-the sandy bay |

# COMMON NAMES AND THEIR MEANINGS

Apple     One who dwells near an apple tree; descendant of Adel, short form of Adalbert (noble bright).

Bank     One who lived near an embankment or mound; does not refer to money.

Barber     Once a surgeon, blood letter and hairdresser.

Beach     Name given to those who lived near an ocean, beech tree or brook.

Butcher     A cutter and seller of meat.

Blacksmith     Iron is the "black" metal; one who worked it.

Carpenter     A woodworker.

Castle     A person who worked in, built, lived in or near yesterday's titans.

Champion     Has its origins in medieval combat; one who would fight for another.

Cliff     A geographic name identifying those who lived near steep slopes or rocks.

Cook     A preparer of food, you are right.

Creek     Those who once lived in or near marshes, creeks or wetlands.

Cross     Saints would often have a cross erected to them at roadsides or intersections. A "Cross" was one who lived near the marker.

Deal     Original inhabitants of the Deal (Valley) in Kent, England.

Deer     Those emigrants from Aberdeenshire, Scotland. Dwellers in the Deer (forest).

Dove     Either one who dwelled near the Dove (black, dark) or a possessor of the gentle characteristics of the bird of peace.

| | |
|---|---|
| Drum(m) | A person who originated from the Drum, a back hill or ridge. |
| Duck | A possessor of the characteristics of a duck. Also a pet form of Marmaduke, a sea leader. |
| Eagle | Aegel means noble and Eagle means descendant of noble ones; also one who dwelled at the sign of the Eagle or came from Eagle, oakwood, in Lincolnshire. |
| Earth | A farmer, one who tilled the soil. |
| Edge | A dweller on a hillside, cliff or edge. Common geographical reference name. |
| Emperor | Originally a commander or leader, ultimately the supreme commander or sovereign. |
| End | One who lived near a boundary or at an end of a row. |
| Fabric | Variant for one who worked in metals, was a smith. |
| Fair | Descriptive for those who were beautiful, descendant from beautiful ones. |
| Falls | A geographic term describing those who lived near waterfalls or on a slope. |
| Farmer | Despite the inclination to identify this name as another soil tiller, it describes one who tilled the revenue, in other words, a tax collector. |
| Fern | A place name describing those who lived near the alder tree or Fern. |
| Field | Those who lived in open, treeless, fenceless tracts of arabale land. |
| Fisherman | One who caught, sold or lived near the fishing industry. |
| Flax | One who dealt in, made or sold linen from the Flax plant. |
| Flower(s) | A maker of arrows or a descendant of same. |
| Fortune | Indeed, those who were considered lucky or fortunate. |
| Fox | One who possesses the characteristics of a fox or who lives near the sign of the fox. |
| Friend | A person held in the highest regard. |
| Gale | Those who lived near a jail or prison; an unusually happy person. |
| Gem | A highly cherished person. |
| Glove(ver) | A maker and/or seller of gloves. |
| Goat | An occupational and place name for one who raised goats |

| | | | |
|---|---|---|---|
| | or lived near where goats grazed. | Hook | A geographic, denoting one who lived near some natural feature with a bend in it. |
| Gold | Personal names given those who traded or worked with the metal. | Horn | Does not relate to the musical instrument, rather it denotes those who lived near a protruding hill or mountain. |
| Gravel | Those who lived in small groves. | Horse | Short form for Englishmen who resided in or near a horse pasture or came from the horse island, Horsey. |
| Green | Around each village green people lived. Those who did so were named Green. | Hunter | Occupational name for huntsmen, seekers of game for the Lord. |
| Grove | Place name given those who lived in large groves. | Iron(s) | Originally one who came from Airaines, which means brass, in the country of France. |
| Guard | Occupational name for watchmen or guards. | Ivory | Ivory is a province in Normandy and also means archer. This name has either site or occupational origins. |
| Hail | One who saluted or acclaimed. | Jack(et) | Jack is the pet name for John. Most names with Jack as the prefix are derivatives of John in some form. |
| Hawk | One who either lived near a hawk sign or possessed the characteristics of a hawk. Also, a pet form of Harry or Henry. | Jewel | The term Jewell refers to descendants of Jehovah the God. Jewel is likely the short form. |
| Heaven | Evan is the Welsh form of John, the gracious gift of Jehovah. Heavens are descendants of Evan. | Judge | English or Irish denoting the ones who held and exercised the powers of some judicial function. |
| Herd | Tenders of the flocks and herds, shepherds and carers for domestic animals. | | |
| Hoe | Geographical name identifying those who lived at or near the spur of a hill. | | |

| | | | |
|---|---|---|---|
| Junior | Derived from the Latin Junius, refers to descendants of someone, the youthful ones. | Leather | Those who worked with leather or were descendants of Hleothor, which means melody, tune. |
| Keen | Those who possessed sharp insights, were quick of thought and action. | Lilac | Those who lived near the fragrant flower. |
| Keeper | Can be used as a single name or in compound form, i.e., Housekeeper. Those who attended to things in their care. | Lion | Place and sign name from the English. Used to describe courage. |
| Kernel | German name of place and occupation. Can refer to millers, cart drivers or emigrants from Kern, Germany. | Little | Used in compound names as well as to describe size, i.e., Littleman, Littlejohn. |
| King | Those who imitated the role of king in some manner or had direct connections with regal ones. | Lord | Another name carried over from the middle ages and the feudal system. Those who are in fact or mind superior. |
| Knight | Medieval role where for service to the king, land and/or privilege was granted. | Love | Those who have wolflike characteristics or are descendants from Lufa, England. |
| Lad(d) | Servants or attendants to gentlemen. | Major | As in Major or Minor, one who is larger, a larger man, a descriptive name. |
| Lamb | In feudal times, public places placed signs in front of their establishments. Thus, one who had characteristics of the gentle animal or who lived near a place where the Lamb sign was hung. | Marsh | Swamp dwellers or people living near wetlands. |
| | | Mason | Occupational name for those who worked with brick or stone. |
| | | Mayor | Title or position, name derived from the post held. |
| Law | Those who lived near grave yards or burial mounds. | Minister | Variant of Minster, an assistant to some official. |

| | |
|---|---|
| Mire | |
| Moon | The one who was monastic or lived near a moon sign. |
| Moor(e) | As in Othello, a dark one or one who lived on or near the wastelands of Scotland. |
| Mountain | Those who lived on, near or came from the higher elevations. |
| North | The geographic/directional name given to those who came from the north of where they currently resided. |
| Owl | Descriptive and sign name for persons possessing the bird-like characteristics or living near the Owl sign. |
| Painter | Occupational name for artists of Rembrandt quality or your local house painter. |
| Palm | Refers to the palm tree and religious ceremonies rather than the hand. |
| Parents | Connected with the clergy, priests and fathers, usually simply the father. |
| Parson | The child of a minister or par son. Par also is a form of Peter, or Peter's son. |
| Pasture | Another term denoting shepherd or flock tender. |

| | |
|---|---|
| Peace | Name given to those born during the Easter season when the Christian King of Peace prevailed. |
| Pebble | Does not refer to little rocks, rather those who lived near or came from a place of assembly. |
| Peer | Variant of Peter, the rock; name given to the descendants. |
| People | Similar to Pebble, those from a place of assembly. |
| Pigeon | Descriptive name for those possessing the characteristics. |
| Pillar | Germanic in origin; Bilihar meant army, Pillar(s) were descendants of Bilihar. |
| Plow | Those who followed the spring ritual of plowing. |
| Poet | Name given to those workers of rhyme and verse. |
| Pond | Those who lived on or near small bodies of water. |
| Pope | Those who assumed the role in fact or fiction; also, unusually austere, sometimes saintly people. |
| Printer | Occupational name for those who composed the printed page. |

Queen — Those who would play the role of a queen in drama or were in some manner attached to the Queen's retinue.

Rain — Descendants of counsels or mighty ones. Connected with the term regent. Also, the term was used to identify those from wetlands.

Ransom — Randal refers to a shield or wolf; Rand is short for Randolph, the son of one who was shield-like.

Reed — Form of red describing ruddy people, or people who lived in reedy areas.

Regal — Descendant of nobility, or royal in nature.

Rice — Form of the Welsh name Rhys, or ardor.

Rich — Short for Richard, a ruler or hard person, refers to the descendants.

Ridge — Those who lived on or near the geographic feature.

Robber — Robert refers to bright, famous people. Variant of Robert; descendant of Rob.

Roman — Those who pilgrimmed to Rome or came from Rome.

Rood — Another variant for red or ruddy-like people. Those who dwelled near roadside crosses from medieval times.

Sailor — Festive dancers and/or ship-workers or seamen.

Saint — Used in compounds to refer to Catholic saints, i.e., St. George, or places named after saints.

Seal — Those who lived near or at the seal or hall. Name of many places in Great Britain.

Sheep — Those who tended or were connected with the flocks.

Shepherd — Occupational term of ancient use and origin.

Ship — Worker on or near ships and shipyards. Those who lived near the Ship's sign, even if they never went to sea.

Shoemaker — Occupational name for workers in footwear.

Shore — Those who live near the ocean. Hebrew variants refer to Joseph who is Bullock-like. Those who lived near the Bullock sign.

Singer — Connected with Church singing in English; place name; Singer in the German.

Sparrow — Sign name for those living near the Sparrow sign; one

| | |
|---|---|
| | possessing cheerful characteristics. |
| Spear | Watchmen, lookouts and/or guards from antiquity. |
| Steel | Refers not to the metal, but to descendants of those who live near a place where climbing was necessary, the Stile. |
| Sweet | A dear or beloved one used most often as part of a compound, i.e., Sweeten or son of the sweet man. |
| Teacher | An instructor, one would hope, pure and simple. Occupational name. |
| Temple | Those who lived in or near religious buildings as well as their descendants. |
| Tower | Persons who lived in or near large buildings or towers. |
| Town | Manor dwellers in Medieval times, those who lived in enclosed areas. |
| Treat | Another expression for dear, well-loved people. |
| Valley | Those who lived in the geographic area, connected by topography, not necessarily blood. |
| Victor | Conquerors and their descendants. |
| Vine | Workers in or people who lived near the vineyards. |
| Virgin | Those who lived near statues of the Virgin Mary. Medieval in origin. |
| Waiter | Guards and watchmen, not those who serve tables. |
| Weave(r) | Occupational name for makers of cloth. |
| White | Descriptive name for fair people. |
| Wood | Forest dwellers from old England before settled agriculture became the way of life. |
| Young | For two in a family who bore the same first name, i.e., John the Young, the descendants of the young(er) of the two. |

# Common Names and Translations

| English | French | German | Italian | Spanish | Swedish | Polish |
|---|---|---|---|---|---|---|
| Apple | Pomme | Apfel | Mela | Manzana | Apple | Jablko |
| Bank | Rive | Ufer | Riva | Ribera | Strand | Bank |
| Barber | Coiffeur | Frisor | Barbiere | Barbero | Barberare | Fryzjer |
| Beach | Plage | Strand | Spiaggia | Playa | Strand | Plaza |
| Blacksmith | Forgeron | Schmied | Ferraio | Herrero | Smed | Kowal |
| Butcher | Boucher | Fleischer | Macellaio | Carnicero | Slaktare | Rzeznik |
| Carpenter | Charpentier | Zimmermann | Falegname | Carpintero | Snickare | Ciesla |
| Castle | Chateau | Schloss | Castello | Castillo | Slott | Zamek |
| Champion | Champion | Meister | Campione | Campeon | Mastare | Mistrz |
| Cliff | Falaise | Klippe | Precipizio | Risco | Klippa | Urwisko |
| Cook | Cuisinier | Koch | Cuoco | Cocinero | Kock | Kucharz |
| Creek | Ruisseau | Bach | Ruscello | Arroyo | Back | Zatoka |
| Cross | Croix | Kreuz | Croce | Cruz | Kors | Krzyz |
| Deal | Commercer | Handeln | Trattare | Tratar | Handla | Rozdanie Kart |
| Deer | Cert | Hirsch | Cervo | Ciervo | Radjur | Zwierzyna |
| Dove | Colombe | Taube | Colomba | Paloma | Duva | Golab |
| Drum | Tambour | Trommel | Tamburo | Tambor | Tramma | Beben |
| Duck | Canard | Ente | Anitra | Pato | Anka | Kaczka |
| Eagle | Aigle | Adler | Aquila | Aquila | Orn | Orzel |
| Earth | Terre | Boden | Terra | Tierra | Jord | Ziemia |
| Edge | Tranchant | Schneide | Filo | Filo | Egg | Ostrze |
| Emperor | Empereur | Kaiser | Imperature | Emperador | Kejsare | Cesarz |
| End | Fin | Schluss | Fine | Fin | Slut | Zabonczenie |
| Fabric | Tissu | Stoff | Tessuto | Tela | Tyg | Gmach |
| Fair | Beau | Schon | Chiaro | Despejado | Klar | Jarmark |
| Falls | Chutes | Wasserfall | Cuscata | Cuscada | Vattenfall | Wodospad |
| Farmer | Fermier | Bauer | Coltivatore | Agricultor | Bonde | Dzierzawca |
| Fern | Fougere | Farn | Felce | Helecho | Ormbunke | Paproc |
| Field | Champ | Feld | Campo | Campo | Falt | Polebitwy |
| Fisherman | Pecheur | Fischer | Pescatore | Pescador | Fiskare | Rybak |
| Flax | Lin | Flachs | Lino | Lino | Lin | Len |
| Flower | Fleur | Blume | Fiore | Flor | Blomma | Kwiat |
| Fortune | Fortune | Gluck | Fortuna | Fortuna | Tur | Fortuna |
| Fox | Renard | Fuchs | Volpe | Zorra | Rav | Lis |
| Friend | Ami | Freund | Amico | Amigo | Van | Przyjaciel |

| English | French | German | Italian | Spanish | Swedish | Polish |
|---|---|---|---|---|---|---|
| Gale | Vent | Sturm | Bufera | Ventarron | Blast | Wiatr |
| Gem | Gemme | Edelstein | Gemma | Gema | Adelsten | Klejnot |
| Glove | Gant | Handschuh | Guanto | Guante | Handske | Rekawiczka |
| Goat | Chevre | Ziege | Capra | Cabra | Get | Koza |
| Gold | Or | Gold | Oro | Oro | Guld | Zloto |
| Gravel | Gravier | Kies | Ghiaia | Grava | Grus | Zwir |
| Green | Vert | Grun | Verde | Verde | Gron | Zielonosc |
| Grove | Bosquet | Waldchen | Boschetto | Arboleda | Dunge | Gaj |
| Guard | Garde | Wache | Guardino | Guarda | Vakt | Stroz |
| Hail | Greler | Hageln | Grandinare | Granizar | Hagla | Grad |
| Hawk | Faucon | Habicht | Falco | Halcon | Hok | Sokol |
| Heaven | Ciel | Himmel | Cielo | Cielo | Himmel | Niebo |
| Herd | Troupeau | Herde | Mandria | Rebano | Hjord | Trzoda |
| Hoe | Hove | Hacke | Zappa | Azada | Hacka | Graca |
| Hook | Crochet | Haken | Gancio | Guncho | Krok | Hak |
| Horn | Corne | Horn | Corno | Cuerno | Horn | Rog |
| Horse | Cheval | Pferd | Cavallo | Caballo | Hast | Kon |
| Hunter | Chasseur | Jager | Cacciatore | Cazador | Jagare | Mysliwy |
| Iron | Fer | Eisen | Ferro | Hierro | Jarn | Zelazo |
| Ivory | Ivoire | Elfenbein | Avorio | Marfil | Elfenben | Kosc |
| Jacket | Jaquette | Jacke | Giacca | Chaqueta | Jacka | Zakiet |
| Jewel | Bijou | Juwel | Gioiello | Joya | Jurel | Klejnot |
| Judge | Juge | Richter | Giudice | Juez | Domare | Sedzia |
| Junior | Cadet | Junger | Minore | Menor | Yugre | Junior |
| Keen | Aigo | Scharf | Aguzzo | Agudo | Skarp | Ostry |
| Keeper | Gardien | Warter | Costode | Guarda | Vakt | Dozorca |
| Kernel | Graine | Kern | Chicco | Grano | Katna | Ziarnko |
| King | Roi | Konig | Re | Rey | Kung | Krol |
| Knight | Chevalier | Ritter | Cavaliere | Caballero | Riddare | Rycerz |
| Lad | Garcon | Junge | Giovanetto | Mozalbete | Pojke | Chlopiec |
| Lamb | Agneau | Lamm | Agnello | Cordero | Lamm | Baranek |
| Law | Droit | Recht | Legge | Ley | Lag | Prawo |
| Leather | Cuir | Leder | Cuoio | Cuero | Lader | Skora |
| Lilac | Lilas | Flieder | Lilla | Lila | Syren | Bez |
| Lion | Lion | Lowe | Leone | Leon | Lejon | Lew |
| Little | Petit | Klein | Piccolo | Pequeno | Liten | Maly |
| Lord | Seigneur | Herr | Padrone | Senor | Herre | Pan |
| Love | Amour | Liebe | Amore | Amor | Karlek | Milosc |
| Major | Majeur | Grosser | Maggiore | Mayor | Storre | Starszy |
| Marsh | Marais | Sumpf | Palude | Pantano | Karr | Bloto |
| Mason | Macon | Maurer | Muratore | Albanil | Murare | Mularz |
| Mayor | Maire | Burgermeister | Sindaco | Alcalde | Borgmastore | Barmistrz |
| Minister | Pastuer | Pfarrer | Ministro | Pastor | Prast | Minister |
| Mire | Boorbier | Sumpf | Fango | Cieno | Karr | Bloto |
| Moon | Lune | Mond | Luna | Luna | Mane | Ksiezyc |
| Moor | Lande | Moor | Landa | Paramo | Hed | Blota |
| Mountain | Montagne | Berg | Montagna | Montana | Berg | Gora |

| English | French | German | Italian | Spanish | Swedish | Polish |
|---|---|---|---|---|---|---|
| North | Nord | Norden | Settentriome | Norte | Nord | Polnoc |
| Owl | Hibou | Eule | Gufo | Buho | Uggla | Sowa |
| Ox | Boeuf | Ochs | Bue | Buey | Oxe | Wol |
| Painter | Peintre | Maler | Pittore | Pintor | Malare | Cuma |
| Palm | Paume | Handflache | Palmo | Palma | Handflata | Dlon |
| Parents | Parents | Eltern | Genitori | Padres | Foraldrar | Rodzice |
| Parson | Cure | Pfarrer | Ministro | Clerigo | Kyrkoherde | Pastor |
| Pasture | Paturage | Weide | Puscolo | Pastura | Betesmark | Pastwisko |
| Peace | Paix | Frieden | Pace | Paz | Fred | Spokoj |
| Pebble | Caillou | Kiesel | Ciottolo | Piedrecilla | Smusten | Kmayk |
| Peer | Pareil | Gleiche | Pari | Par | Like | Rowny |
| People | Peuple | Volk | Popolo | Pueblo | Folk | Ludzie |
| Pigeon | Pigeon | Taube | Piccione | Paloma | Dura | Golab |
| Pillar | Pilier | Pfeiler | Pilastro | Pilar | Pelare | Podpora |
| Plow | Charrve | Pflug | Aratro | Arado | Plog | Plug |
| Poet | Poete | Dichter | Poeta | Poeta | Diktare | Poeta |
| Pond | Etang | Teich | Stagno | Estanque | Damm | Staw |
| Pope | Pape | Papst | Papa | Papa | Pave | Papiez |
| Printer | Imprimeur | Drucker | Tipografo | Impressor | Tryckare | Drukarz |
| Queen | Reine | Konigin | Regina | Reina | Drottning | Krolowa |
| Rain | Pluie | Regen | Pioggia | Lluria | Regn | Deszcz |
| Ransom | Rancon | Losegeld | Riscutto | Rescate | Losen | Wykup |
| Reed | Roseau | Rohr | Canna | Junco | Vass | Trzcina |
| Regal | Royal | Koniglich | Regale | Real | Kunglig | Krolewski |
| Rice | Riz | Reis | Riso | Arroz | Ris | Ryz |
| Rich | Riche | Reich | Ricco | Rico | Rik | Bogaty |
| Ridge | Chaine | Kette | Catena | Sierra | Bergas | Grzbiet |
| Road | Route | Strasse | Strada | Camino | Vag | Droga |
| Robber | Voleur | Rauber | Ladro | Ladron | Runare | Zlodziej |
| Roman | Romain | Romisch | Romano | Romano | Romersk | Rzymianin |
| Sailor | Marin | Matrose | Marinaio | Marinero | Sj'oman | Marynarz |
| Saint | Saint | Heilige | Santo | Santo | Helgon | Swiety |
| Seal | Sceau | Siegel | Timbro | Sello | Sigill | Foka |
| Sheep | Mouton | Schaf | Pecora | Oveja | Far | Owca |
| Shepherd | Berger | Hirt | Pastore | Pastor | Herde | Pasterz |
| Ship | Navire | Schiff | Nave | Barco | Skepp | Okret |
| Shoemaker | Cordonnier | Schuster | Calzolaio | Zapatero | Skomakare | Szewc |
| Shore | Rive | Ufer | Riva | Ribera | Strand | Podporka |
| Singer | Chanteur | Sanger | Cantante | Cantante | Sangare | Spiewak |
| Sparrow | Moineau | Sputz | Pussero | Gorrion | Sparv | Worbel |
| Spear | Lance | Speer | Lancia | Lanza | Spjut | Wlocznia |
| Steel | Acier | Stahl | Acciaio | Acero | Stal | Stal |
| Sweep | Balayer | Fegen | Spazzare | Barrer | Sopa | Zamiatanie |
| Teacher | Instituteur | Lehrer | Maestro | Maestro | Larare | Mauczyciel |
| Temple | Tempe | Schlafe | Tempia | Sien | Tinning | Swiatynia |
| Tower | Tour | Turm | Torre | Torre | Torn | Wieza |
| Town | Ville | Stadt | Citta | Pueblo | Stad | Miasto |

| English | French | German | Italian | Spanish | Swedish | Polish |
|---|---|---|---|---|---|---|
| Treat | Traiter | Behandeln | Trattare | Tratar | Behandla | Poczestunek |
| Valley | Vallee | Tal | Vallata | Valle | Dal | Dolina |
| Victor | Vainqueur | Sieger | Vincitore | Vencedor | Segrare | Zwyciezca |
| Vine | Vigne | Weinstock | Vite | Vid | Vinranka | Winograd |
| Virgin | Virge | Jung frau | Vergine | Virgen | Jungfru | Dziewica |
| Waiter | Garcon | Kellner | Cameriere | Camerero | Kypare | Kelner |
| Weave | Tisser | Weben | Tessere | Tejer | Vava | Tkacz |
| White | Blanc | Weiss | Bianco | Blanco | Vit | Bialy |
| Wood | Boise | Wald | Bosco | Bosque | Skog | Drzewo |
| Young | Jeune | Jung | Giovane | Joven | Ung | Mlode |

# THE REFERENCE BOOKS

## BIOGRAPHIES

American Biographical Dictionary, The, Allen, William, third edition, Boston, 1857.

Notable American Women, 1607–1950, Editor: James, Edward T., Belknap Press, Cambridge, Mass. 1971.

## ETHNIC

Lists of Swiss Emigrants in the Eighteenth Century to the American Colonies, Vol. I and II, Faust, Albert Bernhardt, A.B., Ph.D., The National Genealogical Society, Washington, D. C., 1920.

Passenger Arrivals, 1819–1820, Genealogical Publishing Co., Baltimore, 1967 (originally published, Washington, D.C., 1821).

Passengers Who Arrived in the United States, September 1821-December 1823, from transcripts made by the State Department, Magna Carta Book Co., 1969, Baltimore.

Pennsylvania German Pioneers, Strassburger, Ralph Beaver, LL.D., Vol. I and II., Genealogical Publishing Co., 1966, Baltimore, second publishing.

## ETYMOLOGY

Concise Etymological Dictionary of Modern English, Weekly, E., revised edition, 1952.

Concise Oxford Dictionary of English Places-Names, The, Ekwall Eilert, Oxford, 1960.

Etymological Dictionary of Modern English, An, Weekly, London, 1921.

Etymological Dictionary of the English Language, 1910.

Etymology, Worterhudider der deutsehen Sprache Kulge.

Growth and Structure of the English Language, Jespersen, Otto, Doubleday & Co., Inc., Garden City, New York, 1955, ninth edition.

International Book of Names, Mawson, New York, 1934.

Langenscheidt's New Muret Sanders Encyclopedic Dictionary, Barnes and Noble.

McKay's Modern Danish-English Dictionary, New York, 1965.

Mother Tongue, The, Hogben, Lancelot, W.W. Norton & Co., Inc., New York, 1965.

Names and Their Histories, Taylor, Issac, second edition, 1898.

Origins, Patridge, London, 1958.

Oxford Dictionary of English Christian Names, The, Withycombe, London, 1947.

Wessely's Dictionary of the Swedish and English Language, New York, 1941.

## GENERAL

American and British Genealogy and Heraldry, P. William Filby, second edition, American Library Association, Chicago, 1975.

Find Your Ancestor, Criswell, Howard D., Washington, D.C., 1973 (The Author Published).

Genealogical Research: Methods and Sources, edited by Rubincan, Milton and Stephenson, Jean, 6th printing, Washington, D.C., 1966.

Man's Rise to Civilization, Farb, Peter, Avon Books, New York, 1968.

Searching for Your Ancestors: The How and Why of Genealogy, Doane Gilbert H., 4th edition, revised, New York, Bantam Books, 1974.

Statistical History of the United States from Colonial Times to the Present, The, Fairfield Publishers, Inc., Stamford, Ct., 1960.

## HERALDRY

Guide to Orders of Chivalry-Hartwell, Sir Rodney, Habor City, Calif., Hartwell Co., 1974.

Observer's Book of Heraldry, The, MacKinnon, Charles, of Dunakin, Frederick, Warne & Co., Ltd., London, 1966.

Pageant of Heraldry: An Explanation of Its Principles, Its Uses Today, Rogers, Col. H.C.B., London, O.B.E., Seeley Service & Co., Ltd., Great Britain (196 Shafesbury Avenue).

## MILITARY

Complete Army and Navy Register of the United States of America from 1776 to 1887. Thomas H.S. Hamersly, New York, 1888 (Army Only).

History of the Pennsylvania Volunteers, 1861–1865, Bates, Samuel P., 5 Volumes, Prepared in Compliance with Acts of the Liegislature, Harrisburg, Singerly, B., State Printer, 1869.

List of Officers of the Navy of the United States and of the Marine Corps, from 1775 to 1900, Haskell House, New York, Reprint 1901 Edition by Edward W. Callahan.

Register of the Volunteer Force of the U.S. Army, 1861–1865, Washington, D.C., 1865–1867.

Tracing Your Civil War Ancestor, Groene, Beramtram H., Winston-Salem, N.C., 1973.

U.S. National Archives and Records Service General Information No. 7, National Archives, Washington, D.C.

## REFERENCES

American Ethnic Groups and the Revival of Cultural Pluralism, Evaluative Sourcebook for the 1970's, Kinton, Jack F., 1974, fourth edition.

American Indian, 1492–1970: A Chronology and Fact Book, Dennis, Henry C., Oceana Pub., 1971.

Americans of Jewish Descent: A Compendium of Genealogy, Stern, Malcolm H., Ktav Pub. House, 1960.

Bibliography of American Ethnology, Cashman, Marc, Editor, Todd Publications, Rye, New York, 1976. Sixty-seven indian tribes covered black Americans and other minorities-extensive and excellent!

Bibliographic Guide to Materials on Greeks in the United States, A, 1890–1968, Custumbis, Michael N., Center for Migration Studies, 1970.

Bibliography on German Settlements in Colonial North America, Meynen, Emil, Gale Research, Reprint of the 1937 edition.

Chinese Immigration, Roberts, Mary, Coolidge Arno Press, Reprint of the 1909 edition.

Chinese in America, The: A Chronology and Factbook, 1820 to 1973, Tung, William, Oceana Pub., 1974.

Dutch Emigration to North America, 1624 to 1860, Wabeke, Bertus Harry, Books for Libraries, Inc., Reprint of the 1944 edition.

Early Germans of New Jersey, The: Their History, Churches and Genealogies, Chambers, Theodore Frelinghuvsen, Genealogical Publishing Co., Reprint of the 1895 edition.

Europe: From the Renaissance to Waterloo, Ergang, Robert, D.C. Heath & Co., Boston, 1939.

First American, The, Ceram, C.W., Harcourt Brace Jovanovich, Inc., New York, 1971.

Hispanic Society of America, The, Catalogue of the Library of the Hispanic Society of America, 10 Volumes, G.K. Hall & Co., 1962.

History of England, Anderson, John J., Effingham Maynard & Co., Publishers, New York, 1889.

History of the Irish Settlers of North America from the Earliest Period to the Census of 1850, A, McGee, Thomas D'Arcy, Rand E. Research Associates, Pubs., Reprint of the 1852 edition, Genealogical Publishing Co.

History of the Negro Race in America from 1619 to 1880, Williams, George W., Arno Press, Reprint of the 1833 edition.

Homeward to Zion: The Mormon Migration from Scandinavia, Mulder, William, University of Minnesota Press, 1957.

Hungarians in the United States of America, An Immigration Study, Konnyu, Leslie, American Hungarian Review, 1967.

Italian-Americans, The: Their History and Culture, Rolle, Andrew F., Wadsworth Publishing Co.

Italians in America, The: A Chronology and Factbook, 1492 to 1972, LoGatto, Anthony L., Oceana Pubns., 1972.

Japanese Immigration, Ichihashi, Yamato, R and E Research Associates, Pubs., Reprint of 1915 edition.

List of Emigrants to America from Liverpool, 1697–1707, French, Elizabeth, Genealogical Publishing Co., Reprint of 1913 edition.

Moravians in Georgia, The, 1735 to 1740, Fries, Adelaide L. Genealogical Publishing Co., Repring of 1905 edition.

Norwegian Migration to America: 1825–1860, Blegen, Theodore C., Arno Press., Reprint of the 1931 edition.

Pennsylvania Genealogies: Chiefly Scotch-Irish and German, Egle, William Henry, Genealogical Publishing Co., Reprint of the 1896 edition.

Poles in New York in the 17th and 18th Centuries, Mieczyslau, Haiman, R & E Research Associates, Reprint of the 1938 edition.

Russian Immigrant, The, Davis, Jerome, Arno Press, Reprint of the 1922 edition.

Tlingit Indians, The: Results of a Trip to the Northwest Coast of America and the Bearing Straits, Krause, Aurel, University of Washington Press, 1970.

Topographical Dictionary of 2,885 English Emigrants to New England, 1620 to 1650, Banks, Charles Edward, Genealogical Publishing Co., Reprint of 1937 edition.

# RELIGIOUS

Biographical Dictionary of Early American Jews, A, Colonial Times Through 1800, Rosenbloom, Joseph A., University Press of Ky., Lexington, Ky., 1960.

Index to Names, Hayward, Elizabeth, Chester (now Rochester), N.Y. American Baptist Historical Society, 1951.

Index to Selected Amish Genealogies, Cross, Harold E. and Hostetler, B., Baltimore, Div. of Medical Genetics, Johns Hopkins University.

Microfilm Index and Bibliography of the Concordia Historical Institute, Department of Archives and History, The Lutheran Church, Missouri Synod., St. Louis, Mo., 1954–1963. Concordia Press, 1966, St. Louis, Mo.

Naturalizations of Foreign Protestants in the American and West Indian Colonies, Guiseppi, Montague S., Genealogical Publishing Co., Baltimore, 1969, Reprint of 1921 edition.

Preliminary Guide to Church Records Repositories, A, Washington, D.C., The Society, 1969.

Records of Huguenots in the United States, Canada, and the West Indies, Allen, Cameron, World Conference on Records, Area F-10 Paper, Salt Lake City: Genealogical Society, L.D.S., 1969.

Records of the Roman Catholic Church in the United States, Curry, Cora C., National Genealogical Society, Special Pub. 5, Washington, D.C., 1935.

# STATES

Abstracts of Wills in the District of Columbia, 1776–1815, Bell, Mrs. Alexander H., Washington, D.C., 1945–1946 (covers 1776–1815).

Alabama Genealogical Register, Vol. I–X, Tuslocaloosa, Ala., 1959–1968. Separate Index by Nelle M. Jenkins, ca., 1965.

Ancestry of Thirty-Three Rhode Islanders, 1889, Austin, John O., Reprint, Tuttle, Rutland, Vt., 1970.

Annals of Wyoming, Vol. 1, State Archives and Historical Department, 1923, Cheyenne, Wyo.

Annual Reports, Hawaiian Historical Society, Honolulu, 1892–1967.

Bibliography of the State of Maine, Bangor Public Library, G.K. Hall, Boston, 1962.

Bibliography of West Virginia, A, Parts 1–2, Davis, Innis C., Charleston, W.Va., 1939.

Biographical and Historical Memoirs of Eastern Arkansas, Chicago, 1890, Goodspeed Pub. Co.

Biographical and Historical Memoirs of Western Arkansas, Chicago, 1891, Southern Book Co.

Biographical, Genealogical and Descriptive History of the State of New Jersey, Brown, William M., Newark, New Jersey, 1900.

California Pioneer Register and Index, 1542–1848, Bancroft, Hubert H., Genealogical Pub. Co., Baltimore, 1964.

Colorado Genealogist, The, Colorado Genealogical Society, Denver, Co. Periodicals.

Contributions, Volumes 1–10, Historical Society of Montana, Reprint: Pub-Canner, Boston, 1966.

Dakota Territory, Volumes, Rogers, Bernice L. (editor), Phoenix, Ariz., 1969.

Delaware: Original Land Titles in Delaware Commonly Known as the Duke of York Record, Available from Public Archives Commission, Dover, Del.

Early Missouri Marriages to and Including 1840, 3 Volumes, Carter, Genevieve L., Sedalia, Mo., 1969–1972.

Early Settlers of New York State, Their Ancestors and Descendants, Foley, Janet W., Akron, N.Y., 1934–1942.

First Families of Louisiana, The, 2 Volumes, 1970, Conrad, Glen R., Claitor's, Baton Rouge, La.

First Ownership of Ohio Lands, Dyer, Albion M., Genealogical Pub. Co., Baltimore, 1969, Reprint.

Florida Genealogical Research Quarterly, Florida Society for Genealogical Research, Inc., Pinellas Park, Fla.

Gazeteer of the State of Michigan (and Directory of Emigrants), Blois, John T., Detroit, Mich., 1839.

Genealogical and Family History of the State of Vermont, 2 Vols., Carleton, Hiram, New York, 1903.

Genealogical Manuscript Material Index, The Genealogical Society of Pennsylvania, Philadelphia, 1964.

Genealogical Notes, South Carolina and Virginia, Brown, Richard L. and Brown, R.E., West Greenville, S.C., 1937.

Genealogies of the State of New York, Bergen, Teumis G., Long Island Edition, 3 Vol., New York, 1915.

Germans in Texas, The: A Study in Immigration, Benjamin, Gilbert G., R & E Research Assocs., Reprint of 1910 edition, San Francisco, 1970.

Gleanings of Virginia History, Boogher, William F., Genealogical Pub. Co., Baltimore, 1965, Reprinted from 1903 edition.

Guide to the Wisconsin State Archives, Delgado, David J., Wisconsin State Historical Society, Madison, Wisc., 1966.

Historical and Genealogical Materials in the North Dakota State, The, Historical Society Library, 1973, Burns, Betty S., Bismarck-Mandan, Historical Genealogical Society, Bismark, N.D., 1974.

History of Arizona, Peplou, Edward H., 3 Vols., New York, 1958.

History of Idaho, French, Hiram T., 3 Volumes, Chicago, ca 1914. (Volumes 2 and 3 have individual biographies.)

History of Southeastern Dakota: Its Settlement and Growth, Sioux City, Iowa, 1881.

Illinois State Genealogical Society Quarterly, The Illinois State Genealogical Society, since 1969. Springfield, Ill.

Index to the First Federal Census, Territory of Washington (1860), Stucki, J.U., Century Enterprises, Huntsville, Ark., 1972.

1820 Indiana Federal Census, Cox, Evelyn M., Ellensburgh, Wash., 1973.

Iowa Genealogical Society Surname Index, The, Volume I, 1972, The Iowa Genealogical Society, Des Moines, Iowa.

Kansas Memorial, The, Gleed, Charles S., Kansas City, Mo., 1880, (Lists of Settlers and Dates of Birth.)

Kentucky Records, Ardery, Julia H, (Spencer), Genealogical Pub. Co., 1969, Baltimore (Court Records—Old Bible Records —Tombstones)

Land Office and Prerogative Court Records of 1968 Colonial Maryland, Hartsook, Elisabeth and Skordas, Gust., Genealogical Pub. Co., Baltimore.

List of Early Settlers of Georgia, A, Coulter, Ellis M., and Saye, A.B., second printing, University of Georgia Press, Athans, Ga., 1967.

Missions of New Mexico, The, 1776–1956, Adams, Eleanor B., and Chavez, A., Santa Fe, N.M., 1956.

Mississippi Court Records, King, Junie Estelle S., Genealogical Pub., Co., Baltimore, 1969.

Nebraska and Midwest Genealogical Records, Volumes 1–22, Nebraska Genealogical Society, Lincoln, Nebr., 1923–1944.

Nevada: Historical Records Survey, Reno, Nevada, 1941.

New Hampshire Genealogical Research Guide, Towle, Laird C., Prince George's Genealogical Society, Bowie, Md., 1973.

North and South Carolina Marriage Records from Earliest Colonial Days to the Civil War, Clemens, William M., Reprint Genealogical Pub. Co., 1973, Baltimore.

Old Philadelphia Families, Du Bin, Alexander, Philadelphia, 1939.

Peirce's Colonial Lists, Civil, Military and Professional Lists of Rhode Island and Plymouth, 1621–1700, Peirce, Ebenezer W., 1881, reprint 1968 by Genealogical Pub. Co., Baltimore.

Pioneers and Prominent Men of Utah, Esshom, Frank, 1913, Reprinted Western Epics, Salt Lake City, 1966.

Pioneers of Alaska: The Trail Blazers of Bygone Days, Chase, Will H., Kansas City, Ka., 1951.

Portrait and Biographical Records of Oklahoma, Chicago, 1901. (Sketches of Early Citizens.)

Redemptioners and Indentured Servants in the Colony and Commonwealth of Pa., Geiser, Karl F., New Haven, Conn., 1901.

Reference Guide to Minnesota History, Brook, Michael, Minnesota Historical Society, St. Paul, Minn., 1974.

Roster of Ancestors (Oregon), Goodrich, Mrs. George R., D.A.R., Tillamook, Ore., 1963.

Shenandoah Valley, Virginia, Marriage Bonds, 1772–1850, Ashby, Bernice M., Virginia Book Co., Berryville, Va., 1967.

Sources for Genealogical Searching in Connecticut and Massachusetts, Barlou, Claude W., Central New York, Genealogical Society, Syracuse, N.Y., 1973.

Tennessee Books—A Preliminary Guide, Allen, Ronald R., Knoxville, Tenn., 1969.

Trek to Texas, 1770–1870, Foster, Pearl, Fort Worth, Tx., 1966.

*Four Gettysburg Union Generals. Seated: Major General Winfield Scott Hancock. Standing: Generals Francis Barlow, John Gibbon, David B. Birney, 1863.*
*Hancock was assigned by General Meade to command Union Forces following the death of Major General J. F. Reynolds by a sharpshooter's bullet early during the first day of battle. Barlow was known as the boy General.*

*Confederate soldier: Private Edwin E. Jennison of Georgia regiment, Killed at Malvern Hill.*

*The camp and regimental drill of the 96th Pennsylvania Infantry at Camp Northumberland, 1861.*

# How To Use
# The Reference Directories:

The Reference Directories are a current listing of families with your surname and are made available to you for your personal research. The directories are to be used in conjunction with your Heritage and Lineage Charts, and Personal History Sheets. At the same time that you have received your book and are working on completing your reference sheets, other people with your name across the country are working on theirs. These people may be parents, grandparents, aunts, uncles, nieces, nephews or cousins.

## The Forward Lineage Chart:

The Lineage Chart records the parents, children and grandchildren of an ancestor plus their births, deaths, and spouses. It is designed to provide a means for more distant relatives to determine a common ancestor and then to work forward in time. In this way, you may establish a particular relative as first cousin, second cousin or third, and then determine if you are of the same generation, or REMOVED.

## The Individual Heritage Chart:

The Heritage Chart represents your actual direct line forebearers. Each generation back represents the addition of one, then two, then four, etc. new family names into your heritage. Along with the names, each generation can represent the addition of a meaningful history of rich or poor, royal or slave, adventurer, farmer, tradesman, hunter or soldier.

## The Personal History Sheet:

The personal History is what we would like to know about every one of our relatives. It is also what we currently know about ourselves, our parents, and most likely our grandparents. It is information, which unless recorded today, can be lost as a generation passes on. This is the information that other members of your family will want to know about the people and places which make up their heritage.

## Family Signature Sheet:

A signature is a close and personal representation of the personality, psychological attitude and physical aptitude of an individual. It is more representative of a person than any other single item. It is an item that should be collected on every member of your family NOW. Generations from now, this book, this signature sheet, and these signatures will still represent these people.

HUSBAND _____

WIFE (Maiden Name) _____

Birth Date _____          Birth Date _____

Death Date _____          Death Date _____

*For large families complete 2 charts*

CHILD'S NAME _____     CHILD'S NAME _____     CHILD'S NAME _____

Birth Date _____          Birth Date _____          Birth Date _____

Death Date _____          Death Date _____          Death Date _____

Married to: _____          Married to: _____          Married to: _____

SPOUSE'S NAME _____   SPOUSE'S NAME _____   SPOUSE'S NAME _____

**G R A N D C H I L D R E N**

1) _____    1) _____    1) _____

B _____ D _____    B _____ D _____    B _____ D _____

2) _____    2) _____    2) _____

B _____ D _____    B _____ D _____    B _____ D _____

3) _____    3) _____    3) _____

B _____ D _____    B _____ D _____    B _____ D _____

4) _____    4) _____    4) _____

B _____ D _____    B _____ D _____    B _____ D _____

5) _____    5) _____    5) _____

B _____ D _____    B _____ D _____    B _____ D _____

6) _____    6) _____    6) _____

B _____ D _____    B _____ D _____    B _____ D _____

7) _____    7) _____    7) _____

B _____ D _____    B _____ D _____    B _____ D _____

**N A M E S**

# FORWARD LINEAGE CHART

HUSBAND _____

Birth Date _____

Death Date _____

WIFE (Maiden Name) _____

Birth Date _____

Death Date _____

*For large families complete 2 charts.*

| CHILD'S NAME _____ | CHILD'S NAME _____ | CHILD'S NAME _____ |
| Birth Date _____ | Birth Date _____ | Birth Date _____ |
| Death Date _____ | Death Date _____ | Death Date _____ |
| Married to: _____ | Married to: _____ | Married to: _____ |
| SPOUSE'S NAME | SPOUSE'S NAME | SPOUSE'S NAME |

1) _____   B _____ D _____

2) _____   B _____ D _____

3) _____   B _____ D _____

4) _____   B _____ D _____

5) _____   B _____ D _____

6) _____   B _____ D _____

7) _____   B _____ D _____

G R A N D C H I L D R E N

N A M E S

# FORWARD LINEAGE CHART

HUSBAND _____

WIFE (Maiden Name) _____

Birth Date _____

Birth Date _____

Death Date _____

Death Date _____

_For large families complete 2 charts_

| CHILD'S NAME _____ | CHILD'S NAME _____ | CHILD'S NAME _____ |
|---|---|---|
| Birth Date _____ | Birth Date _____ | Birth Date _____ |
| Death Date _____ | Death Date _____ | Death Date _____ |
| Married to: _____ | Married to: _____ | Married to: _____ |
| SPOUSE'S NAME _____ | SPOUSE'S NAME _____ | SPOUSE'S NAME _____ |

G R A N D C H I L D R E N

N A M E S

| 1) _____ | 1) _____ | 1) _____ |
| B _____ D _____ | B _____ D _____ | B _____ D _____ |
| 2) _____ | 2) _____ | 2) _____ |
| B _____ D _____ | B _____ D _____ | B _____ D _____ |
| 3) _____ | 3) _____ | 3) _____ |
| B _____ D _____ | B _____ D _____ | B _____ D _____ |
| 4) _____ | 4) _____ | 4) _____ |
| B _____ D _____ | B _____ D _____ | B _____ D _____ |
| 5) _____ | 5) _____ | 5) _____ |
| B _____ D _____ | B _____ D _____ | B _____ D _____ |
| 6) _____ | 6) _____ | 6) _____ |
| B _____ D _____ | B _____ D _____ | B _____ D _____ |
| 7) _____ | 7) _____ | 7) _____ |
| B _____ D _____ | B _____ D _____ | B _____ D _____ |

# FORWARD LINEAGE CHART

HUSBAND _____

Birth Date _____

Death Date _____

WIFE (Maiden Name) _____

Birth Date _____

Death Date _____

*For large families complete 2 charts.*

| CHILD'S NAME _____ | CHILD'S NAME _____ | CHILD'S NAME _____ |
|---|---|---|
| Birth Date _____ | Birth Date _____ | Birth Date _____ |
| Death Date _____ | Death Date _____ | Death Date _____ |
| Married to: _____ | Married to: _____ | Married to: _____ |
| SPOUSE'S NAME _____ | SPOUSE'S NAME _____ | SPOUSE'S NAME _____ |

G R A N D C H I L D R E N

1) _____
B _____ D _____

2) _____
B _____ D _____

3) _____
B _____ D _____

4) _____
B _____ D _____

5) _____
B _____ D _____

6) _____
B _____ D _____

7) _____
B _____ D _____

N A M E S

1) _____
B _____ D _____

2) _____
B _____ D _____

3) _____
B _____ D _____

4) _____
B _____ D _____

5) _____
B _____ D _____

6) _____
B _____ D _____

7) _____
B _____ D _____

# FORWARD LINEAGE CHART

# PERSONAL HISTORY SHEET

## Of

Full Name: _____

Place of Birth: City _____ State _____ County _____

Date of Birth: Month _____ Day _____ Year _____

Spouse's Name _____ Marriage Date _____

Father's Name _____

Mother's Name _____

Occupation _____

Current or last address: Street _____

City _____ State _____ County _____

Previous Address: Street _____

City _____ State _____ County _____

In what country or countries did this name originate? _____

Has the last name ever been changed or misspelled? Other versions are: _____

_____

This Surname or last name means: _____

_____

Does this surname have a Coat of Arms? _____ yes _____ no

If yes, where is it recorded? _____

Other Important Information: _____

_____

_____

_____

_____

_____

_____

# PERSONAL HISTORY SHEET

## Of

Full Name: _____

Place of Birth: City _____ State _____ County _____

Date of Birth: Month _____ Day _____ Year _____

Spouse's Name _____ Marriage Date _____

Father's Name _____

Mother's Name _____

Occupation _____

Current or last address:    Street _____

City _____ State _____ County _____

Previous Address:    Street _____

City _____ State _____ County _____

In what country or countries did this name originate? _____

Has the last name ever been changed or misspelled?  Other versions are: _____

_____

This Surname or last name means: _____

_____

Does this surname have a Coat of Arms?  _____ yes    _____ no

If yes, where is it recorded? _____

Other Important Information: _____

_____

_____

_____

_____

_____

# PERSONAL HISTORY SHEET

## Of

_____

Full Name: _____

Place of Birth: City _____ State _____ County _____

Date of Birth: Month _____ Day _____ Year _____

Spouse's Name _____ Marriage Date _____

Father's Name _____

Mother's Name _____

Occupation _____

Current or last address: Street _____

City _____ State _____ County _____

Previous Address: Street _____

City _____ State _____ County _____

In what country or countries did this name originate? _____

Has the last name ever been changed or misspelled? Other versions are: _____

_____

This Surname or last name means: _____

_____

Does this surname have a Coat of Arms? _____ yes _____ no

If yes, where is it recorded? _____

Other Important Information: _____

_____

_____

_____

_____

_____

_____

# PERSONAL HISTORY SHEET

## Of _____

Full Name: _____

Place of Birth:  City _____ State _____ County _____

Date of Birth:  Month _____ Day _____ Year _____

Spouse's Name _____ Marriage Date _____

Father's Name _____

Mother's Name _____

Occupation _____

Current or last address:  Street _____

City _____ State _____ County _____

Previous Address:  Street _____

City _____ State _____ County _____

In what country or countries did this name originate? _____

Has the last name ever been changed or misspelled?  Other versions are: _____

_____

This Surname or last name means: _____

_____

Does this surname have a Coat of Arms? _____ yes _____ no

If yes, where is it recorded? _____

Other Important Information: _____

_____

_____

_____

_____

_____

_____

# PERSONAL HISTORY SHEET

## Of

Full Name: _____

Place of Birth: City _____ State _____ County _____

Date of Birth: Month _____ Day _____ Year _____

Spouse's Name _____ Marriage Date _____

Father's Name _____

Mother's Name _____

Occupation _____

Current or last address: Street _____

City _____ State _____ County _____

Previous Address: Street _____

City _____ State _____ County _____

In what country or countries did this name originate? _____

Has the last name ever been changed or misspelled? Other versions are: _____

_____

This Surname or last name means: _____

_____

Does this surname have a Coat of Arms? _____ yes _____ no

If yes, where is it recorded? _____

Other Important Information: _____

_____

_____

_____

_____

_____

_____

# PERSONAL HISTORY SHEET

## Of

Full Name: _____

Place of Birth: City _____ State _____ County _____

Date of Birth: Month _____ Day _____ Year _____

Spouse's Name _____ Marriage Date _____

Father's Name _____

Mother's Name _____

Occupation _____

Current or last address: Street _____

City _____ State _____ County _____

Previous Address: Street _____

City _____ State _____ County _____

In what country or countries did this name originate? _____

Has the last name ever been changed or misspelled? Other versions are: _____

_____

This Surname or last name means: _____

_____

Does this surname have a Coat of Arms? _____ yes _____ no

If yes, where is it recorded? _____

Other Important Information: _____

_____

_____

_____

_____

_____

_____

Individual
Heritage
Chart
of

Father

Mother

Paternal Grandfather

Paternal Grandmother

Maternal Grandfather

Maternal Grandmother

Great Grandfather

Great Grandmother

Great Grandfather

Great Grandmother

Great Grandfather

Great Grandmother

Great Grandfather

Great Grandmother

Great Great Grandfather

Great Great Grandmother

Great Great Grandfather

Great Great Grandmother

Great Great Grandfather

Great Great Grandmother

Great Great Grandfather

Great Great Grandmother

Great Great Grandfather

Great Great Grandmother

Great Great Grandfather

Great Great Grandmother

Great Great Grandfather

Great Great Grandmother

Great Great Grandfather

Great Great Grandmother

# INDIVIDUAL HERITAGE CHART

Individual
Heritage
Chart
of

Father
Paternal Grandfather
Paternal Grandmother

Great Grandfather
Great Great Grandfather
Great Great Grandmother

Great Grandmother
Great Great Grandfather
Great Great Grandmother

Great Grandfather
Great Great Grandfather
Great Great Grandmother

Great Grandmother
Great Great Grandfather
Great Great Grandmother

Mother
Maternal Grandfather
Maternal Grandmother

Great Grandfather
Great Great Grandfather
Great Great Grandmother

Great Grandmother
Great Great Grandfather
Great Great Grandmother

Great Grandfather
Great Great Grandfather
Great Great Grandmother

Great Grandmother
Great Great Grandfather
Great Great Grandmother

# INDIVIDUAL HERITAGE CHART

Individual
Heritage
Chart
of

Father

Mother

Paternal Grandfather

Paternal Grandmother

Maternal Grandfather

Maternal Grandmother

Great Grandfather

Great Grandmother

Great Grandfather

Great Grandmother

Great Grandfather

Great Grandmother

Great Grandfather

Great Grandmother

Great Great Grandfather

Great Great Grandmother

Great Great Grandfather

Great Great Grandmother

Great Great Grandfather

Great Great Grandmother

Great Great Grandfather

Great Great Grandmother

Great Great Grandfather

Great Great Grandmother

Great Great Grandfather

Great Great Grandmother

Great Great Grandfather

Great Great Grandmother

Great Great Grandfather

Great Great Grandmother

# INDIVIDUAL HERITAGE CHART

Individual
Heritage
Chart
of

_____

| | |
|---|---|
| Father | |
| | |

Paternal Grandfather

Great Grandfather

Great Great Grandfather

Great Great Grandmother

Great Grandmother

Great Great Grandfather

Great Great Grandmother

Paternal Grandmother

Great Grandfather

Great Great Grandfather

Great Great Grandmother

Great Grandmother

Great Great Grandfather

Great Great Grandmother

Mother

Maternal Grandfather

Great Grandfather

Great Great Grandfather

Great Great Grandmother

Great Grandmother

Great Great Grandfather

Great Great Grandmother

Maternal Grandmother

Great Grandfather

Great Great Grandfather

Great Great Grandmother

Great Grandmother

Great Great Grandfather

Great Great Grandmother

## INDIVIDUAL HERITAGE CHART

# INDIVIDUAL HERITAGE CHART

Individual
Heritage
Chart
of

Father

Mother

Paternal Grandfather

Paternal Grandmother

Maternal Grandfather

Maternal Grandmother

Great Grandfather

Great Grandmother

Great Grandfather

Great Grandmother

Great Grandfather

Great Grandmother

Great Grandfather

Great Grandmother

Great Great Grandfather

Great Great Grandmother

Great Great Grandfather

Great Great Grandmother

Great Great Grandfather

Great Great Grandmother

Great Great Grandfather

Great Great Grandmother

Great Great Grandfather

Great Great Grandmother

Great Great Grandfather

Great Great Grandmother

Great Great Grandfather

Great Great Grandmother

Great Great Grandfather

Great Great Grandmother

# FAMILY SIGNATURE SHEET

These are the signatures of the relatives of _____

| SIGNATURE | PRINTED NAME | RELATIONSHIP TO ABOVE |
|-----------|--------------|------------------------|
| _____ | _____ | _____ |
| _____ | _____ | _____ |
| _____ | _____ | _____ |
| _____ | _____ | _____ |
| _____ | _____ | _____ |
| _____ | _____ | _____ |
| _____ | _____ | _____ |
| _____ | _____ | _____ |
| _____ | _____ | _____ |
| _____ | _____ | _____ |
| _____ | _____ | _____ |
| _____ | _____ | _____ |
| _____ | _____ | _____ |
| _____ | _____ | _____ |
| _____ | _____ | _____ |
| _____ | _____ | _____ |
| _____ | _____ | _____ |
| _____ | _____ | _____ |
| _____ | _____ | _____ |
| _____ | _____ | _____ |
| _____ | _____ | _____ |
| _____ | _____ | _____ |
| _____ | _____ | _____ |
| _____ | _____ | _____ |

# FAMILY SIGNATURE SHEET

These are the signatures of the relatives of _____

| SIGNATURE | PRINTED NAME | RELATIONSHIP TO ABOVE |
|---|---|---|
| | | |
| | | |
| | | |
| | | |
| | | |
| | | |
| | | |
| | | |
| | | |
| | | |
| | | |
| | | |
| | | |
| | | |
| | | |
| | | |
| | | |
| | | |
| | | |
| | | |
| | | |
| | | |
| | | |

# THE REFERENCE DIRECTORIES

Following is a directory of all of the families in the United States with this surname, which we have been able to locate through the computer scanning of government, utility and other reputable records. It is provided for your personal use in the search for your family ancestors. Since these surnames are unique, they quite often represent a common heritage or place of origin. For instance, the name "Deal" represents families who were original inhabitants of the Deal (Valley) in Kent, England. If you can trace your family name back to a particular foreign country, then you can refer to the reference books and begin your foreign search.

The last page of this directory provides a state count of the families with this last name. Even though people in the United States are mobile, the state count gives you an excellent beginning for determining where heavy concentrations of the family surname exists. These are the areas where you should start looking for early census information.

The first names of the families in this directory are most interesting because we have a very nice habit of naming our children after relatives. If you spot an uncommon first name which also runs in your family, you may have come upon a lost relative.

## THE FAMILY HERITAGE BOOK CERTIFICATE

On the next page you will find a Certificate of Authenticity showing the original owner of this book. When turning to the reverse side you will find that space has been provided to transfer this book from the original owner to future generations. It is our intention that the proper use of this certificate will provide your family with a permanent record of ownership which will be of historical interest for years to come.

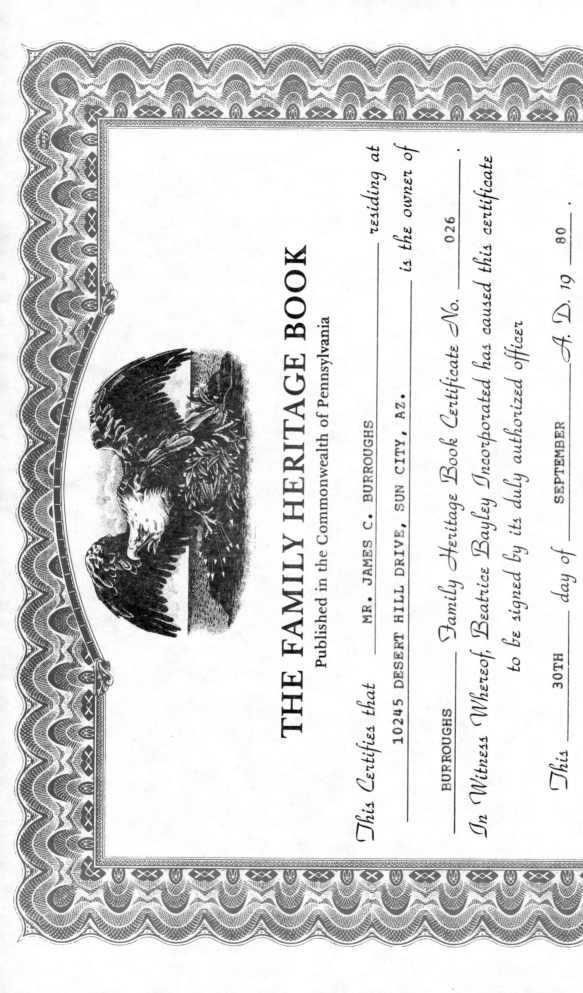

# THE FAMILY HERITAGE BOOK

### Published in the Commonwealth of Pennsylvania

*This Certifies that*    MR. JAMES C. BURROUGHS    *residing at*

10245 DESERT HILL DRIVE, SUN CITY, AZ.    *is the owner of*

BURROUGHS    *Family Heritage Book Certificate No.*    026 .

*In Witness Whereof, Beatrice Bayley Incorporated has caused this certificate*

*to be signed by its duly authorized officer*

*This*    30TH    *day of*    SEPTEMBER    *A.D. 19* 80 .

*Beatrice Bayley*

**First Transferral:**

On this _____ Day of _____ in the year _____ , I transfer to

(name) _____ (city) _____

(state) _____ the ownership of this Family Heritage Book

as indicated on this Certificate.

(signature) _____
First Owner

**Second Transferral:**

On this _____ Day of _____ in the year _____ , I transfer to

(name) _____ (city) _____

(state) _____ the ownership of this Family Heritage Book

as indicated on this Certificate.

(signature) _____
Second Owner

**Third Transferral:**

On this _____ Day of _____ in the year _____ , I transfer to

(name) _____ (city) _____

(state) _____ the ownership of this Family Heritage Book

as indicated on this Certificate.

(signature) _____
Third Owner

**Fourth Transferral:**

On this _____ Day of _____ in the year _____ , I transfer to

(name) _____ (city) _____

(state) _____ the ownership of this Family Heritage Book

as indicated on this Certificate.

(signature) _____
Fourth Owner

**Fifth Transferral:**

On this _____ Day of _____ in the year _____ , I transfer to

(name) _____ (city) _____

(state) _____ the ownership of this Family Heritage Book

as indicated on this Certificate.

(signature) _____
Fifth Owner

DONALD D. BURROUGHS
970 MAIN ST.
AGAWAM, MA. 01001

CLARA O. BURROUGHS
181 SHERIDAN ST.
CHICOPEE, MA. 01020

J. D. BURROUGHS
LONG PLAIN RD.
LEVERETT, MA. 01054

ROBERT B. BURROUGHS
7 SCHOOL
WARREN, MA. 01083

D. L. BURROUGHS
1582 MEMORIAL AV.
W SPRINGFIELD, MA. 01089

K. S. BURROUGHS
533 MAIN ST.
W SPRINGFIELD, MA. 01089

DANIEL E. BURROUGHS
490 WHITE ST.
SPRINGFIELD, MA. 01108

WATERS J. BURROUGHS
361 EVERGREEN RD.
SPRINGFIELD, MA. 01119

ALFRED E. BURROUGHS
55 NAGLE ST.
SPRINGFIELD, MA. 01151

STEPHEN M. BURROUGHS
MAIN
SUNDERLAND, MA. 01375

WENDELL BURROUGHS
SANDRSN RD.
LITTLETON, MA. 01460

STUART M. BURROUGHS
156 HARWOOD AV.
LITTLETON, MA. 01460

RICHARD P. BURROUGHS
150 PAKACHOAG ST.
AUBURN, MA. 01501

ARTHUR T. BURROUGHS
FISHER RD.
MILLVILLE, MA. 01529

WAYNE G. BURROUGHS
314 PROVIDENCE RD.
SOUTH GRAFTON, MA. 01560

WILLIAM E. BURROUGHS
28 HARTFORD AV. R1
UXBRIDGE, MA. 01569

ROY BURROUGHS
23 PURGATORY RD.
WHITINSVILLE, MA. 01588

GEORGE H. BURROUGHS
22 BERGIN LN.
WORCESTER, MA. 01602

ALFRED J. BURROUGHS
49 DARNELL RD.
WORCESTER, MA. 01606

GEORGE E. BURROUGHS, JR.
20 PATTERSON RD.
BEDFORD, MA. 01730

C. B. BURROUGHS
1354 MAIN ST.
CONCORD, MA. 01742

E. A. BURROUGHS
755 WASHINGTON ST.
HOLLISTON, MA. 01746

RICHD C. BURROUGHS
77 REGAL ST.
HOLLISTON, MA. 01746

S. R. BURROUGHS
210 SALEM ST.
WOBURN, MA. 01801

HOBART M. BURROUGHS
15 CLANCY ST.
CHELMSFORD, MA. 01824

ROBERT H. BURROUGHS
9 NALLY AV.
GLOUCESTER, MA. 01930

WILLIAM A. BURROUGHS
594 WASHINGTON ST.
GLOUCESTER, MA. 01930

GORDON J. BURROUGHS
513 ESSEX AV.
GLOUCESTER, MA. 01930

M. E. BURROUGHS
58 CHERRY ST.
GLOUCESTER, MA. 01930

WILLIAM W. BURROUGHS
19 SCHOOL ST.
MANCHESTER, MA. 01944

WILLIAM W. BURROUGHS
21 SCHOOL ST.
MANCHESTER, MA. 01944

M. S. BURROUGHS
SALEM RD. R1
TOPSFIELD, MA. 01983

ALFRED L. BURROUGHS
13 MARSH ST.
HINGHAM, MA. 02043

JOHN H. BURROUGHS, JR.
KINGS LANDNG ST.
NORWELL, MA. 02061

YVONNE BURROUGHS
16 ISABELLA ST.
BOSTON, MA. 02116

FRANK B. BURROUGHS
72 RIDGEWOOD ST.
DORCHESTER, MA. 02122

J. BURROUGHS
270 SUMNER ST.
EAST BOSTON, MA. 02128

MICHAEL BURROUGHS
26 ROBESON ST.
JAMAICA PLAIN, MA. 02130

B. J. BURROUGHS
279 BROADWAY ST.
CAMBRIDGE, MA. 02139

JANET C. BURROUGHS
15 CALVIN ST.
SOMERVILLE, MA. 02143

ARTHUR A. BURROUGHS
152 ASPINWALL AV.
BROOKLINE, MA. 02146

ROBERT F. BURROUGHS
287 LYNN ST.
MALDEN, MA. 02148

D. A. BURROUGHS
840 BROADHAY ST.
CHELSEA, MA. 02150

JOHN E. BURROUGHS
36 BRIGHAM RD.
WALTHAM, MA. 02154

JAMES F. BURROUGHS
23 CAPPY CIR.
WEST NEWTON, MA. 02165

WARREN H. BURROUGHS
112 GORDON RD.
WABAN, MA. 02168

FRED T. BURROUGHS
5 FLORENCE TER.
ARLINGTON, MA. 02174

S. R. BURROUGHS
9 PARK AV.
BELMONT, MA. 02178

JAMES A. BURROUGHS
21 PARTRIDGE RD.
S. WEYMOUTH, MA. 02190

CHARLES BURROUGHS
569 BEDFORD ST. R2 N.
E BRIDGEWATER, MA. 02333

WILLIAM W. BURROUGHS
THOMPSON ST.
HALIFAX, MA. 02338

JOHN BURROUGHS
1860 WAREHAM R4
MIDDLEBORO, MA. 02346

DONALD J. BURROUGHS
65 ELM ST.
NORTH EASTON, MA. 02356

DONALD E. BURROUGHS
67 ELM ST.
NORTH EASTON, MA. 02356

GEORGE R. BURROUGHS
49 COCHATO PARK
RANDOLPH, MA. 02368

TONY BURROUGHS
24 PARK ST.
BROCKTON, MA. 02401

S. R. BURROUGHS
STATE RD.
CHILMARK, MA. 02535

R. S. BURROUGHS
SUMMER
EDGARTOWN, MA. 02539

NELSON M. BURROUGHS
80 DALECOURT RD.
CHATHAM, MA. 02633

WILLIAM P. BURROUGHS
MARY CHASE RD.
EASTHAM, MA. 02642

EDGAR E. BURROUGHS
64 HIGHLAND
MASHPEE, MA. 02649

S. E. BURROUGHS
4 SHOREWD DR.
MASHPEE, MA. 02649

DONALD BURROUGHS
56 DEAN ST.
TAUNTON, MA. 02780

NOYES G. BURROUGHS
675 KNOTY OAK RD. R3
COVENTRY, R.I. 02816

EDWARD A. BURROUGHS
35 CANONICUS TER.
E. GREENWICH, R.I. 02818

JOHN J. BURROUGHS
BLACK PLAIN RD.
EXETER, R.I. 02822

WILLIAM P. BURROUGHS
B426 BLACK PL. R1
EXETER, R.I. 02822

MARIAN L. BURROUGHS
SNELL RD.
LTL COMPTON, R.I. 02837

WALTER I. BURROUGHS
1120 TOWER HL RD. R1
N. KINGSTOWN, R.I. 02852

THOMAS BURROUGHS
39 CLAY ST. CF
PAWTUCKET, R.I. 02863

LUCILE BURROUGHS
32 ANGELL RD. CU R5
PAWTUCKET, R.I. 02864

LUCILLE B. BURROUGHS
32 ANGELL RD.
PAWTUCKET, R.I. 02865

JOHN A. BURROUGHS
396 SANDY PT AV. R3
PORTSMOUTH, R.I. 02871

LEROY F. BURROUGHS
124 BLACKSTONE BL APT. 1
PROVIDENCE, R.I. 02906

EDWIN E. BURROUGHS
100 FORBES ST. RI
PROVIDENCE, R.I. 02915

WILLIAM B. BURROUGHS
14 JUNE AV.
PROVIDENCE, R.I. 02920

ELEANOR J. BURROUGHS
425 HOPE RD. R5
PROVIDENCE, R.I. 02920

ALBERT C. BURROUGHS
85 BACK RIVER RD.
MERRIMACK, N.H. 03054

HOBART M. BURROUGHS
631 MAIN ST.
NASHUA, N.H. 03060

KEITH E. BURROUGHS
4 GEORGE AV.
SALEM, N.H. 03079

JOHN BURROUGHS
749 CORNING RD. R3
MANCHESTER, N.H. 03103

ROBERT P. BURROUGHS
1280 UNION ST.
MANCHESTER, N.H. 03104

GEORGE E. BURROUGHS
85 ASH ST.
MANCHESTER, N.H. 03104

NORMA J. BURROUGHS
109 SKY VIEW DR.
MANCHESTER, N.H. 03104

MORRIS R. BURROUGHS
21 FRIENDSHP AV. R1
SUNCOOK, N.H. 03275

R. G. BURROUGHS
NELSON SR.
KEENE, N.H. 03431

DENNIS L. BURROUGHS
75 DAVIS ST.
KEENE, N.H. 03431

RANDOLPH A. BURROUGHS
R3 BX. 383
KEENE, N.H. 03431

CHERYL A. BURROUGHS
NELSON SR.
KEENE, N.H. 03431

HARRY E. BURROUGHS
R32
KEENE, N.H. 03431

HARRY E. BURROUGHS
R2
WINCHESTER, N.H. 03470

DORIS M. BURROUGHS
R123
ALSTEAD, N.H. 03602

GEORGE H. BURROUGHS
MINE RD.
ALSTEAD, N.H. 03602

MARY C. BURROUGHS
ALSTEAD RD. SRE
ALSTEAD, N.H. 03602

HAROLD W. BURROUGHS
BX. 203
CHARLESTOWN, N.H. 03603

WILLARD R. BURROUGHS
R2 BX. 430K
CLAREMONT, N.H. 03743

KENNETH R. BURROUGHS
PIPER HILL R2
CLAREMONT, N.H. 03743

BRUCE BURROUGHS
R1
CLAREMONT, N.H. 03743

FLORENCE H. BURROUGHS
263 ROCKLAND ST. APT. 55
PORTSMOUTH, N.H. 03801

ALBERT BURROUGHS
BX. 314
PORTSMOUTH, N.H. 03801

CATHERINE J. BURROUGHS
LITTLE BAY RD.
PORTSMOUTH, N.H. 03801

STEPHEN BURROUGHS
MAIN ST.
CENTER CONWAY, N.H. 03813

JOHN BURROUGHS
MAIN ST.
CENTER CONWAY, N.H. 03813

EVELYN T. BURROUGHS
CHARLES ST.
MILTON, N.H. 03851

WILFRED BURROUGHS
MAIN ST. S.
MILTON, N.H. 03851

RALPH J. BURROUGHS, SR.
BURROUGHS AV.
SANBORNVILLE, N.H. 03872

JOSEPHINE D. BURROUGHS
5 SWEETSER ST.
BERWICK, ME. 03901

FRANKLIN G. BURROUGHS, J
R2
BOWDOINHAM, ME. 04008

FRANKLIN G. BURROUGHS
R1 BX. 55
ORRS ISLAND, ME. 04066

ROBERT W. BURROUGHS
BX. 1194
PORTLAND, ME. 04104

JOSEPH J. BURROUGHS
FROST HILL AV.
LISBON FALLS, ME. 04252

GLENN BURROUGHS
RIDGE RD. R1
LISBON FALLS, ME. 04252

GLENN BURROUGHS
2 RIDGE RD.
LISBON FALLS, ME. 04252

WILLIAM BURROUGHS
R2 BX. 206
MECHANIC FLS, ME. 04256

MURIEL BURROUGHS
R2
MECHANIC FLS, ME. 04256

STEVEN BURROUGHS
PLEASANT HL R2
AUGUSTA, ME. 04330

PATRICK BURROUGHS
BX. 92
COOPERS MILLS, ME. 04341

ISABELLE H. BURROUGHS
R1
BUCKSPORT, ME. 04416

LINDA C. BURROUGHS
2 PINE ST.
ORONO, ME. 04473

GEORGE BURROUGHS
R4 BX. 87
HOULTON, ME. 04730

DEAN BURROUGHS
33 KELLERAN ST.
HOULTON, ME. 04730

PATRICIA BURROUGHS
R1
ALBION, ME. 04910

GEORGE T. BURROUGHS
R1 BX. 68
DIXMONT, ME. 04932

HENRIETTE M. BURROUGHS
FAIRGROUND RD.
BRADFORD, VT. 05033

ELEANOR H. BURROUGHS
CORINTH, VT. 05039

KAETE M. BURROUGHS
BX. 31
NEWBURY, VT. 05051

HELEN M. BURROUGHS
BX. 102
S. ROYALTON, VT. 05068

REX P. BURROUGHS
R1
WELLS RIVER, VT. 05081

DAVID F. BURROUGHS
RFD
WELLS RIVER, VT. 05081

LARRIE O. BURROUGHS
RFD
WELLS RIVER, VT. 05081

ROBERT O. BURROUGHS
WELLS RIVER, VT. 05081

MARY L. BURROUGHS
PEACHBROOK RD.
WELLS RIVER, VT. 05081

WILLIAM G. BURROUGHS, SR.
WEST NEWBURY, VT. 05085

BERTHA R. BURROUGHS
PEACH BROOK RD.
WEST NEWBURY, VT. 05085

RONALD E. BURROUGHS
SR. 2 BX. 93
WINDSOR, VT. 05089

ALFRED W. BURROUGHS
19 TYLER ST.
BRATTLEBORO, VT. 05301

JOHN P. BURROUGHS
R1
E. FAIRFIELD, VT. 05448

JOHN P. BURROUGHS
BX. 118
ESSEX, VT. 05451

ELIZABETH B. BURROUGHS
21 GRANDVIEW AV.
ESSEX JCT., VT. 05452

GLEN A. BURROUGHS
OAK PARK R2 14
ESSEX JCT., VT. 05452

JOHN B. BURROUGHS
38 CASCADE ST.
ESSEX JCT, VT. 05452

JULIET G. BURROUGHS
R1 BX. 82
HINESBURG, VT. 05461

FRANCIS H. BURROUGHS
R2
MILTON, VT. 05468

ROLAND A. BURROUGHS
BX. 84
UNDERHILL CTR., VT. 05490

STUART H. BURROUGHS
PETERSON LN.
WILLISTON, VT. 05495

VIRGIE E. BURROUGHS
EAST BARRE, VT. 05649

AUDRA L. BURROUGHS
BX. 71
GRANITEVILLE, VT. 05654

CLIFTON J. BURROUGHS
PEARL ST.
GRANITEVILLE, VT. 05654

HOWARD C. BURROUGHS
PLAINFIELD, VT. 05667

ROY A. BURROUGHS
PITTSFORD, VT. 05763

RUDOLPH J. BURROUGHS
BX. 82
DERBY, VT. 05829

JANET A. BURROUGHS
BX. 402
DERBY, VT. 05829

RUDOLPH J. BURROUGHS
BX. 72
DERBY, VT. 05829

CHARLES R. BURROUGHS
MORGAN CENTER, VT. 05854

RONALD BURROUGHS
24 LINWOOD DR. R2
BLOOMFIELD, CT. 06002

C. A. BURROUGHS
23 MT. VERNON APTS.
VERNON-ROCKVL, CT. 06066

EDWARD BURROUGHS, JR.
89 MAPLE AV.
WILLIMANTIC, CT. 06226

EDWARD BURROUGHS
FLANDERS RD.
COVENTRY, CT. 06238

N. BURROUGHS
PLAINS RD.
WINDHAM, CT. 06280

ELLIOTT W. BURROUGHS
BARSTOW RD.
CANTERBURY, CT. 06331

ROLAND E. BURROUGHS, JR.
BARSTOW RD.
CANTERBURY, CT. 06331

OLIVER BURROUGHS
14 HANCOX ST.
STONINGTON, CT. 06378

IRVING F. BURROUGHS
6 ANTIONETTE ST.
PAWCATUCK, CT. 06379

ROBERT S. BURROUGHS
10 MAIN ST.
CHESHIRE, CT. 06410

GEORGE BURROUGHS
96 LUDLOWE RD.
FAIRFIELD, CT. 06430

LESTER BURROUGHS
PARMALE HILL R3
NEWTOWN, CT. 06470

G. N. BURROUGHS
13 BRENTLEY DR.
SHELTON, CT. 06484

ROBERT O. BURROUGHS
LAKEMERE RD. R3
SOUTHBURY, CT. 06488

DAVID BURROUGHS
32 BASSETT ST.
NEW HAVEN, CT. 06511

L. BURROUGHS
123 CARMEL ST.
NEW HAVEN, CT. 06511

W. M. BURROUGHS
523 SHERMAN AV.
NEW HAVEN, CT. 06511

HENRY BURROUGHS
76 UNION AV. WH
NEW HAVEN, CT. 06516

SUSAN S. BURROUGHS
814 PARK AV.
BRIDGEPORT, CT. 06604

SANFORD BURROUGHS
301 PARK AV. N.
BRIDGEPORT, CT. 06612

ROBERT O. BURROUGHS
83 CHURCH RD.
BRIDGEPORT, CT. 06612

DAVID BURROUGHS
34 FAIRMONT ST.
WATERBURY, CT. 06706

A. BURROUGHS
30 BLISS ST.
WATERBURY, CT. 06708

EARL B. BURROUGHS
153 ALLERTON FARM
MIDDLEBURY, CT. 06762

BRUCE BURROUGHS
WEST CORNWALL, CT. 06796

W. J. BURROUGHS
15 MAPLE LN.
BROOKFLD CTR., CT. 06805

POLLY BURROUGHS
PORCHUCK RD.
GREENWICH, CT. 06830

RICHARD P. BURROUGHS
102 RIVERSIDE DR. R4
RIDGEFIELD, CT. 06877

RAIN BURROUGHS
124 COMPO RD. S.
WESTPORT, CT. 06880

BERNARD BURROUGHS
10 WAKEMAN PL.
WESTPORT, CT. 06880

DOROTHY BURROUGHS
791 ATLANTIC ST.
STAMFORD, CT. 06902

REGINALD C. BURROUGHS
198 SAWMILL RD.
STAMFORD, CT. 06903

WALTER D. BURROUGHS
151 2ND ST. W.
BAYONNE, N.J. 07002

J. BURROUGHS
66 LINCOLN ST.
EAST ORANGE, N.J. 07017

ROSLEE BURROUGHS
45 18TH ST. N.
EAST ORANGE, N.J. 07017

N. BURROUGHS
23 LAUREL AV.
MAPLEWOOD, N.J. 07040

FRANK BURROUGHS
2 CLAIRIDGE CT.
MONTCLAIR, N.J. 07042

R. BURROUGHS
97 MAPLE AV.
MONTCLAIR, N.J. 07042

T. BURROUGHS
195 PARK AV.
ORANGE, N.J. 07050

L. L. BURROUGHS
318 GRANT AV.
PLAINFIELD, N.J. 07060

E. BURROUGHS
726 WATCHUNG AV.
PLAINFIELD, N.J. 07060

RAY T. BURROUGHS
287 SOMERSET ST.
PLAINFIELD, N.J. 07060

T. BURROUGHS
320 EMERSON AV.
PLAINFIELD, N.J. 07062

H. BURROUGHS
721 FRONT ST. E.
PLAINFIELD, N.J. 07062

ALEXANDER BURROUGHS
908 3RD ST. W.
PLAINFIELD, N.J. 07063

RUFUS BURROUGHS
906 3RD ST. W.
PLAINFIELD, N.J. 07063

E. BURROUGHS
240 VAN BUREN ST.
RUTHERFORD, N.J. 07071

JAMES J. BURROUGHS
75 TUXEDO PL.
VAUXHALL, N.J. 07088

J. BURROUGHS
182 ORANGE ST.
NEWARK, N.J. 07103

DORIS BURROUGHS
78 BOYLAN ST.
NEWARK, N.J. 07106

CLARA BURROUGHS
30 11TH AV.
NEWARK, N.J. 07107

WILLIAM BURROUGHS
261 6TH ST. N.
NEWARK, N.J. 07107

STEVEN W. BURROUGHS
37 WAVERLY AV.
NEWARK, N.J. 07108

S. BURROUGHS
188 WAVERLY AV.
NEWARK, N.J. 07108

OLIVER BURROUGHS, JR.
202 RUNYON ST. W.
NEWARK, N.J. 07108

C. BURROUGHS, JR.
40 UNION AV. NU
NUTLEY, N.J. 07110

N. BURROUGHS
55 LESLIE PL.
IRVINGTON, N.J. 07111

D. BURROUGHS
237 OSBORNE TER.
NEWARK, N.J. 07112

FREDERICK D. BURROUGHS, JR.
1601 SUMMIT AV.
ELIZABETH, N.J. 07205

R. J. BURROUGHS
12 MC DOUGAL ST.
JERSEY CITY, N.J. 07304

JAMES BURROUGHS
6 BOLTWOOD ST.
JERSEY CITY, N.J. 07304

L. BURROUGHS
79 BERGEN AV.
JERSEY CITY, N.J. 07305

L. BURROUGHS
206 BIDWELL AV.
JERSEY CITY, N.J. 07305

M. A. BURROUGHS
23 OGDEN TER.
BUTLER, N.J. 07405

CHARLES BURROUGHS
10 10 12TH ST.
FAIR LAWN, N.J. 07410

CHARLES A. BURROUGHS
23 MOORE RD. R5
WEST MILFORD, N.J. 07480

M. BURROUGHS
203 17TH AV.
PATERSON, N.J. 07504

M. BURROUGHS
155 22ND ST. E.
PATERSON, N.J. 07514

RONALD BURROUGHS
281 GARDEN ST.
ENGLEWOOD, N.J. 07631

CHARLES V. BURROUGHS
347 ROSS RD.
PARAMUS, N.J. 07652

ROBERT R. BURROUGHS
200 PALISADES AV.
WESTWOOD, N.J. 07675

G. H. BURROUGHS
49 LEWIS PL.
WESTWOOD, N.J. 07675

G. BURROUGHS
162 KINDERKAMACK RD.
WESTWOOD, N.J. 07675

CHIP BURROUGHS
14 SYCAMORE LN.
RED BANK, N.J. 07701

HARRY S. BURROUGHS
222 MAPLE PL.
KEYPORT, N.J. 07735

EARL L. BURROUGHS
9 HILLTOP CIR.
BROOKSIDE, N.J. 07926

JAMES E. BURROUGHS
87 LACKAWANA BL
GILLETTE, N.J. 07933

JOHN R. BURROUGHS
US HWY 206
GLADSTONE, N.J. 07934

ELIZABETH M. BURROUGHS
27 HANOVER RD.
EAST HANOVER, N.J. 07936

ABEL I. BURROUGHS
42 COOK AV.
MADISON, N.J. 07940

S. BURROUGHS
29 CENTRAL AV.
MADISON, N.J. 07940

G. BURROUGHS
30 COOK AV.
MADISON, N.J. 07940

A. E. BURROUGHS
21 KINNEY ST.
MADISON, N.J. 07940

ALFRED E. BURROUGHS
34 WALNUT ST.
MADISON, N.J. 07940

D. BURROUGHS
20 GRANT ST.
MORRISTOWN, N.J. 07960

F. H. BURROUGHS
209 AUSTIN AV.
BARRINGTON, N.J. 08007

ROBERT A. BURROUGHS
18 CYPRESS RD.
BURLINGTON, N.J. 08016

B. R. BURROUGHS
74 2ND ST. E.
BURLINGTON, N.J. 08016

NATHANIEL H. BURROUGHS
19 6TH ST. W.
BURLINGTON, N.J. 08016

EDWARD BURROUGHS
326 YORK ST.
BURLINGTON, N.J. 08016

H. BURROUGHS
315 ELLIS AV.
LAWNSIDE, N.J. 08045

M. E. BURROUGHS
1331 MILLCREEK RD.
MANAHAWKIN, N.J. 08050

DAVID B. BURROUGHS
200 CHIPPEWA TRL
MEDFORD, N.J. 08055

EDWARD F. BURROUGHS, JR.
531 STEVENS DR.
MOUNT HOLLY, N.J. 08060

YVETTE BURROUGHS
617 2ND ST. W.
PALMYRA, N.J. 08065

C. E. BURROUGHS, JR.
106 COOPER AV. CW
CAMDEN, N.J. 08108

M. E. BURROUGHS
116 WALNUT AV. E.
CAMDEN, N.J. 08109

M. E. BURROUGHS
120 WALNUT AV. E.
CAMDEN, N.J. 08109

FRED BURROUGHS
314 PINE ST.
ABSECON, N.J. 08201

R. C. BURROUGHS
318 PINE ST.
ABSECON, N.J. 08201

CHARLES W. BURROUGHS
22 SUMMIT AV.
ABSECON, N.J. 08201

GEORGE J. BURROUGHS
12 8TH AV.
ABSECON, N.J. 08201

GEORGE BURROUGHS
402 ALBERT AV.
NORTHFIELD, N.J. 08225

GEORGE E. BURROUGHS
720 MILL RD.
NORTHFIELD, N.J. 08225

WILLIAM H. BURROUGHS
130 BRIGHTON AV.
PLEASANTVILLE, N.J. 08232

L. BURROUGHS
23 DAWES AV. E.
SOMERS POINT, N.J. 08244

B. F. BURROUGHS
225 3RD ST. W.
WILDWOOD, N.J. 08260

JILL BURROUGHS
534 CHESTNUT AV.
BRIDGETON, N.J. 08302

JAMES A. BURROUGHS
1117 ADRIATIC AV.
ATLANTIC CITY, N.J. 08401

JAMES BURROUGHS
821 BALTIC AV.
ATLANTIC CITY, N.J. 0840

JAMES M. BURROUGHS
139 LIBERTY AV.
ATLANTIC CITY, N.J. 08401

E. BURROUGHS
503 TENNESSEE AV. N. APT
ATLANTIC CITY, N.J. 08401

ANDREW BURROUGHS
1536 READING AV. APT. B.
ATLANTIC CITY, N.J. 08401

RICHARD BURROUGHS
209 DUDLEY AV. N.
ATLANTIC CITY, N.J. 0840

GLADYS M. BURROUGHS
MONMOUTH RD.
CREAMRIDGE, N.J. 08514

J. E. BURROUGHS
MONMOUTH RD.
CREAMRIDGE, N.J. 08514

EARL BURROUGHS
820 2ND ST. W.
FLORENCE, N.J. 08518

K. A. BURROUGHS
43 CLINTON ST.
LAMBERTVILLE, N.J. 08530

JACOB F. BURROUGHS
44 MAIN ST. S.
LAMBERTVILLE, N.J. 08530

JOHN D. BURROUGHS
165 UNION ST. N.
LAMBERTVILLE, N.J. 08530

JOHN BURROUGHS
36 UNION ST. S.
LAMBERTVILLE, N.J. 08530

A. BURROUGHS
105 QUARRY ST. R. 2
LAMBERTVILLE, N.J. 08530

DIANA BURROUGHS
8 MADISON ST.
PRINCETON, N.J. 08540

ROBERT F. BURROUGHS, JR.
FORREST EDGE
TITUSVILLE, N.J. 08560

R. H. BURROUGHS
182 LOCUST ST.
TRENTON, N.J. 08609

M. BURROUGHS
2035 BROAD ST. S.
TRENTON, N.J. 08610

REGINALD L. BURROUGHS
10 KERR DR.
TRENTON, N.J. 08610

ABRAM B. BURROUGHS
47 BRENWAL AV.
TRENTON, N.J. 08618

D. BURROUGHS
610 WESTMORELAND DR.
TRENTON, N.J. 08618

HARRY J. BURROUGHS
16 WALTON AV.
TRENTON, N.J. 08618

W. A. BURROUGHS, 3D
321 HANOVER ST. W.
TRENTON, N.J. 08618

EDGAR J. BURROUGHS
87 SAYBROOK AV.
TRENTON, N.J. 08619

SAMUEL F. BURROUGHS
30 ELMORE AV.
TRENTON, N.J. 08619

EDWARD F. BURROUGHS
16 DELOTTA DR.
TRENTON, N.J. 08619

RAYMOND J. BURROUGHS
5 WHITMAN RD.
TRENTON, N.J. 08619

CHARLES W. BURROUGHS
34 SCOTCH RD.
TRENTON, N.J. 08628

IRVING D. BURROUGHS
393 ATLANTIC AV.
TRENTON, N.J. 08629

RUSSELL H. BURROUGHS
331 GARFIELD AV.
TRENTON, N.J. 08629

ALFRED L. BURROUGHS
19 ORNE AV.
TRENTON, N.J. 08638

PAUL L. BURROUGHS
11 WINDSOR AV.
TRENTON, N.J. 08638

KATHERINE B. BURROUGHS
212 MAPLE ST.
TRENTON, N.J. 08691

L. H. BURROUGHS
315 OCEAN AV.
LAKEWOOD, N.J. 08701

M. BURROUGHS
130 HARBOR INN RD.
BAYVILLE, N.J. 08721

PETER BURROUGHS
2418 RIVERSIDE TER.
MANASQUAN, N.J. 08736

EDGAR J. BURROUGHS
8 KEENE ST.
WHITING, N.J. 08759

SUSAN BURROUGHS
CROTON, NJ R2
FLEMINGTON, N.J. 08822

J. BURROUGHS
136 FIAT AV.
ISELIN, N.J. 08830

L. R. BURROUGHS
74 AMHERST LN.
JAMESBURG, N.J. 08831

R. F. BURROUGHS
928 WASHINGTON AV. S.
PISCATAWAY, N.J. 08854

RAYMOND F. BURROUGHS
8 HADLER DR.
SOMERSET, N.J. 08873

LEOY J. BURROUGHS
37 BALDWIN ST.
NEW BRUNSWICK, N.J. 08901

FREDERICK BURROUGHS
2541 54TH ST. W.
NEW YORK, N.Y. 10019

WILLIE M. BURROUGHS
120 129TH ST. W.
NEW YORK, N.Y. 10027

CHESTER BURROUGHS
2509 7TH AV.
NEW YORK, N.Y. 10039

WILLIAM BURROUGHS
66 HEBERTON AV.
STATEN ISLAND, N.Y. 10302

BETH A. BURROUGHS
2 NARROWS RD. S.
STATEN ISLAND, N.Y. 10305

GEORGE H. BURROUGHS
164 BURBANK AV.
STATEN ISLAND, N.Y. 10306

RONALD G. BURROUGHS
57 SUMMIT AV.
STATEN ISLAND, N.Y. 1030

HOWARD C. BURROUGHS
43 IDAHO AV.
STATEN ISLAND, N.Y. 10309

JONELL BURROUGHS
1262 WEBSTER AV.
BRONX, N.Y. 10456

DONALD C. BURROUGHS
1052 BURKE AV.
BRONX, N.Y. 10469

DEWEY A. BURROUGHS
1860 TILLOTSON AV.
BRONX, N.Y. 10469

WILLIAM BURROUGHS
115 UNION AV.
MOUNT VERNON, N.Y. 10550

WILLIAM BURROUGHS
21 BENNETT ST.
RYE, N.Y. 10580

VALENTINE BURROUGHS
120 LORD KITCHENER
NEW ROCHELLE, N.Y. 10804

ELSIE BURROUGHS
55 ARLENE CT.
PEARL RIVER, N.Y. 10965

DOROTHY M. BURROUGHS
152 ORANGE TPKE
SLOATSBURG, N.Y. 10974

MARTIN BURROUGHS
4 MERRICK DR.
SPRING VALLEY, N.Y. 10977

GEORGE BURROUGHS
164 46TH ST. E.
BROOKLYN, N.Y. 11203

FREDDIE BURROUGHS
1711 DEAN ST.
BROOKLYN, N.Y. 11213

MABEL M. BURROUGHS
776 CROWN ST.
BROOKLYN, N.Y. 11213

DAVE BURROUGHS
1243 PRESIDENT ST.
BROOKLYN, N.Y. 11225

THELMA A. BURROUGHS
618 DECATUR ST.
BROOKLYN, N.Y. 11233

HOOVER E. BURROUGHS
119 54 226TH ST.
JAMAICA, N.Y. 11411

LUELLA B. BURROUGHS
134 22 227TH ST.
JAMAICA, N.Y. 11413

CHRISTINE BURROUGHS
137 27 78TH ST.
JAMAICA, N.Y. 11414

BARBARA BURROUGHS
146 33 175TH ST.
JAMAICA, N.Y. 11434

JOSEPHINE BURROUGHS
144 09 ROCKAWAY BL
JAMAICA, N.Y. 11436

CHARLES K. BURROUGHS
842 LORENZ AV.
BALDWIN, N.Y. 11510

DAVID B. BURROUGHS
PIPING ROCK RD.
GLEN HEAD, N.Y. 11545

RAYMOND BURROUGHS
23 WEIR ST.
HEMPSTEAD, N.Y. 11550

FRANCIS BURROUGHS
63 HART ST.
LYNBROOK, N.Y. 11563

AGNES BURROUGHS
21 PARK PL.
ROOSEVELT, N.Y. 11575

HELEN BURROUGHS
5 BAYVIEW AV.
BAYVILLE, N.Y. 11709

JOHN K. BURROUGHS
71 BRENNER AV.
BETHPAGE, N.Y. 11714

DAVID BURROUGHS
216 BRANCH AV.
CENTRAL ISLIP, N.Y. 1172

A. B. BURROUGHS
9 DUQUESNE DR.
GREENLAWN, N.Y. 11740

MARY L. BURROUGHS
12 MAURICE CT.
HUNTINGTON, N.Y. 11743

WILLIAM T. BURROUGHS
38 SARAH DR.
LAKE GROVE, N.Y. 11755

MARGARET BURROUGHS
4005 ALKEN AV.
SEAFORD, N.Y. 11783

LESLIE V. BURROUGHS
MAIN RD.
CUTCHOGUE, N.Y. 11935

STANLEY C. BURROUGHS
R1
AMSTERDAM, N.Y. 12010

LORRAINE A. BURROUGHS
24 1/2 MINAVILLE ST.
AMSTERDAM, N.Y. 12010

RONALD E. BURROUGHS
R2 BX. 152
AVERILL PARK, N.Y. 12018

ALTON E. BURROUGHS
48 MIDLINE RD.
BALLSTON LAKE, N.Y. 12019

SAMUEL T. BURROUGHS
82 SIDE DR. E.
BALLSTON LAKE, N.Y. 12019

RALPH BURROUGHS
75 DEVON RD.
DELMAR, N.Y. 12054

KENNETH B. BURROUGHS
40 CAROLANNE DR.
DELMAR, N.Y. 12054

PHILIPP H. BURROUGHS
3 TAMARACK LN.
CLIFTON PARK, N.Y. 12065

JAMES W. BURROUGHS
CHURCH ST. E.
FORT HUNTER, N.Y. 12069

RICHARD D. BURROUGHS
34 HIGHLAND AV.
FORT JOHNSON, N.Y. 12070

CRAIG A. BURROUGHS
712 ADAMS CT.
GUILDERLAND, N.Y. 12084

SHARON I. BURROUGHS
R1
MELROSE, N.Y. 12121

SHARON I. BURROUGHS
119 MINERAL SPRINGS B.
MELROSE, N.Y. 12121

J. BURROUGHS
R1 BX. 119
MELROSE, N.Y. 12121

RALPH B. BURROUGHS
31 MELLON AV.
TROY, N.Y. 12180

VALERIE C. BURROUGHS
1007 HOOSICK ST.
TROY, N.Y. 12180

GERALD R. BURROUGHS
7 NORTON ST. RO
ALBANY, N.Y. 12205

FRANCIS BURROUGHS
285 LARK ST. APT. 9
ALBANY, N.Y. 12210

LAWRENCE E. BURROUGHS
447 SHAGGERTOWN RD.
SCHENECTADY, N.Y. 12302

SAMUEL T. BURROUGHS
124 GIFFORD RD.
SCHENECTADY, N.Y. 12304

GEORGE A. BURROUGHS
626 POUTRE AV.
SCHENECTADY, N.Y. 12306

CHANCEY A. BURROUGHS
GRAND GORGE, N.Y. 12434

VELA BURROUGHS
DEPOT ST.
GRAND GORGE, N.Y. 12434

JOHN BURROUGHS
BX. 108
ROXBURY, N.Y. 12474

LOUISE BURROUGHS
307 LIBERTY ST.
NEWBURGH, N.Y. 12550

LOUISE BURROUGHS
298 LIBERTY ST.
NEWBURGH, N.Y. 12550

ROBERT H. BURROUGHS
12 STARR DR.
RHINEBECK, N.Y. 12572

CANDACE M. BURROUGHS
R1 BX. 127
TIVOLI, N.Y. 12583

MAYNARD B. BURROUGHS
241 GRAND AV.
POUGHKEEPSIE, N.Y. 12603

E. W. BURROUGHS
3 PATRICIA RD.
POUGHKEEPSIE, N.Y. 12603

KENNETH T. BURROUGHS
22 VALLEY VIEW RD.
POUGHKEEPSIE, N.Y. 12603

PATRICK T. BURROUGHS
WILSEY RD.
GREENFLD CTR, N.Y. 12833

HENRY P. BURROUGHS
SHORE RD. SRS
HADLEY, N.Y. 12835

DOUGLAS C. BURROUGHS
BX. 318-1
HADLEY, N.Y. 12835

HORACE BURROUGHS
207 THE PORTAGE
TICONDEROGA, N.Y. 12883

JAMES H. BURROUGHS
18 TREADWAY ST.
TICONDEROGA, N.Y. 12883

HAROLD J. BURROUGHS
BREED HILL RD.
CROWN POINT, N.Y. 12928

THOMAS C. BURROUGHS
BX. 146
CROWN POINT, N.Y. 12928

MILDRED E. BURROUGHS
181 GENESEE ST.
AUBURN, N.Y. 13021

EDWARD F. BURROUGHS
65 FRENCH AV.
AUBURN, N.Y. 13021

WILLIAM H. BURROUGHS
305 MC INTOSH DR.
AUBURN, N.Y. 13021

BETTY J. BURROUGHS
6 GARROW ST.
AUBURN, N.Y. 13021

B. R. BURROUGHS
9594 TAGUS LN.
BREWERTON, N.Y. 13029

CECIL M. BURROUGHS
R1
HOMER, N.Y. 13077

SANDRA D. BURROUGHS
COLD BRK RD. R1
HOMER, N.Y. 13077

ALAN G. BURROUGHS
513 1ST ST.
LIVERPOOL, N.Y. 13088

STEVEN J. BURROUGHS
BAPTIST HILL RD. R1
PORT BYRON, N.Y. 13140

FRANKLIN L. BURROUGHS
120 CAYUGA ST.
SENECA FALLS, N.Y. 13148

SARAH M. BURROUGHS
R3 BX. 3183
SENECA FALLS, N.Y. 13148

RACHEL C. BURROUGHS
R2
TULLY, N.Y. 13159

STANLEY BURROUGHS
38 LIBERTY CT. D.
WATERLOO, N.Y. 13165

BRUCE V. BURROUGHS
136 CENTURY DR.
SYRACUSE, N.Y. 13209

DELLA D. BURROUGHS
316 FELLOWS AV.
SYRACUSE, N.Y. 13210

WILLIAM A. BURROUGHS
228 CHINOOK DR.
SYRACUSE, N.Y. 13210

FREDERICK C. BURROUGHS, JR.
111 MARIAN DR.
SYRACUSE, N.Y. 13219

CHARLES R. BURROUGHS
R1
FORT PLAIN, N.Y. 13339

RICHARD J. BURROUGHS
16 GORDON AV.
HERKIMER, N.Y. 13350

HILBERT BURROUGHS
R8
NEW BERLIN, N.Y. 13411

WILBERT BURROUGHS
R1
NEW BERLIN, N.Y. 13411

BEVAN B. BURROUGHS
2029 TITAN CIR. N. APT.
ROME, N.Y. 13440

JEAN BURROUGHS
198 TOWN LIN RD. A.
VERNON, N.Y. 13476

R. J. BURROUGHS
BX. 111
BIBLE SCH PK, N.Y. 13737

JAMES A. BURROUGHS
986 CONKLIN RD.
CONKLIN, N.Y. 13748

CHARLES BURROUGHS
SAND CR RD. SR. 2
HANCOCK, N.Y. 13783

RUTH G. BURROUGHS
16 MASSACHUSTTS ST.
JOHNSON CITY, N.Y. 13790

THERESA B. BURROUGHS
MILL ST. EXT.
MARATHON, N.Y. 13803

DAVID D. BURROUGHS
4 ROSS ST.
OXFORD, N.Y. 13830

MORRELL BURROUGHS
24 WOODLAND RD.
BINGHAMTON, N.Y. 13901

ALFRED E. BURROUGHS
8493 INDIAN FALLS RD.
CORFU, N.Y. 14036

RONALD L. BURROUGHS
2488 BROADWAY RD.
DARIEN CENTER, N.Y. 14040

LLOYD S. BURROUGHS
GEORGE ST.
DELEVAN, N.Y. 14042

DAVID J. BURROUGHS
76 KING ST.
DUNKIRK, N.Y. 14048

KEITH A. BURROUGHS
10537 BETH CENTER
EAST BETHANY, N.Y. 14054

WILLIAM A. BURROUGHS
6989 ACADEMY DR.
LOCKPORT, N.Y. 14094

WALTER J. BURROUGHS
238 GLENDALE DR.
TONAWANDA, N.Y. 14150

DENTON L. BURROUGHS
ARSTIO TRLPK
YORKSHIRE, N.Y. 14173

JOHN H. BURROUGHS
427 BEST ST.
BUFFALO, N.Y. 14208

HENRY BURROUGHS
625 FERRY ST. E.
BUFFALO, N.Y. 14211

HOWARD M. BURROUGHS
148 JOHNSON ST.
BUFFALO, N.Y. 14211

HENRY N. BURROUGHS
244 PHYLLIS AV.
BUFFALO, N.Y. 14215

LOUISE BURROUGHS
57 WYOMING AV.
BUFFALO, N.Y. 14215

KAREN M. BURROUGHS
124 HIGHLAND AV.
BUFFALO, N.Y. 14222

GREGORY BURROUGHS
35 ELKHURST DR.
BUFFALO, N.Y. 14225

LAWRENCE P. BURROUGHS
21 PANAMA LN.
BUFFALO, N.Y. 14225

LAURENCE G. BURROUGHS
24 SIBERLING DR.
BUFFALO, N.Y. 14225

JOHN E. BURROUGHS
313 ALLENHURST RD.
BUFFALO, N.Y. 14226

GEORGE BURROUGHS
24 WILLIAMSTOWN CT. APT.
BUFFALO, N.Y. 14227

CHARLES H. BURROUGHS
4017 GLENN ST.
NIAGARA FALLS, N.Y. 14305

LUTHER P. BURROUGHS
123 MAIN ST. S. APT. 1
ALBION, N.Y. 14411

LEROY BURROUGHS
218 BANK ST. W.
ALBION, N.Y. 14411

CATHERINE BURROUGHS
5 HAVENWD HLW R5
FAIRPORT, N.Y. 14450

G. F. BURROUGHS
7855 MAIN ST.
FISHERS, N.Y. 14453

W. BURROUGHS
NYS SCHOOL OF I.
INDUSTRY, N.Y. 14474

CRAIG G. BURROUGHS
1829 GENESEE ST.
LIMA, N.Y. 14485

EDITH V. BURROUGHS
35 MACEDON TRLPK
MACEDON, N.Y. 14502

JAMES R. BURROUGHS
EELPOT RD. R3
NAPLES, N.Y. 14512

RAYMOND J. BURROUGHS
43 HUBBARD DR.
NORTH CHILI, N.Y. 14514

CHARLES E. BURROUGHS
4 THORNWOOD CIR.
PITTSFORD, N.Y. 14534

VINCENT D. BURROUGHS
2830 RETSOF AV.
RETSOF, N.Y. 14539

PURCELL W. BURROUGHS
56 LIVINGSTON ST.
WARSAW, N.Y. 14569

FRANCIS O. BURROUGHS
144 HEMPEL ST.
ROCHESTER, N.Y. 14605

JEROME BURROUGHS
448 CLINTON AV. N.
ROCHESTER, N.Y. 14605

JOHN M. BURROUGHS
209 LINCOLN ST.
ROCHESTER, N.Y. 14605

WILLIAM J. BURROUGHS
10 VIENNA ST. APT. 4H
ROCHESTER, N.Y. 14605

ROBERT J. BURROUGHS
73 ARDELLA ST.
ROCHESTER, N.Y. 14606

VINCENT J. BURROUGHS
297 ROSSMORE ST.
ROCHESTER, N.Y. 14606

BILLY BURROUGHS
101 NORWOOD AV.
ROCHESTER, N.Y. 14606

KAREN P. BURROUGHS
62 BERKELEY ST.
ROCHESTER, N.Y. 14607

GARY L. BURROUGHS
72 POND VW HTS. ST.
ROCHESTER, N.Y. 14612

WESLEY BURROUGHS
328 GLENWOOD AV.
ROCHESTER, N.Y. 14613

CHARLES D. BURROUGHS
99 MERLIN ST.
ROCHESTER, N.Y. 14613

JOHN R. BURROUGHS
464 LA GRANGE AV.
ROCHESTER, N.Y. 14615

JACOB J. BURROUGHS
1886 PORTLAND AV.
ROCHESTER, N.Y. 14617

BARBARA B. BURROUGHS
918 EASTBROOKE LN.
ROCHESTER, N.Y. 14618

MYRTLE V. BURROUGHS
190 TERRACE PK.
ROCHESTER, N.Y. 14619

ROBERT J. BURROUGHS
69 VIRGINIA AV.
ROCHESTER, N.Y. 14619

LEROY BURROUGHS
294 BERNARD ST.
ROCHESTER, N.Y. 14621

PRINCE L. BURROUGHS
151 SENECA MANOR DR.
ROCHESTER, N.Y. 14621

PEGGY BURROUGHS
605 PORTLAND AV.
ROCHESTER, N.Y. 14621

J. S. BURROUGHS
73 MOHAWK ST.
ROCHESTER, N.Y. 14621

WILLIAM BURROUGHS
134 WILKINS ST.
ROCHESTER, N.Y. 14621

LAURA M. BURROUGHS
682 BEAHAN RD.
ROCHESTER, N.Y. 14624

MARSHALL C. BURROUGHS, JR.
422 MILL RD.
ROCHESTER, N.Y. 14626

HENRIETTA V. BURROUGHS
14 RICHMOND PL.
JAMESTOWN, N.Y. 14701

CINDY L. BURROUGHS
1 1ST ST.
CATTARAUGUS, N.Y. 14719

BERNICE M. BURROUGHS
73 DUNHAM AV.
CELORON, N.Y. 14720

MAVIS R. BURROUGHS
BX. 1008
CHAUTAUQUA, N.Y. 14722

CHRISTINE BURROUGHS
WAHMEDA
CHAUTAUQUA, N.Y. 14722

WILSON BURROUGHS
TOAD HLW RD. R1
LITTLE VALLEY, N.Y. 14755

JULIA M. BURROUGHS
EDDYVILLE RD. R1
LITTLE VALLEY, N.Y. 14755

MILTON BURROUGHS
R1
LITTLE VALLEY, N.Y. 14755

GARY A. BURROUGHS
TOAD HLW RD. R1
LITTLE VALLEY, N.Y. 14755

DENNIS N. BURROUGHS
TOAD HOLLOW RD.
LITTLE VALLEY, N.Y. 14755

HOWARD L. BURROUGHS
MAPLES RD. R1
LITTLE VALLEY, N.Y. 14755

CLEO L. BURROUGHS
BX. 25
LITTLE VALLEY, N.Y. 14755

CLARA A. BURROUGHS
R1 BX. 290
LITTLE VALLEY, N.Y. 14755

EDWARD M. BURROUGHS
1001 IRVING ST.
OLEAN, N.Y. 14760

ROBERT F. BURROUGHS
61 MAIN ST. N.
PORTVILLE, N.Y. 14770

SUSAN M. BURROUGHS
122 MAIN ST. N.
PORTVILLE, N.Y. 14770

GERALD W. BURROUGHS
46 JAMESTOWN ST.
RANDOLPH, N.Y. 14772

JOHN G. BURROUGHS
420 TIFFT AV.
HORSEHEADS, N.Y. 14845

CHARLES A. BURROUGHS
SHAW RD.
LODI, N.Y. 14860

GARY BURROUGHS
4899PINECRST R.D. R1
MILLPORT, N.Y. 14864

MATTHEW O. BURROUGHS
11 TALL MDW APT. R4
PAINTED POST, N.Y. 14870

KERRY F. BURROUGHS
3214 RIVERSIDE ST. R3
WELLSVILLE, N.Y. 14895

DIANE G. BURROUGHS
RIVERSIDE ST. R3
WELLSVILLE, N.Y. 14895

PATRICIA A. BURROUGHS
261 13TH ST. W.
ELMIRA, N.Y. 14903

WILLIAM E. BURROUGHS
105 WESTMONT AV.
ELMIRA, N.Y. 14905

F. BURROUGHS
621 MULBERRY ST.
BEAVER, PA. 15009

JAMES E. BURROUGHS
109 VANDIVORT DR. R2
BEAVER, PA. 15009

GEORGE BURROUGHS
1400 8TH ST.
BEAVER FALLS, PA. 15010

RALPH L. BURROUGHS
611 22ND ST.
BEAVER FALLS, PA. 15010

KENNETH W. BURROUGHS
13 PATRICIA ST. R1
CHARLEROI, PA. 15022

RUTH BURROUGHS
426 DE SOTO ST.
E. MCKEEPORT, PA. 15035

GEORGE A. BURROUGHS
945 GRAHAM AV.
MONESSEN, PA. 15062

F. M. BURROUGHS
670 MC MAHON AV.
MONESSEN, PA. 15062

IDA BURROUGHS
1328 3RD AV.
NEW BRIGHTON, PA. 15066

E. F. BURROUGHS
755 GROVE AV.
NEW BRIGHTON, PA. 15066

R. D. BURROUGHS
2005 PLEASANT ST.
BETHEL PARK, PA. 15102

JAMES V. BURROUGHS
1401 HAYS ST.
HOMESTEAD, PA. 15120

JOHN L. BURROUGHS
3238 WEST ST.
WEST MIFFLIN, PA. 15122

FREDERICK BURROUGHS
1023 PEEBLES LN.
MC KEESPORT, PA. 15132

H. E. BURROUGHS, JR.
434 SULGRAVE RD.
PITTSBURGH, PA. 15211

ALICE BURROUGHS
624 PERRY ST.
PITTSBURGH, PA. 15219

PAUL F. BURROUGHS
1670 DOYLE ST.
PITTSBURGH, PA. 15221

D. C. BURROUGHS, JR.
1035 HIGHMONT RD.
PITTSBURGH, PA. 15232

A. M. BURROUGHS
515 AIKEN AV. S. 517
PITTSBURGH, PA. 15232

JOHN H. BURROUGHS
854 BEECH AV.
PITTSBURGH, PA. 15233

RONALD BURROUGHS
909 NORTH AV. W.
PITTSBURGH, PA. 15233

GEORGE C. BURROUGHS
237 DATURA DR.
PITTSBURGH, PA. 15235

MARTHA BURROUGHS
90 TIMOTHY DR.
PITTSBURGH, PA. 15239

PAUL J. BURROUGHS
337 CLAIR DR.
PITTSBURGH, PA. 15241

SAMUEL BURROUGHS
1775 PARTRIDGE RUN
PITTSBURGH, PA. 15241

BETTY A. BURROUGHS
555 COUNCIL ST.
WASHINGTON, PA. 15301

SHIRLEY M. BURROUGHS
155 COLLEGE ST. N.
WASHINGTON, PA. 15301

LINDA BURROUGHS
R.R. 4
WASHINGTON, PA. 15301

RUSSELL A. BURROUGHS
106 HIGHLAND DR. E.
CANONSBURG, PA. 15317

G. BURROUGHS
JONES MILLS, PA. 15646

CORBETT R. BURROUGHS
239 1/2 EBENSBURG RD.
JOHNSTOWN, PA. 15901

JAMES G. BURROUGHS
142 WINTERWOOD DR.
BUTLER, PA. 16001

CLAUDE G. BURROUGHS
R.D. 1A
RUSSELL, PA. 16345

CLAUDE BURROUGHS, JR.
21 PARK AV.
WARREN, PA. 16365

CHARLES W. BURROUGHS
2311 PEACH ST.
ERIE, PA. 16502

PAUL BURROUGHS
4635 WOLF RD.
ERIE, PA. 16505

JOHN F. BURROUGHS
209 2D ST. E.
ERIE, PA. 16507

JOET BURROUGHS
114 3D ST. W. APT. 3
ERIE, PA. 16507

M. S. BURROUGHS
R.R. 2
JONESTOWN, PA. 17038

RALPH E. BURROUGHS
R.R. 6
CHAMBERSBURG, PA. 17201

ISRAEL BURROUGHS
525 PARK AV.
WILLIAMSPORT, PA. 17701

P. E. BURROUGHS, JR.
205 RONALD AV.
ORWIGSBURG, PA. 17961

RICHARD S. BURROUGHS
R.R. 2
ALLENTOWN, PA. 18103

E. M. BURROUGHS
R.R. 2
ALLENTOWN, PA. 18103

EDWIN E. BURROUGHS
168 COXE ST.
HAZLETON, PA. 18201

PAUL B. BURROUGHS
145 PEBBLE WOODS DR.
DOYLESTOWN, PA. 18901

ROBERT E. BURROUGHS
1375 CHINQUAPIN RD.
SOUTHAMPTON, PA. 18966

ROBERT S. BURROUGHS
1421 MIRANDA LN.
WARMINSTER, PA. 18974

ALFRED B. BURROUGHS
305 7TH AV.
FOLSOM, PA. 19033

LOUISE BURROUGHS
801 MERION SQ. RD.
GLADWYNE, PA. 19035

V. E. BURROUGHS
823 JACKSON AV.
GLENSIDE, PA. 19038

H. J. BURROUGHS, JR.
21 OLDPOND RD.
LEVITTOWN, PA. 19057

M. BURROUGHS
30 10TH ST. E.
MARCUS HOOK, PA. 19061

R. E. BURROUGHS
7 BALTIMORE AV. E.
MEDIA, PA. 19063

ARTHUR B. BURROUGHS
210 FERRY RD. W.
MORRISVILLE, PA. 19067

M. H. BURROUGHS
621 NEWTOWN RD. N.
NEWTOWN SQ, PA. 19073

PAUL BURROUGHS
417 SPRUCE ST.
UPPER DARBY, PA. 19082

JOSEPH BURROUGHS
410 TRENTON CT.
MEDIA, PA. 19086

J. L. BURROUGHS
431 SHORTRIDGE DR.
WYNNEWOOD, PA. 19096

JOHN BURROUGHS
2317 SANSOM ST.
PHILADELPHIA, PA. 19103

D. BURROUGHS
720 38TH ST. N.
PHILADELPHIA, PA. 19104

TROY BURROUGHS
524 33RD ST. N.
PHILADELPHIA, PA. 19104

A. S. BURROUGHS
10602 EVANS ST.
PHILADELPHIA, PA. 19116

ANDREW BURROUGHS
3140 EUCLID ST.
PHILADELPHIA, PA. 19121

ARTHUR BURROUGHS
1843 FRANKFORD AV.
PHILADELPHIA, PA. 19125

CORNELL BURROUGHS
6642 17TH ST. N.
PHILADELPHIA, PA. 19126

J. L. BURROUGHS
4341 MAIN ST.
PHILADELPHIA, PA. 19127

CECIL BURROUGHS
3234 DOVER ST. N.
PHILADELPHIA, PA. 19129

ROBERT BURROUGHS
2511 LEHIGH AV. W.
PHILADELPHIA, PA. 19132

JAMES L. BURROUGHS
2425 CLEVELAND ST. N.
PHILADELPHIA, PA. 19132

JOHN E. BURROUGHS
5733 VANDIKE ST.
PHILADELPHIA, PA. 19135

HENRY W. BURROUGHS
6631 LIMEKILN PKE.
PHILADELPHIA, PA. 19138

C. C. BURROUGHS
32 58TH ST. S.
PHILADELPHIA, PA. 19139

ARTHUR BURROUGHS
5808 12TH ST. N.
PHILADELPHIA, PA. 19141

DONALD BURROUGHS
5837 PINE ST.
PHILADELPHIA, PA. 19143

SHIRLEY BURROUGHS
218 HAINES ST. E.
PHILADELPHIA, PA. 19144

MARTHA BURROUGHS
606 HOFFMAN ST.
PHILADELPHIA, PA. 19148

HENRY BURROUGHS, JR.
1461 60TH ST. N.
PHILADELPHIA, PA. 19151

PAUL B. BURROUGHS
INDIAN RN VLG
HONEY BROOK, PA. 19344

WILLIAM BURROUGHS
54 CAROL LN.
MALVERN, PA. 19355

RICHD J. BURROUGHS
1140 GROVE RD.
WEST CHESTER, PA. 19380

E. H. BURROUGHS
568 SARATOGA RD.
NORRISTOWN, PA. 19406

E. B. BURROUGHS
6 CHERRY CT.
READING, PA. 19606

R. J. BURROUGHS
123 LONGVIEW DR.
NEWARK, DE. 19711

L. J. BURROUGHS
200 DELAWARE ST.
NEW CASTLE, DE. 19720

MICHAEL BURROUGHS
140 RIVERVIEW DR.
NEW CASTLE, DE. 19720

JOHN A. BURROUGHS
13 PAUL DR.
NEW CASTLE, DE. 19720

T. BURROUGHS
178 RIVERVIEW DR.
NEW CASTLE, DE. 19720

SIMEON BURROUGHS
304 ROOSEVELT AV. E. APT
NEW CASTLE, DE. 19720

MABEL BURROUGHS
107 STATE LINE RD.
WILMINGTON, DE. 19803

CHARLES BURROUGHS
1109 LINCOLN ST. N.
WILMINGTON, DE. 19805

JOHN W. BURROUGHS
829 9TH AV.
WILMINGTON, DE. 19808

BETTY BURROUGHS
2131 DELAVIEW AV.
WILMINGTON, DE. 19810

M. BURROUGHS
R1 BX. 24
DOVER, DE. 19901

K. S. BURROUGHS
1ST ST. N.
BETHANY BEACH, DE. 19930

S. L. BURROUGHS
103 PINE ST. W.
GEORGETOWN, DE. 19947

C. E. BURROUGHS
R3 BX. 210
MILLSBORO, DE. 19966

HENRY BURROUGHS
1505 E. ST. S.E.
WASHINGTON, D.C. 20003

J. BURROUGHS
1423 33RD ST. N.W.
WASHINGTON, D.C. 20007

ROGER M. BURROUGHS
1825 CONNECTCT AV. N.W.
WASHINGTON, D.C. 20009

CYNTHIA D. BURROUGHS
2108 16TH ST. N.W.
WASHINGTON, D.C. 20009

WESSER L. BURROUGHS
611 JEFFERSON ST. N.W.
WASHINGTON, D.C. 20011

CHARLES W. BURROUGHS
5833 3RD PL. N.W.
WASHINGTON, D.C. 20011

FRANKLIN P. BURROUGHS, SR.
4500 JONES BRIDGE RD.
WASHINGTON, D.C. 20014

ELIZABETH K. BURROUGHS
4926 BATTERY LN. APT. 4
WASHINGTON, D.C. 20014

JOHN W. BURROUGHS
4405 FARADAY PL. N.W.
WASHINGTON, D.C. 20016

MELVIN R. BURROUGHS
2901 SOUTH DAKOTA N.E.
WASHINGTON, D.C. 20018

JOHN A. BURROUGHS
1409 DOWNING ST. N.E.
WASHINGTON, D.C. 20018

ALLEN E. BURROUGHS
3430 MINNESOTA AV. S.E.
WASHINGTON, D.C. 20019

JOSEPH E. BURROUGHS
2201 16TH ST. S.E.
WASHINGTON, D.C. 20020

LEONA BURROUGHS
2828 31ST ST. S.E.
WASHINGTON, D.C. 20020

LAWRENCE W. BURROUGHS
2105 BELFAST DR. S.E.
WASHINGTON, D.C. 20022

WILLIAM H. BURROUGHS
2314 BROOKS DR. S.E. APT
WASHINGTON, D.C. 20023

JAMES R. BURROUGHS
6251 MAXWELL DR. S.E.
WASHINGTON, D.C. 20023

O. J. BURROUGHS
7004 CANYON DR. N.E.
WASHINGTON, D.C. 20027

B. E. BURROUGHS
400 ROLLINS AV. S.E.
WASHINGTON, D.C. 20027

ERNEST J. BURROUGHS, JR.
314 ROLLINS AV. S.E.
WASHINGTON, D.C. 20027

RALPH J. BURROUGHS
5535 MARLBORO PKE. S.E.
WASHINGTON, D.C. 20028

T. R. BURROUGHS
7302 MALDEN LN. S.E.
WASHINGTON, D.C. 20028

FRANCIS D. BURROUGHS
5601 JOAN LN. S.E.
WASHINGTON, D.C. 20031

F. BURROUGHS
5731 FISHER RD. S.E.
WASHINGTON, D.C. 20031

M. L. BURROUGHS
5900 HOLTON LN. S.E.
WASHINGTON, D.C. 20031

BENJAMIN E. BURROUGHS
633 CONDON TER. S.E.
WASHINGTON, D.C. 20032

JOHN A. BURROUGHS
9202 EWING DR.
WASHINGTON, D.C. 20034

WALTON H. BURROUGHS, SR.
14411 SPRINGFIELD RD. SE
BRANDYWINE, MD. 20613

ROGER L. BURROUGHS
CALIFORNIA, MD. 20619

MARY I. BURROUGHS
CHAPTICO, MD. 20621

LAWRENCE BURROUGHS
OLD R5
CHARLOTE HALL, MD. 20622

JOHN D. BURROUGHS
R1 BX. 90
CHARLOTE HALL, MD. 20622

GEORGE D. BURROUGHS, JR.
R234
CLEMENTS, MD. 20624

JOHN M. BURROUGHS
COLTONS POINT, MD. 20626

J. E. BURROUGHS, JR.
MT. AIR RD.
FAULKNER, MD. 20632

B. L. BURROUGHS
LANGLEY TR PK.
GREAT MILLS, MD. 20634

THOMAS M. BURROUGHS
HOLLYWOOD, MD. 20636

EUGENE S. BURROUGHS
R1 BX. 44
HUGHESVILLE, MD. 20637

DONALD R. BURROUGHS
HUGHESVILLE MANOR R1
HUGHESVILLE, MD. 20637

CLYDE BURROUGHS
R.R. 2
INDIAN HEAD, MD. 20640

C. P. BURROUGHS
17 IRVING PL.
INDIAN HEAD, MD. 20640

CLYDE D. BURROUGHS, SR.
STUCKEY RD. R425
INDIAN HEAD, MD. 20640

W. B. BURROUGHS
SR3 BX. 112
LA PLATA, MD. 20646

EVERETT B. BURROUGHS, JR.
R2 BX. 2056
LA PLATA, MD. 20646

J. H. BURROUGHS, JR.
LEONARDTOWN, MD. 20650

BENJAMIN L. BURROUGHS
17 OFFICERS CT.
LEXINGTON PK, MD. 20653

WILLIAM BURROUGHS
MECHANICSVL, MD. 20659

THOMAS M. BURROUGHS
R3 BX. 10
MECHANICSVL, MD. 20659

LUTHER K. BURROUGHS
FL RD. R2
MECHANICSVL, MD. 20659

ROBERT R. BURROUGHS
MECHANICSVL, MD. 20659

PAUL N. BURROUGHS
MORGANZA TURNER
MECHANICSVL, MD. 20659

JAMES H. BURROUGHS, JR.
R2 BX. 480
MECHANICSVL, MD. 20659

DEBRACY BURROUGHS
R. 1
MECHANICSVL, MD. 20659

E. S. BURROUGHS
R5 BX. 1
MECHANICSVL, MD. 20659

BERNARD BURROUGHS
MECHANICSVL, MD. 20659

MARY H. BURROUGHS
MORGANZA, MD. 20660

WILLIAM F. BURROUGHS
R1 BX. 210
NANJEMOY, MD. 20662

SADIE E. BURROUGHS
R. 1
NEWBURG, MD. 20664

GERALD E. BURROUGHS
PINEY POINT, MD. 20674

GEORGE W. BURROUGHS
BX. 292
SAINT LEONARD, MD. 20685

G. S. BURROUGHS
SR. 20677
SAINT LEONARD, MD. 20685

CHARLES E. BURROUGHS, SR.
LEXINGTON AND MARKET
ANNAPOLIS JCT. MD. 20701

GARY L. BURROUGHS
11372 CHERRY HILL RD. AP
BELTSVILLE, MD. 20705

EDWARD W. BURROUGHS, SR.
13222 RONEHILL DR.
BELTSVILLE, MD. 20705

STEVEN P. BURROUGHS
13304 YORKTOWN DR.
BOWIE, MD. 20715

EDGAR W. BURROUGHS
1318 PALMYRA LN.
BOWIE, MD. 20716

PAUL P. BURROUGHS
3201 DAMSCS RD.
BROOKEVILLE, MD. 20729

H. L. BURROUGHS
8513 RENO CT.
CLINTON, MD. 20735

JOHN F. BURROUGHS
9690 BRASSIE WY.
GAITHERSBURG, MD. 20760

WILLIAM M. BURROUGHS
11440 GAME PRESERVE
GAITHERSBURG, MD. 20760

WILLIAM E. BURROUGHS
427 GAITHER ST.
GAITHERSBURG, MD. 20760

MARY S. BURROUGHS
401 RUSSELL AV. APT. 105
GAITHERSBURG, MD. 20760

ROBERT C. BURROUGHS
408 DEER PARK DR. W.
GAITHERSBURG, MD. 20760

HEATH C. BURROUGHS
7462 MINK HOLLW RD.
HIGHLAND, MD. 20777

JOHN J. BURROUGHS
5610 GALLATIN PL.
HYATTSVILLE, MD. 20781

LEON P. BURROUGHS, SR.
800 RITTENHOUSE ST.
HYATTSVILLE, MD. 20783

WILLIAM A. BURROUGHS
2001 HANNON ST.
HYATTSVILLE, MD. 20783

JOHN E. BURROUGHS
2409 LACKAHANNA ST.
HYATTSVILLE, MD. 20783

ALFREDA M. BURROUGHS
10910 DEVIN PL.
KENSINGTON, MD. 20795

HELEN P. BURROUGHS
3409 WAKE DR.
KENSINGTON, MD. 20795

EDWARD G. BURROUGHS
9416 FRANKLIN AV.
LANHAM-SEABRK, MD. 20801

JACK BURROUGHS
6605 WEAVER CT.
LAUREL, MD. 20810

ROBERT P. BURROUGHS
378 OLD LINE AV.
LAUREL, MD. 20810

DAVID B. BURROUGHS
1610 AUBURN AV.
ROCKVILLE, MD. 20850

CHARLES BURROUGHS
686 COLLEGE PKWY.
ROCKVILLE, MD. 20850

LEROY B. BURROUGHS
303 LAWRENCE DR.
ROCKVILLE, MD. 20850

ATLEE I. BURROUGHS
804 GRANDIN AV.
ROCKVILLE, MD. 20850

PAUL M. BURROUGHS
4804 CREEK SHORE DR.
ROCKVILLE, MD. 20852

BERNARD R. BURROUGHS
11012 SCHUYKILL RD.
ROCKVILLE, MD. 20852

WALTER B. BURROUGHS
12522 ROSEBUD DR.
ROCKVILLE, MD. 20853

N. A. BURROUGHS
17700 RIDGE DR.
ROCKVILLE, MD. 20853

LILLIE M. BURROUGHS
10272 RIVER RD.
ROCKVILLE, MD. 20854

DOUGLAS J. BURROUGHS
7803 MUIRFIELD CT.
ROCKVILLE, MD. 20854

FRANCIS E. BURROUGHS
10813 STANMORE DR.
ROCKVILLE, MD. 20854

WILLIAM E. BURROUGHS, SR.
7512 NEEDWOOD RD.
ROCKVILLE, MD. 20855

CECIL T. BURROUGHS
14303 RECTORY LN.
UPR MARLBORO, MD. 20870

RICHARD D. BURROUGHS
17610 CLAGGTT LNDG R2
UPR MARLBORO, MD. 20870

GEORGE T. BURROUGHS, JR.
15500 CROOM ARPRT R3
UPR MARLBORO, MD. 20870

JAMES E. BURROUGHS
404 WILLIAMSBURG DR.
SILVER SPRING, MD. 20901

JAMES H. BURROUGHS, JR.
1510 MOFFETT RD.
SILVER SPRING, MD. 20903

JOHN A. BURROUGHS, JR.
14728 FLINTSTONE LN.
SILVER SPRING, MD. 20904

GEORGE W. BURROUGHS
607 QUAINTACRES DR.
SILVER SPRING, MD. 20904

WILBUR C. BURROUGHS
16005 CHESTER MLL TER.
SILVER SPRING, MD. 20906

JOHN N. BURROUGHS
14106 BALDWIN MILL RD.
BALDWIN, MD. 21013

T. M. BURROUGHS
7456 FLAMEWOOD DR.
CLARKSVILLE, MD. 21029

MARSHAL BURROUGHS
231 OAKWOOD RD.
EDGEWATER, MD. 21037

JOHN M. BURROUGHS
710 LONDONTOWN RD.
EDGEWATER, MD. 21037

GEORGE W. BURROUGHS
1389 BAYSIDE DR.
EDGEWATER, MD. 21037

ROBT. M. BURROUGHS
211 RIVERSIDE RD.
EDGEWATER, MD. 21037

CHARLES B. BURROUGHS
7006 FOLDED PALM ST.
COLUMBIA, MD. 21045

LLOYD H. BURROUGHS, JR.
9937 FERNDALE AV.
COLUMBIA, MD. 21046

HARVEY J. BURROUGHS
51 CHESTER CIR.
GLEN BURNIE, MD. 21061

JAMES F. BURROUGHS
1701 SAUNDERS WY.
GLEN BURNIE, MD. 21061

WILLIAM G. BURROUGHS, JR.
1208 CLEARFIELD CIR.
LTHRVL-TIMNUM, MD. 21093

M. BURROUGHS
15 MISSION WOOD WY.
REISTERSTOWN, MD. 21136

DAVID L. BURROUGHS
721 BENNINGHAUS RD.
BALTIMORE, MD. 21212

ANN T. BURROUGHS
1 GOODALE PL.
BALTIMORE, MD. 21212

GERARD T. BURROUGHS
3308 AILSA AV.
BALTIMORE, MD. 21214

ATLA M. BURROUGHS
3203 BATAVIA AV.
BALTIMORE, MD. 21214

SYLVESTER BURROUGHS
3405 HILTON RD.
BALTIMORE, MD. 21215

JEREMIAH M. BURROUGHS
3401 LUDGATE RD.
BALTIMORE, MD. 21215

BRISTO BURROUGHS
2921 BAKER ST.
BALTIMORE, MD. 21216

LEO W. BURROUGHS, SR.
3011 BAKER ST.
BALTIMORE, MD. 21216

STANLEY M. BURROUGHS
2824 NORTH AV. W.
BALTIMORE, MD. 21216

ROY V. BURROUGHS
2307 MADISON AV.
BALTIMORE, MD. 21217

JEFFREY W. BURROUGHS
2416 PENNSYLVANIA AV.
BALTIMORE, MD. 21217

RAYMOND H. BURROUGHS
916 LEMMON ST.
BALTIMORE, MD. 21223

HARVEY B. BURROUGHS
902 VICTORY AV.
BALTIMORE, MD. 21225

WILLIAM E. BURROUGHS
41 MORLEY ST. S.
BALTIMORE, MD. 21229

ANNE M. BURROUGHS
610 ALDERSHOT RD.
BALTIMORE, MD. 21229

MILDRED G. BURROUGHS
1000 STAMFORD RD.
BALTIMORE, MD. 21229

J. BURROUGHS
262 DUNCAN ST. S.
BALTIMORE, MD. 21231

B. BURROUGHS
R. 1
STEVENSVILLE, MD. 21666

ROY J. BURROUGHS
BRADDOCK HTS., MD. 21714

PAUL F. BURROUGHS
111 WINDSOR CIR. R7
HAGERSTOWN, MD. 21740

PAUL M. BURROUGHS
GREEN RIDGE D.
MONROVIA, MD. 21770

ROBERT W. BURROUGHS
GREEN VLLY DEVL
MONROVIA, MD. 21770

JOSEPH P. BURROUGHS
13125 FORSYTHE RD.
SYKESVILLE, MD. 21784

ARTHUR D. BURROUGHS
609 THIN TREE RD.
SALISBURY, MD. 21801

THOMAS F. BURROUGHS
10 BURLEY ST.
BERLIN, MD. 21811

ALAN BURROUGHS
84TH ST.
OCEAN CITY, MD. 21842

GEORGE BURROUGHS
GEORGETOWN, MD. 21930

CERELDA J. BURROUGHS
4918 BRISTOW DR.
ANNANDALE, VA. 22003

MELVIN D. BURROUGHS
11701 VALLEY RD. R8
FAIRFAX, VA. 22030

HARRY F. BURROUGHS
8902 SOUTHWICK ST.
FAIRFAX, VA. 22031

KATHLYN J. BURROUGHS
3479 LAKE ST. APT. 202
FALLS CHURCH, VA. 22041

AUSTIN C. BURROUGHS
6632 BEACON LN.
FALLS CHURCH, VA. 22043

CHIP BURROUGHS
2910 WILLSTON PL.
FALLS CHURCH, VA. 22044

THOMAS BURROUGHS
2900 PEYTON RANDOLPH
FALLS CHURCH, VA. 22044

EUGENE B. BURROUGHS
10103 MINBURN
GREAT FALLS, VA. 22066

JAMES BURROUGHS
711 HEMLOCK CT.
HERNDON, VA. 22070

ELISE S. BURROUGHS
1350 NORTHGATE SQ.
HERNDON, VA. 22090

STEVEN BURROUGHS
1440 INGLESIDE AV.
MC LEAN, VA. 22101

H. F. BURROUGHS
8856 TEAKWOOD CT.
MANASSAS, VA. 22110

DOUGLAS J. BURROUGHS
9075 MC CLELLAN CT.
MANASSAS, VA. 22110

ERVIN W. BURROUGHS
4020 QUARTERS
QUANTICO, VA. 22134

THOMAS R. BURROUGHS
6109 AMHERST AV.
SPRINGFIELD, VA. 22150

DAVID M. BURROUGHS
6601 SANDOVER CT.
SPRINGFIELD, VA. 22152

WILLIAM D. BURROUGHS
2540 GLENGYLE DR.
VIENNA, VA. 22180

FREDERICK M. BURROUGHS
124 MELODY LN. S.W.
VIENNA, VA. 22180

RICHARD T. BURROUGHS
1889 COLD CREEK R7
VIENNA, VA. 22180

JAMES C. BURROUGHS
1811 MIDLOTHIAN CT.
VIENNA, VA. 22180

JULIA E. BURROUGHS
1911 15TH ST. N.
ARLINGTON, VA. 22201

GEORGE R. BURROUGHS
1300 CLEVELAND ST. S. AP
ARLINGTON, VA. 22204

WALTER W. BURROUGHS
2000 ILLINOIS ST. N.
ARLINGTON, VA. 22205

F. P. BURROUGHS, JR.
1518 BUCHANAN ST. N.
ARLINGTON, VA. 22205

WILLIAM S. BURROUGHS, JR.
2019 POTOMAC ST. N.
ARLINGTON, VA. 22205

J. P. BURROUGHS
2991 COLUMBUS ST. S.
ARLINGTON, VA. 22206

KENT D. BURROUGHS
2541 GRANADA ST. N.
ARLINGTON, VA. 22207

VA E. BURROUGHS
2139 QUEBEC ST. N.
ARLINGTON, VA. 22207

W. S. BURROUGHS
3825 WAKEFIELD ST. N.
ARLINGTON, VA. 22207

JOHN BURROUGHS
3232 WOODROW ST. N.
ARLINGTON, VA. 22207

FRED A. BURROUGHS, 3D
4524 32ND ST. N. !
ARLINGTON, VA. 22207

JAMES H. BURROUGHS
108 WALNUT ST. W.
ALEXANDRIA, VA. 22301

L. BURROUGHS
5 MONROE AV. E. APT. 304
ALEXANDRIA, VA. 22301

LORENZO W. BURROUGHS
8703 TRIUMPH CT.
ALEXANDRIA, VA. 22308

C. BURROUGHS
8764 WALUTES CIR.
ALEXANDRIA, VA. 22309

ELDRIDGE N. BURROUGHS
4600 EATON PL.
ALEXANDRIA, VA. 22310

THOMAS P. BURROUGHS
4717 BRADDOCK RD. W. APT
ALEXANDRIA, VA. 22311

JAMES D. BURROUGHS
301 BEAUREGARD ST. APT.
ALEXANDRIA, VA. 22312

LLOYD E. BURROUGHS
1025 LOSSING AV.
COLONIAL BCH., VA. 22443

JOHN BURROUGHS
R.R. 6
WINCHESTER, VA. 22601

EARL E. BURROUGHS
SILER SR.
WINCHESTER, VA. 22601

PERRY BURROUGHS
STEPHENS CITY, VA. 22655

HARRY L. BURROUGHS
STEPHENS CITY, VA. 22655

R. BURROUGHS
BOSTON, VA. 22713

ARGIE BURROUGHS
BERKLEY ST. R. 3
ASHLAND, VA. 23005

RONALD C. BURROUGHS
BAVON, VA. 23013

N. C. BURROUGHS
BAVON, VA. 23013

WILL BURROUGHS
BAVON, VA. 23013

WATSON BURROUGHS
DELTAVILLE, VA. 23043

G. G. BURROUGHS
DIGGS, VA. 23045

JOE BURROUGHS
DIGGS, VA. 23045

JOSEPH BURROUGHS
102 BEAL ST. E.
HIGHLAND SPG, VA. 23075

WILMA D. BURROUGHS
LOUISA, VA. 23093

GEORGE BURROUGHS, 3D
MATHEWS, VA. 23109

GEORGE L. BURROUGHS
NEW POINT, VA. 23125

HOLMES BURROUGHS
NEW POINT, VA. 23125

L. W. BURROUGHS
NEW POINT, VA. 23125

WALTER BURROUGHS
NEW POINT, VA. 23125

HENRY G. BURROUGHS
PORT HAYWOOD, VA. 23138

R. H. BURROUGHS
PORT HAYWOOD, VA. 23138

GLENN BURROUGHS
SUSAN, VA. 23163

LISLE BURROUGHS
308 INDIAN SPGS RD.
WILLIAMSBURG, VA. 23185

WILLIAM H. BURROUGHS
1177 DUNCAN DR.
WILLIAMSBURG, VA. 23185

ELSIE H. BURROUGHS
1261 LAKEVIEW AV.
RICHMOND, VA. 23220

GEORGE H. BURROUGHS, JR.
1413 WINDER ST.
RICHMOND, VA. 23220

MARION L. BURROUGHS
612 LANCASTER RD. W.
RICHMOND, VA. 23222

RONALD M. BURROUGHS
3801 PATRICK AV.
RICHMOND, VA. 23222

JOSEPH D. BURROUGHS
718 ARNOLD AV.
RICHMOND, VA. 23222

G. T. BURROUGHS
3018 4TH AV.
RICHMOND, VA. 23222

GRACE E. BURROUGHS
3350 NINE MILE RD.
RICHMOND, VA. 23223

ALICE H. BURROUGHS
2413 GRACE ST. E.
RICHMOND, VA. 23223

DARNELL BURROUGHS
663 LABURNUM AV. N. APT.
RICHMOND, VA. 23223

JAMES H. BURROUGHS
109 ROANOKE ST. E.
RICHMOND, VA. 23224

E. B. BURROUGHS
3103 TANNERS HY. APT. L.
RICHMOND, VA. 23224

GLADYS BURROUGHS
209 JEFFERSN VLG DR. APT
RICHMOND, VA. 23225

GEORGE W. BURROUGHS
1301 43RD ST. W.
RICHMOND, VA. 23225

GILBERT C. BURROUGHS
1321 WENTBRIDGE RD.
RICHMOND, VA. 23227

IRVIN J. BURROUGHS, JR.
1305 WENTBRIDGE RD.
RICHMOND, VA. 23227

MARGUERITE R BURROUGHS
7107 FERNWOOD ST. APT. 2
RICHMOND, VA. 23228

RICHARD L. BURROUGHS
4105 FAIRLAKE CT.
RICHMOND, VA. 23229

RICHARD L. BURROUGHS
9104 WHITEMONT RD.
RICHMOND, VA. 23229

CECIL L. BURROUGHS
2217 BAILEY DR.
RICHMOND, VA. 23231

FREDERICK L. BURROUGHS
9104 MINNA DR.
RICHMOND, VA. 23233

EUGENE W. BURROUGHS, 3D
1906 SWEETWATER LN.
RICHMOND, VA. 23233

WALTER B. BURROUGHS, JR.
3008 BICKNELL RD.
RICHMOND, VA. 23235

R. K. BURROUGHS
524 SOUTHFIELD DR.
CHESAPEAKE, VA. 23320

W. L. BURROUGHS
350 PEACEFUL RD. R6
CHESAPEAKE, VA. 23320

LINWOOD J. BURROUGHS
705 PARKER RD.
CHESAPEAKE, VA. 23320

EUGENE W. BURROUGHS, JR.
4401 DEBORAH CT. APT. 2
CHESAPEAKE, VA. 23321

CHARLES J. BURROUGHS, JR.
1632 GAFF RD.
CHESAPEAKE, VA. 23321

WILLIAM T. BURROUGHS, JR.
817 GEO WASH HWY N.
CHESAPEAKE, VA. 23323

JAMES L. BURROUGHS
SMITH BEACH VIA
EASTVILLE, VA. 23347

FRED H. BURROUGHS
HALLWOOD, VA. 23359

CHARLES F. BURROUGHS, JR.
PUNGOTEAGUE, VA. 23422

EUG W. BURROUGHS
403 MAYFLOWER APTS.
VIRGINIA BCH, VA. 23451

ALLAN A. BURROUGHS
168 CORAL GABLES CT. APT
VIRGINIA BCH, VA. 23452

DOROTHY K. BURROUGHS
700 NORTHGATE CT.
VIRGINIA BCH, VA. 23452

KENNETH G. BURROUGHS
975 CLUB HOUSE RD. S.
VIRGINIA BCH, VA. 23452

THOMAS A. BURROUGHS
4628 HERMITAGE RD.
VIRGINIA BCH, VA. 23455

ROBERT A. BURROUGHS
4721 WINDERMERE CT.
VIRGINIA BCH, VA. 23455

RONALD E. BURROUGHS
916 FOWLER CT.
VIRGINIA BCH, VA. 23456

JOSEPH E. BURROUGHS
2893 SEA BOARD RD. R1
VIRGINIA BCH, VA. 23456

EDGAR R. BURROUGHS
1205 ACREDALE RD.
VIRGINIA BCH, VA. 23462

THERESA L. BURROUGHS
4725 JEANNE ST. APT. 101
VIRGINIA BCH, VA. 23462

RONALD BURROUGHS
1127 RIVIERA DR.
VIRGINIA BCH, VA. 23462

WILLIAM E. BURROUGHS
5209 JULIANNA DR.
NORFOLK, VA. 23502

R. A. BURROUGHS
1563 NORCOVA AV.
NORFOLK, VA. 23502

JOSEPH D. BURROUGHS
1128 OCEAN VIEW AV. W.
NORFOLK, VA. 23503

HARRY T. BURROUGHS
3933 GRANBY ST. APT. E2
NORFOLK, VA. 23504

RUTH BURROUGHS
1723 BROWN AV.
NORFOLK, VA. 23504

MATTIE BURROUGHS
815 29TH ST. E. APT. 4
NORFOLK, VA. 23504

CHARLES F. BURROUGHS, JR.
7721 ARGYLE AV.
NORFOLK, VA. 23505

ROBERT L. BURROUGHS
7714 NESBITT DR.
NORFOLK, VA. 23505

CARL D. BURROUGHS
7862 WHERRY DR. APT. B.
NORFOLK, VA. 23505

LINWOOD G. BURROUGHS
526 STERLING ST.
NORFOLK, VA. 23505

EDWARD O. BURROUGHS, JR.
156 SIR OLIVER RD.
NORFOLK, VA. 23505

H. V. BURROUGHS
1627 LONGWOOD DR.
NORFOLK, VA. 23508

LARRY T. BURROUGHS
6129 ROLFE AV.
NORFOLK, VA. 23508

WARNER V. BURROUGHS
1000 ROCKBRIDGE AV. APT.
NORFOLK, VA. 23508

ALLAN C. BURROUGHS
2700 SOMME AV.
NORFOLK, VA. 23509

CHARLES J. BURROUGHS
3118 ARIZONA AV.
NORFOLK, VA. 23513

LUTHER J. BURROUGHS
6443 SEWELLS PT RD. E.
NORFOLK, VA. 23513

MARGARET H. BURROUGHS
6231 SEDGEFIELD DR. APT.
NORFOLK, VA. 23513

KENNETH BURROUGHS
5403 HENNEMAN DR.
NORFOLK, VA. 23513

CURTIS L. BURROUGHS
3496 BONNER DR. E.
NORFOLK, VA. 23513

CARL D. BURROUGHS
4705 KRICK ST.
NORFOLK, VA. 23513

CAREY L. BURROUGHS
7854 AZALEA GARDEN APT.
NORFOLK, VA. 23518

NORMAN C. BURROUGHS
6905 OLD MILL RD.
NORFOLK, VA. 23518

CAREY L. BURROUGHS
8244 BUFFALO AV.
NORFOLK, VA. 23518

DOUGLAS L. BURROUGHS
92 CALDRONEY DR.
NEWPORT NEWS, VA. 23602

RONALD B. BURROUGHS
820 VENTNOR DR.
NEWPORT NEWS, VA. 23602

ROBERT C. BURROUGHS
763 OYSTER PT RD.
NEWPORT NEWS, VA. 23602

LUCILLE BURROUGHS
5134 GOLDSBORO DR.
NEWPORT NEWS, VA. 23605

BYRON V. BURROUGHS
40 TOWNE SQ. DR.
NEWPORT NEWS, VA. 23607

SAMUEL N. BURROUGHS
23 ROBERTA DR.
HAMPTON, VA. 23666

JERRY L. BURROUGHS
3242 BUTTERNUT DR. APT.
HAMPTON, VA. 23666

PAUL R. BURROUGHS
307 SOURWOOD DR.
HAMPTON, VA. 23666

JERRY L. BURROUGHS
3202 BUTTERNUT DR. APT.
HAMPTON, VA. 23666

MELVIN BURROUGHS
1405 CAVALIER BL
PORTSMOUTH, VA. 23701

E. BURROUGHS
208 NAVAJO TRL APT. 35
PORTSMOUTH, VA. 23701

LYNDENA BURROUGHS
94 CUSHING ST. APT. B.
PORTSMOUTH, VA. 23702

MELVIN BURROUGHS
1 SUBURBAN CIR. APT. D.
PORTSMOUTH, VA. 23702

GEORGE H. BURROUGHS, JR.
3650 WESTERN BR BL APT.
PORTSMOUTH, VA. 23707

CHARLES D. BURROUGHS
3719 WESTERN BR BL
PORTSMOUTH, VA. 23707

L. E. BURROUGHS, II
464 MONTIBELLO ST.
PETERSBURG, VA. 23803

ARLINE S. BURROUGHS
2211 WARREN ST.
PETERSBURG, VA. 23803

LAWRENCE E. BURROUGHS
2141 WARREN ST.
PETERSBURG, VA. 23803

JAMES BURROUGHS
R.R. 2
BLACKSTONE, VA. 23824

GEO D. BURROUGHS
4417 DUDLEY DR.
CHESTER, VA. 23831

DANIEL R. BURROUGHS
16500 HULL ST. RD.
CHESTERFIELD, VA. 23832

C. L. BURROUGHS
231 SPRING DR.
COLONIAL HTS. VA. 23834

DONALD L. BURROUGHS
105 BUCKINGHAM DR.
COLONIAL HTS. VA. 23834

PATRICIA BURROUGHS
1605 ATLANTIC ST.
HOPEWELL, VA. 23860

JAMES A. BURROUGHS
2112 POYTHRESS ST. H.
HOPEWELL, VA. 23860

WILLIAM BURROUGHS
HWY 40
CHARLOTTE C, VA. 23923

J. M. BURROUGHS
DILLWYN, VA. 23936

RONNIE W. BURROUGHS
HWY 690
KEYSVILLE, VA. 23947

ALVIS BURROUGHS
R.R. 1
MEHERRIN, VA. 23954

WILLIAM M. BURROUGHS
439 FLEMING AV. N.E.
ROANOKE, VA. 24012

WILLIAM M. BURROUGHS, JR.
1667 BARNETTE RD. N.W.
ROANOKE, VA. 24017

JOHN D. BURROUGHS
1910 LYTHAM DR. S.W.
ROANOKE, VA. 24018

SHERMAN V. BURROUGHS
2758 WHITE PELICN S.W.
ROANOKE, VA. 24018

FRED C. BURROUGHS, 3D
812 CAMBRIDGE RD. N.W.
BLACKSBURG, VA. 24060

FRANK R. BURROUGHS
LEE HWY
BUCHANAN, VA. 24066

CHARLES BURROUGHS
R.R. 1
CHRISTIANBG, VA. 24073

FRED C. BURROUGHS
CHURCH
DUBLIN, VA. 24084

DANNY W. BURROUGHS
54 SHEPPARD DR.
DUBLIN, VA. 24084

N. R. BURROUGHS
910 MULBERRY RD.
MARTINSVILLE, VA. 24112

J. B. BURROUGHS
R.R. 2
PEARISBURG, VA. 24134

ORRIN P. BURROUGHS
R.R. 2
PEARISBURG, VA. 24134

DANIEL A. BURROUGHS
R.R. 1
SHAWSVILLE, VA. 24162

S. V. BURROUGHS, 3D
1844 TERRY DR.
VINTON, VA. 24179

SALLY BURROUGHS
MOSBY APTS.
BRISTOL, VA. 24201

WENDELL BURROUGHS
GRAY HILL VIA
SAINT PAUL, VA. 24283

JOHN R. BURROUGHS
THORNSPG HTS. R1
PULASKI, VA. 24301

JACK J. BURROUGHS
624 FRANKLIN AV.
PULASKI, VA. 24301

RONALD H. BURROUGHS
107 ROBINHOOD RD. R6
GALAX, VA. 24333

JERRY D. BURROUGHS
R.R. 1
LEXINGTON, VA. 24450

LOUISE BURROUGHS
R.R. 3
BEDFORD, VA. 24523

BARBARA B. BURROUGHS
307 HAMPTON DR.
DANVILLE, VA. 24541

WILLIAM C. BURROUGHS
3220 WESTOVER DR.
DANVILLE, VA. 24541

HARLAN BURROUGHS
BX. 97
AVONDALE, W.V. 24811

STAFFORD W. BURROUGHS
1936 LINCOLN AV.
SAINT ALBANS, W.V. 25177

NELSON D. BURROUGHS
8701 CAROLINA AV.
CHARLESTON, W.V. 25315

D. E. BURROUGHS
8603 OHIO AV.
CHARLESTON, W.V. 25315

JUANITA BURROUGHS
701 HENRY ST.
MARTINSBURG, W.V. 25401

WILLIAM R. BURROUGHS
BX. 242
FALLING WTRS, W.V. 25419

BETTY J. BURROUGHS
COOL RIDGE, W.V. 25825

MARTIN D. BURROUGHS
COOL RIDGE, W.V. 25825

JERRY L. BURROUGHS
R86 BX. 103
JUMPING BR, W.V. 25969

EVELYN C. BURROUGHS
R4 BX. 350
WHEELING, W.V. 26003

T. W. BURROUGHS
9 CARTER AV.
TRIADELPHIA, W.V. 26059

HOWARD D. BURROUGHS
507 17TH ST.
PARKERSBURG, W.V. 26101

HOWARD D. BURROUGHS
507 17TH ST. VI
VIENNA, W.V. 26105

FRED BURROUGHS
GRANTSVILLE, W.V. 26147

DONALD M. BURROUGHS
BLAIR AV. R1
MINERALWELLS, W.V. 26150

B. L. BURROUGHS
602 ORCHARD DR.
RAVENSWOOD, W.V. 26164

CHARLES J. BURROUGHS
WAVERLY, W.V. 26184

FORREST BURROUGHS
10 MORGAN ADD
BUCKHANNON, W.V. 26201

LANA BURROUGHS
20 MYLEM ST.
RICHWOOD, W.V. 26261

A. L. BURROUGHS
517 MILFORD ST.
CLARKSBURG, W.V. 26301

JAMES F. BURROUGHS
BALDWIN, W.V. 26326

KENNETH BURROUGHS
R.R. 1
JANE LEW, W.V. 26378

EUGENE BURROUGHS
R3 BX. 272
HESTON, W.V. 26452

JAMES BURROUGHS
36 FREELAND ST.
FAIRMONT, W.V. 26554

RONALD BURROUGHS
1501 MORGANTOWN AV. APT.
FAIRMONT, W.V. 26554

DONALD BURROUGHS
R65 BX. 43A
HEATERS, W.V. 26627

AVAH BURROUGHS
HEATERS, W.V. 26627

O. P. BURROUGHS
HEATERS, W.V. 26627

HAROLD BURROUGHS
HEATERS, W.V. 26627

RAYMOND BURROUGHS, JR.
BX. 43
MATHIAS, W.V. 26812

NELLIE BURROUGHS
MATHIAS, W.V. 26812

BOBBY G. BURROUGHS
R1 BX. 218A
MAYODAN, N.C. 27027

FRED J. BURROUGHS
909 ANDOVER ST.
MOUNT AIRY, N.C. 27030

CURTIS M. BURROUGHS
R3 BX. 232
STONEVILLE, N.C. 27048

POLLY J. BURROUGHS
R3
STONEVILLE, N.C. 27048

SAMUEL E. BURROUGHS
R3
STONEVILLE, N.C. 27048

DAVID R. BURROUGHS, SR.
R3 BX. 185
STONEVILLE, N.C. 27048

JAMES M. BURROUGHS
R2 BX. 45C
STONEVILLE, N.C. 27048

LARRY F. BURROUGHS
R3
STONEVILLE, N.C. 27048

MAMIE L. BURROUGHS
1643 SANDERSTEAD RD.
WINSTON SALEM, N.C. 27103

JOHN K. BURROUGHS
715 WESTOVER AV.
WINSTON SALEM, N.C. 27104

RALPH C. BURROUGHS, JR.
479 PLYMOUTH AV.
WINSTON SALEM, N.C. 27104

JULIAN C. BURROUGHS, JR.
2116 FACULTY DR.
WINSTON SALEM, N.C. 27106

EULA S. BURROUGHS
507 HALL ST.
ASHEBORO, N.C. 27203

JAMES M. BURROUGHS
R7 BX. 33
ASHEBORO, N.C. 27203

JAMES B. BURROUGHS
R4 BX. 341B
ASHEBORO, N.C. 27203

PEGGY F. BURROUGHS
BX. 443
BISCOE, N.C. 27209

CHARLES R. BURROUGHS
1406 COVENTRY RD.
HIGH POINT, N.C. 27260

BECKY BURROUGHS
1520 WOODSIDE AV. APT. C
HIGH POINT, N.C. 27260

AUBREY C. BURROUGHS
719 HENDRIX ST.
HIGH POINT, N.C. 27260

EVA P. BURROUGHS
521 WALNUT ST.
EDEN, N.C. 27288

MICHAEL D. BURROUGHS
820 STUART ST.
EDEN, N.C. 27288

FRANK O. BURROUGHS
R3 BX. 180
EDEN, N.C. 27288

DONALD F. BURROUGHS
919 WEST AV.
EDEN, N.C. 27288

ROBERT G. BURROUGHS
826 ELM ST.
EDEN, N.C. 27288

DELORIES B. BURROUGHS
322 SUNSET DR.
EDEN, N.C. 27288

GEORGE A. BURROUGHS
BX. 175
LIBERTY, N.C. 27298

D. R. BURROUGHS
R2 BX. 210
MC LEANSVILLE, N.C. 27301

CAROL B. BURROUGHS
R3 BX. 40
MEBANE, N.C. 27302

LARRY E. BURROUGHS
BX. 112
MOUNT GILEAD, N.C. 27306

HOWARD N. BURROUGHS
BX. 321
MOUNT GILEAD, N.C. 27306

FANNIE M. BURROUGHS
BX. 465
MOUNT GILEAD, N.C. 27306

JOEL BURROUGHS
R2 BX. 59A
MOUNT GILEAD, N.C. 27306

CLYDE BURROUGHS, JR.
R2 BX. 155B
MOUNT GILEAD, N.C. 27306

KATHELEEN B. BURROUGHS
R1 BX. 227
PITTSBORO, N.C. 27312

ROY T. BURROUGHS
U. S. HWY 29 R6 S.
REIDSVILLE, N.C. 27320

BARBARA B. BURROUGHS
1409 NORTHUP ST.
REIDSVILLE, N.C. 27320

BARBARA B. BURROUGHS
R3 BX. 383
REIDSVILLE, N.C. 27320

DOROTHY W. BURROUGHS
U. S. HWY 29 R6 S.
REIDSVILLE, N.C. 27320

WILLIAM H. BURROUGHS
204 BOYD ST.
REIDSVILLE, N.C. 27320

JESSIE M. BURROUGHS
BX. 392
ROBBINS, N.C. 27325

MARY H. BURROUGHS
R1 BX. 70
STAR, N.C. 27356

BRENDA F. BURROUGHS
R1
STAR, N.C. 27356

WILLIAM H. BURROUGHS, JR.
R2 BX. 113A
STOKESDALE, N.C. 27357

JUDITH F. BURROUGHS
R1 BX. 108A
WHITSETT, N.C. 27377

DONNIE R. BURROUGHS
5113 MC CONNELL RD.
WHITSETT, N.C. 27377

BERNARD D. BURROUGHS
230 PARK DR. S. APT. 6
GREENSBORO, N.C. 27401

WILLIAM A. BURROUGHS
2210 CAMEO DR.
GREENSBORO, N.C. 27403

JOHNNY BURROUGHS
2807 CANDLENUT RD.
GREENSBORO, N.C. 27405

VINCENT L. BURROUGHS
916 CONE BL E. APT. C.
GREENSBORO, N.C. 27405

MICHAEL L. BURROUGHS
R2 BX. 267
GREENSBORO, N.C. 27405

JOHN L. BURROUGHS
R5 BX. 480AA
GREENSBORO, N.C. 27405

CLAUDETTE G. BURROUGHS
1411 WAYSIDE DR.
GREENSBORO, N.C. 27405

KEITH L. BURROUGHS
5403 ROPLEY DR.
GREENSBORO, N.C. 27405

LOTTIE W. BURROUGHS
308 MURRAY ST.
GREENSBORO, N.C. 27406

FLOYD W. BURROUGHS
3 MYSTIC CT.
GREENSBORO, N.C. 27406

BERNARD D. BURROUGHS
107 SHERATON PK. R15
GREENSBORO, N.C. 27406

ELDON J. BURROUGHS
3210 EUCLID ST.
GREENSBORO, N.C. 27407

B. D. BURROUGHS
2407 PINECROFT RD.
GREENSBORO, N.C. 27407

HARVEY L. BURROUGHS
2521 WOODVIEW DR.
GREENSBORO, N.C. 27408

H. D. BURROUGHS
2619 ROBIN HOOD DR.
GREENSBORO, N.C. 27408

DALLAS S. BURROUGHS
206 AIKEN ST. N.
FUQUAY VARINA, N.C. 27526

JAMES D. BURROUGHS
R6 BX. 139
GOLDSBORO, N.C. 27530

RALPH H. BURROUGHS
102 CAMELLIA DR. R5
GOLDSBORO, N.C. 27530

ELEANOR C. BURROUGHS
R8 BX. 103
GOLDSBORO, N.C. 27530

BOBBY D. BURROUGHS
614 RIDGE DR. R6
GOLDSBORO, N.C. 27530

JAMES H. BURROUGHS
R5 BOX 193
HENDERSON, N.C. 27536

EVELYN C. BURROUGHS
R4
HENDERSON, N.C. 27536

JACKSON H. BURROUGHS, JR
R2 BX. 700
HENDERSON, N.C. 27536

JACK E. BURROUGHS
R1 BX. 1364
HENDERSON, N.C. 27536

ULICE C. BURROUGHS
316 HIGH ST.
HENDERSON, N.C. 27536

ROBERT I. BURROUGHS, JR.
R3 BX. 273
HENDERSON, N.C. 27536

JOAN D. BURROUGHS
R6 BX. 386
HENDERSON, N.C. 27536

CURTIS A. BURROUGHS
R3
HENDERSON, N.C. 27536

CHARLIE A. BURROUGHS
602 ARCH ST.
HENDERSON, N.C. 27536

JOHN W. BURROUGHS
R2
MORRISVILLE, N.C. 27560

GLADYS L. BURROUGHS
R2 BX. 30C
MORRISVILLE, N.C. 27560

JOHN W. BURROUGHS
R1
MORRISVILLE, N.C. 27560

WILLIAM W. BURROUGHS, JR.
R3 BX. 190
OXFORD, N.C. 27565

W. A. BURROUGHS
110 SPRING ST. E.
OXFORD, N.C. 27565

ELVINA D. BURROUGHS
R2 BX. 100
SELMA, N.C. 27576

WALTER C. BURROUGHS
R2 BX. 62
WARRENTON, N.C. 27589

WILLIAM H. BURROUGHS
BX. 368
WENDELL, N.C. 27591

CHARLES W. BURROUGHS
R2 BX. 613
WENDELL, N.C. 27591

FREDERICK D. BURROUGHS
5405 EDINGTON LN.
RALEIGH, N.C. 27604

WILLIAM D. BURROUGHS
5701 HIGH ROCK CT.
RALEIGH, N.C. 27604

SUSAN L. BURROUGHS
523 WADE AV. APT. 27
RALEIGH, N.C. 27605

SEAN BURROUGHS
210 PARK AV. APT. A.
RALEIGH, N.C. 27605

SHANNON D. BURROUGHS
2246 THE CIRCLE
RALEIGH, N.C. 27608

RUTH BURROUGHS
2024 QUAIL RIDGE DR.
RALEIGH, N.C. 27609

PAUL L. BURROUGHS, JR.
3605 WILLIAMSBORO CT.
RALEIGH, N.C. 27609

HERBERT W. BURROUGHS, JR.
1305 KIMBERLEY DR.
RALEIGH, N.C. 27609

GRACE R. BURROUGHS
323 SUNNYBROOK RD.
RALEIGH, N.C. 27610

EVA BURROUGHS
608 EVA ST.
DURHAM, N.C. 27701

NELLIE T. BURROUGHS
1140 MERRICK ST. APT. E.
DURHAM, N.C. 27701

WALTER BURROUGHS
1116 LIBERTY ST. APT. B.
DURHAM, N.C. 27703

J. R. BURROUGHS
R1 BX. 184A
DURHAM, N.C. 27705

JOHNNY L. BURROUGHS
B1 MUTUAL CT.
DURHAM, N.C. 27707

LOIS M. BURROUGHS
314 PRICE ST. APT. B.
DURHAM, N.C. 27707

LOUISE BURROUGHS
410 1/2 DUPREE ST.
DURHAM, N.C. 27707

KENNETH W. BURROUGHS
2805 MEADOWBRK RD. R2
ROCKY MOUNT, N.C. 27801

POLK P. BURROUGHS
1618 ROSEWOOD AV.
ROCKY MOUNT, N.C. 27801

GARREY A. BURROUGHS
3220 WINSTEAD RD.
ROCKY MOUNT, N.C. 27801

SARAH D. BURROUGHS
1 COURTNEY SQ. APT.
GREENVILLE, N.C. 27834

CEDRIC W. BURROUGHS
309 SYLVAN DR. N.
GREENVILLE, N.C. 27834

JOEY R. BURROUGHS
2001 GREENVILLE BL E.
GREENVILLE, N.C. 27834

CHARLES A. BURROUGHS
R4 BX. 513
GREENVILLE, N.C. 27834

QUINCY A. BURROUGHS
R9 BX. 582
GREENVILLE, N.C. 27834

BRENDA L. BURROUGHS
R2 BX. 91
GREENVILLE, N.C. 27834

ETHEL C. BURROUGHS
R2 BX. 2904
GREENVILLE, N.C. 27834

LESLIE D. BURROUGHS
R6 BX. 279
GREENVILLE, N.C. 27834

JAMES A. BURROUGHS
R1 BX. 142
GRIMESLAND, N.C. 27837

CEDRIC B. BURROUGHS
BX. 58
HASSELL, N.C. 27841

THOMAS C. BURROUGHS
R1 BX. 97
HOBGOOD, N.C. 27843

DAVID L. BURROUGHS
314 SPRING AV.
MURFREESBORO, N.C. 27855

JAMES BURROUGHS, JR.
BX. 12
ROANOKE RPDS, N.C. 27870

CURTIS L. BURROUGHS, 3D
206 DANIEL ST.
TARBORO, N.C. 27886

KATHERINE S. BURROUGHS
R5 BX. 243V
WASHINGTON, N.C. 27889

BOBBY L. BURROUGHS
R4 BX. 449
WASHINGTON, N.C. 27889

NINA S. BURROUGHS
R4 BX. 63
WASHINGTON, N.C. 27889

SAMUEL M. BURROUGHS
105 6TH ST. H.
WASHINGTON, N.C. 27889

DOROTHY L. BURROUGHS
R2 BX. 735
WILLIAMSTON, N.C. 27892

JULIA B. BURROUGHS
409 PEMBROKE AV.
AHOSKIE, N.C. 27910

EDWARD G. BURROUGHS
60 QUEEN ANNES PL.
EDENTON, N.C. 27932

BERNARD P. BURROUGHS
BX. 43
EDENTON, N.C. 27932

FRANKLIN D. BURROUGHS
BX. 248
HATTERAS, N.C. 27943

JACK R. BURROUGHS
BX. 491
NAGS HEAD, N.C. 27959

MINNIE D. BURROUGHS
R3 BX. 778A
ALBEMARLE, N.C. 28001

EZRA BURROUGHS
R5 BX. 600
ALBEMARLE, N.C. 28001

EARL P. BURROUGHS
R6 BX. 436
ALBEMARLE, N.C. 28001

MAUD M. BURROUGHS
COLLEGE ST. E.
BOILING SPG, N.C. 28017

LOUISE M. BURROUGHS
3909 LINWOOD RD. S.
GASTONIA, N.C. 28052

PAULETTE G. BURROUGHS
2139 CAMELOT ST.
GASTONIA, N.C. 28052

VALENTINO BURROUGHS
201 BIGGERS ST.
GASTONIA, N.C. 28052

JAMES O. BURROUGHS
CAMP ROTARY R1
GASTONIA, N.C. 28052

WILLIAM A. BURROUGHS
BX. 812
GASTONIA, N.C. 28052

ARLENE S. BURROUGHS
PEARSON TRLR R1 LT 19
GASTONIA, N.C. 28052

ROGER D. BURROUGHS
1910 PENNSYLVANIA AV.
KANNAPOLIS, N.C. 28081

D. N. BURROUGHS
R1 BX. 9A
LILESVILLE, N.C. 28091

JABIE L. BURROUGHS
R1 BX. 21A
LILESVILLE, N.C. 28091

ARLIE C. BURROUGHS
R1 BX. 12A
LILESVILLE, N.C. 28091

JOSHUAY P. BURROUGHS
R1
NEW LONDON, N.C. 28127

RICHARD G. BURROUGHS
R10 BX. 639
SALISBURY, N.C. 28144

GREGORY D. BURROUGHS
R8 BOX 534
SALISBURY, N.C. 28144

ROBERT C. BURROUGHS
R1 BX. 145
TROUTMAN, N.C. 28166

JOAN L. BURROUGHS
BX. 953
WADESBORO, N.C. 28170

GRACE P. BURROUGHS
405 LEAK AV.
WADESBORO, N.C. 28170

GRADY BURROUGHS
442 BROOKHILL RD.
CHARLOTTE, N.C. 28203

JOHN D. BURROUGHS
5317 BUENA VISTA AV.
CHARLOTTE, N.C. 28205

HELYN L. BURROUGHS
1707 CLUB RD. APT. 2
CHARLOTTE, N.C. 28205

LUEVENIA C. BURROUGHS
3608 FREW RD. APT. A.
CHARLOTTE, N.C. 28206

SAM L. BURROUGHS
1408 NORRIS AV. APT. B.
CHARLOTTE, N.C. 28206.

NORA W. BURROUGHS
110 COLVILLE RD. APT. 12
CHARLOTTE, N.C. 28207

FRANK E. BURROUGHS
R6 BX. 748A
CHARLOTTE, N.C. 28208

THERRON R. BURROUGHS
1400 STERLING RD.
CHARLOTTE, N.C. 28209

MOSES BURROUGHS
8313 LAMPLIGHTER PL.
CHARLOTTE, N.C. 28210

WILLIAM E. BURROUGHS
6916 FOLGER DR.
CHARLOTTE, N.C. 28211

LAWRENCE A. BURROUGHS
4911 HARDWICK RD.
CHARLOTTE, N.C. 28211

JULIAN C. BURROUGHS
2401 CLOISTER DR.
CHARLOTTE, N.C. 28211

ROBERT M. BURROUGHS
3813 TABLE ROCK RD.
CHARLOTTE, N.C. 28211

TONY L. BURROUGHS
8507 LAWYERS RD. APT. 1
CHARLOTTE, N.C. 28212

AMOS L. BURROUGHS
10704 CONNELL RD. R1
CHARLOTTE, N.C. 28212

AMOS L. BURROUGHS
10704 CONNELL RD.
CHARLOTTE, N.C. 28212

WILMAR BURROUGHS
3327 CEDARHURST DR.
CHARLOTTE, N.C. 28213

ROBERT O. BURROUGHS
2133 JENNIE LINN DR.
CHARLOTTE, N.C. 28215

PATRICIA W. BURROUGHS
4380 CORAL CT.
FAYETTEVILLE, N.C. 28301

THOMAS C. BURROUGHS
233 VIVIAN DR.
FAYETTEVILLE, N.C. 28301

ROBERT G. BURROUGHS
308 MILBURN ST.
FAYETTEVILLE, N.C. 28304

RALPH C. BURROUGHS
102 ELM ST.
ABERDEEN, N.C. 28315

RALPH C. BURROUGHS
BX. 1201
ABERDEEN, N.C. 28315

ETHEL M. BURROUGHS
R3 BX. 75
CLINTON, N.C. 28328

AMY S. BURROUGHS
R3 BX. 572
DUDLEY, N.C. 28333

JAMES E. BURROUGHS
R1 BX. 131
DUDLEY, N.C. 28333

JEFFREY M. BURROUGHS
R3 BX. 357
DUDLEY, N.C. 28333

BETTY J. BURROUGHS
BX. K14
LAURINBURG, N.C. 28352

LONNIE BURROUGHS
BX. K8
LAURINBURG, N.C. 28352

MITCHELL W. BURROUGHS
BX. 86
LAURINBURG, N.C. 28352

MAXIE L. BURROUGHS, JR.
800 WILEY CIR.
LAURINBURG, N.C. 28352

LONNIE BURROUGHS
126 KISER RD.
LAURINBURG, N.C. 28352

ELIZABETH G. BURROUGHS
R5 BX. 413C
MOUNT OLIVE, N.C. 28365

PHILLIP A. BURROUGHS
R5
MOUNT OLIVE, N.C. 28365

DURWOOD E. BURROUGHS
R5 BX. 125
MOUNT OLIVE, N.C. 28365

JULIAN C. BURROUGHS
801 MAIN ST. S.
RED SPRINGS, N.C. 28377

DOROTHY M. BURROUGHS
BX. 108
RED SPRINGS, N.C. 28377

HARVEY C. BURROUGHS
422 ROBERDELL RD.
ROCKINGHAM, N.C. 28379

RUBY L. BURROUGHS
R1 BX. 213
ROCKINGHAM, N.C. 28379

M. H. BURROUGHS
101 BOYD LN.
SOUTHRN PINES, N.C. 28387

JACK R. BURROUGHS
3313 BRAGG DR.
WILMINGTON, N.C. 28403

WILMA H. BURROUGHS
PORT O. PINES R6 LT 44
WILMINGTON, N.C. 28403

AUBRY J. BURROUGHS
R1
CLARENDON, N.C. 28432

EARL G. BURROUGHS
R1 BX. 132A
HAMPSTEAD, N.C. 28443

CHARLES C. BURROUGHS
R4 BX. 324
LELAND, N.C. 28451

CHARLES C. BURROUGHS
R3 BX. 409A
LELAND, N.C. 28451

DEBORAH L. BURROUGHS
115 SHRIMP ST.
SUPPLY, N.C. 28462

HOMER E. BURROUGHS
BX. 583
TABOR CITY, N.C. 28463

DIXIE C. BURROUGHS
R2 BX. 4C
TABOR CITY, N.C. 28463

VOLLEY R. BURROUGHS, JR.
111 BROWN ST.
TABOR CITY, N.C. 28463

VOLLEY R. BURROUGHS, SR.
121 LEWIS ST.
TABOR CITY, N.C. 28463

FRED J. BURROUGHS
303 RALEIGH ST. N.
WALLACE, N.C. 28466

FRED D. BURROUGHS
300 SOUTHERLAND ST. W.
WALLACE, N.C. 28466

CHARLES H. BURROUGHS
R5 BX. 317
WHITEVILLE, N.C. 28472

ROBERT J. BURROUGHS
R3
WHITEVILLE, N.C. 28472

WILLIS M. BURROUGHS
R3
WHITEVILLE, N.C. 28472

PAUL M. BURROUGHS
BX. 341
WHITEVILLE, N.C. 28472

SAMUEL C. BURROUGHS
R3 BX. 329
WHITEVILLE, N.C. 28472

JOHN B. BURROUGHS
1301 GREENBRIAR RD.
KINSTON, N.C. 28501

CLARENCE L. BURROUGHS
R3 BX. 180
AYDEN, N.C. 28513

DAVID M. BURROUGHS
115 LEGION DR.
BEAUFORT, N.C. 28516

BRUCE H. BURROUGHS
BX. 735
BEAUFORT, N.C. 28516

HOSTEN R. BURROUGHS
BX. 158
BRIDGETON, N.C. 28519

STELLA W. BURROUGHS
R1 BX. 25
GRANTSBORO, N.C. 28529

JOYE B. BURROUGHS
BX. 997
GRIFTON, N.C. 28530

HAROLD L. BURROUGHS
14 CENTRAL ST.
HAVELOCK, N.C. 28532

NORMAN E. BURROUGHS
3 CHATHAM RD.
HAVELOCK, N.C. 28532

BOBBY B. BURROUGHS
121 SMITH CIR.
HAVELOCK, N.C. 28532

HUGH W. BURROUGHS, JR.
121 KENNETH BL
HAVELOCK, N.C. 28532

VELVA T. BURROUGHS
409 KETNER BL R2
HAVELOCK, N.C. 28532

WILLIAM T. BURROUGHS
BX. 824
HAVELOCK, N.C. 28532

ARLENE W. BURROUGHS
R2 BX. 266A
HAVELOCK, N.C. 28532

RUTH L. BURROUGHS
R2 BX. 422
HUBERT, N.C. 28539

PAUL E. BURROUGHS
R3 BX. 153D
HUBERT, N.C. 28539

CHARLES R. BURROUGHS
156 LESLIE DR.
HUBERT, N.C. 28539

RAYMOND A. BURROUGHS
R1 BX. 125A
LA GRANGE, N.C. 28551

LETHA J. BURROUGHS
R4 BX. 266A
LA GRANGE, N.C. 28551

GRADY L. BURROUGHS
1012 KAREN DR.
NEW BERN, N.C. 28560

PAUL E. BURROUGHS
2106 OPAL ST.
NEW BERN, N.C. 28560

RACHEL E. BURROUGHS
SPRING GDN R2
NEW BERN, N.C. 28560

ELMER R. BURROUGHS, SR.
1712 NATIONAL ST.
NEW BERN, N.C. 28560

GLENN M. BURROUGHS
118 HICKORY HL R4
NEW BERN, N.C. 28560

BOBBIE J. BURROUGHS
1314 HAZEL AV.
NEW BERN, N.C. 28560

AGNES H. BURROUGHS
R1 BX. 91
VANCEBORO, N.C. 28586

CLARENCE R. BURROUGHS
753 7TH ST. S.E.
HICKORY, N.C. 28601

JAMES R. BURROUGHS
134 MORNINGSIDE DR.
NEWTON, N.C. 28658

JACK T. BURROUGHS
1259 H. ST. E.
NEWTON, N.C. 28658

MICHAEL K. BURROUGHS
300 CHURCH ST. N.W. APT.
VALDESE, N.C. 28690

DONNIE L. BURROUGHS
R2
BAKERSVILLE, N.C. 28705

JOHN H. BURROUGHS
BAT CAVE, N.C. 28710

ROBERT H. BURROUGHS
1028 HEBRON ST.
HENDERSONVL, N.C. 28739

ELIZ. BURROUGHS
117 LOVETT RD. R2
CAMDEN, S.C. 29020

MAGGIE BURROUGHS
R1 BX. 315
CAMDEN, S.C. 29020

CHARLES BURROUGHS
R1 BX. 228
CAMDEN, S.C. 29020

BERNARD A. BURROUGHS, JR.
HWY 215 NORTH
CARLISLE, S.C. 29031

LULA BURROUGHS
R1 BX. 61
CASSATT, S.C. 29032

BERNARD A. BURROUGHS
411 NEW STATE RD.
CAYCE, S.C. 29033

JENKINS BURROUGHS
R1 BX. 58A
LAMAR, S.C. 29069

ARTHUR BURROUGHS
R2 BX. 373B
LYNCHBURG, S.C. 29080

LESSIE L. BURROUGHS
R1 BX. 112
PELION, S.C. 29123

JAMES L. BURROUGHS
934 BAILEY ST.
SUMTER, S.C. 29150

MABLE E. BURROUGHS
306 BARTLETTE ST. W.
SUMTER, S.C. 29150

JAMES BURROUGHS
123 NEWBERRY AV. E.
SUMTER, S.C. 29150

HENRY BURROUGHS
280 WILLIAMS ST. W.
SUMTER, S.C. 29150

YIRGIL L. BURROUGHS
15 HOSPITAL CIR.
SUMTER, S.C. 29150

KENLY BURROUGHS, JR.
BX. 195
SUMTER, S.C. 29150

PAUL BURROUGHS
42 L. ST.
SUMTER, S.C. 29150

SUE N. BURROUGHS
1355 WILMA DR.
WEST COLUMBIA, S.C. 29169

C. E. BURROUGHS, JR.
R2 BX. 24G
WINNSBORO, S.C. 29180

CHARLES H. BURROUGHS, JR.
3419 PARK ST.
COLUMBIA, S.C. 29201

CHARLES H. BURROUGHS
3414 PARK ST.
COLUMBIA, S.C. 29201

ROY W. BURROUGHS
804 OHIO ST.
COLUMBIA, S.C. 29201

ODESSA M. BURROUGHS
1322 DOVER ST.
COLUMBIA, S.C. 29201

IRIE J. BURROUGHS
4324 CATHERINE AV.
COLUMBIA, S.C. 29203

JOHN BURROUGHS
3902 WATER ST.
COLUMBIA, S.C. 29203

DONALD M. BURROUGHS
4708 TRENHOLM RD.
COLUMBIA, S.C. 29206

LAVERNE BURROUGHS
8565 OLD PERCIVAL RD. AP
COLUMBIA, S.C. 29206

WILLIAM J. BURROUGHS
608 POPLAR ST.
SPARTANBURG, S.C. 29302

DANNY L. BURROUGHS
R1
CLINTON, S.C. 29325

BRYAN T. BURROUGHS
R1 BX. 39BB
LAURENS, S.C. 29360

JOHNNIE BURROUGHS
1807 1/2 GRAYSON ST.
CHARLESTON, S.C. 29405

HORACE BURROUGHS, JR.
SR. 1 BX. 19A
GEORGETOWN, S.C. 29440

WILLIAM R. BURROUGHS
R1 BX. 206D
GEORGETOWN, S.C. 29440

WILLIAM R. BURROUGHS
R6 BX. 206D
GEORGETOWN, S.C. 29440

CLARENCE BURROUGHS
5 AVANT CT.
GEORGETOWN, S.C. 29440

E. O. BURROUGHS
R3 BX. 196
GEORGETOWN, S.C. 29440

SKIPPER BURROUGHS
R1 BX. 49
MT PLEASANT, S.C. 29464

JAMES S. BURROUGHS
109 HOPE DR.
SUMMERVILLE, S.C. 29483

DORIS D. BURROUGHS
1453 IRBY ST. N.
FLORENCE, S.C. 29501

WILLIE B. BURROUGHS
805 FRASER ST.
FLORENCE, S.C. 29501

SANFORD BURROUGHS
1800 GREGG AV.
FLORENCE, S.C. 29501

J. BURROUGHS
819 GREGG AV. APT. C.
FLORENCE, S.C. 29501

ROSE BURROUGHS
3323 DINGLE DR. R9
FLORENCE, S.C. 29501

OLIVER BURROUGHS
BX. 524
ANDREWS, S.C. 29510

W. BURROUGHS
R1
BLENHEIM, S.C. 29516

CLYDE E. BURROUGHS
R1 BX. 160
CADES, S.C. 29518

NAZIE BURROUGHS
R2 BX. 64
CHERAW, S.C. 29520

WILMONT BURROUGHS
BX. 2501
CONWAY, S.C. 29526

HOWARD L. BURROUGHS
600 LAKESIDE DR.
CONWAY, S.C. 29526

J. E. BURROUGHS
605 LAKESIDE DR.
CONWAY, S.C. 29526

MARGERY T. BURROUGHS
BX. 606
CONWAY, S.C. 29526

THERON M. BURROUGHS
R7 BX. 236
CONWAY, S.C. 29526

LLOYD G. BURROUGHS
903 LAKESIDE DR.
CONWAY, S.C. 29526

HENRY B. BURROUGHS
503 MAIN ST.
CONWAY, S.C. 29526

FRANK A. BURROUGHS
509 LAUREL ST.
CONWAY, S.C. 29526

FRANKLIN G. BURROUGHS
500 LAKESIDE DR.
CONWAY, S.C. 29526

WILLMONT BURROUGHS
2501 MARION ST.
CONWAY, S.C. 29526

MARGERY T. BURROUGHS
700 LAKESIDE DR.
CONWAY, S.C. 29526

H. B. BURROUGHS
BX. 571
CONWAY, S.C. 29526

NITA L. BURROUGHS
BX. 332
CONWAY, S.C. 29526

JACKSON BURROUGHS
1614 SUGGS ST.
CONWAY, S.C. 29526

GEORGE BURROUGHS
186 LAKELAND DR.
CONWAY, S.C. 29526

JAMES C. BURROUGHS
910 HWY 378
CONWAY, S.C. 29526

B. B. BURROUGHS
402 PALMETTO ST.
CONWAY, S.C. 29526

ROBERT S. BURROUGHS
R1
CONWAY, S.C. 29526

BILLY W. BURROUGHS
R6 BX. 206
CONWAY, S.C. 29526

J. E. BURROUGHS
BX. 1536
CONWAY, S.C. 29526

R. B. BURROUGHS
BX. 147
CONWAY, S.C. 29526

TOM BURROUGHS, JR.
R1 BX. 15
BUCKSPORT, S.C. 29527

CHARLES E. BURROUGHS
R2 BX. 242
DARLINGTON, S.C. 29532

ELIJAH N. BURROUGHS
701 JOE LOUIS BL
DARLINGTON, S.C. 29532

KAY T. BURROUGHS
R1
EFFINGHAM, S.C. 29541

HARRY BURROUGHS
R1 BX. 34
EFFINGHAM, S.C. 29541

ELIZABETH BURROUGHS
R1 BX. 31
FORK, S.C. 29543

INA BURROUGHS
R2 BX. 50
GALIVANTS FRY, S.C. 29544

RABON BURROUGHS
R3 BX. 68
GALIVANTS FRY, S.C. 2954

CORA L. BURROUGHS
905 MYRTLE ST.
HARTSVILLE, S.C. 29550

GLORIA P. BURROUGHS
R1 BX. 101
HEMINGWAY, S.C. 29554

MINNIE O. BURROUGHS
R1 BX. 81
HEMINGWAY, S.C. 29554

CAROLYN G. BURROUGHS
R3 BX. 161
KINGSTREE, S.C. 29556

WEBSTER BURROUGHS
725 ST. JOHN ST.
KINGSTREE, S.C. 29556

JOHN W. BURROUGHS
R1 BX. 205
KINGSTREE, S.C. 29556

FLOSSIE S. BURROUGHS
R1 BX. 31
KINGSTREE, S.C. 29556

ROSA L. BURROUGHS
BX. 001
KINGSTREE, S.C. 29556

WILLIE BURROUGHS
R1 BX. 66F
KINGSTREE, S.C. 29556

RAYMOND M. BURROUGHS
1321 FLORA ST.
KINGSTREE, S.C. 29556

HENRY BURROUGHS
120 BENTON ST.
LAKE CITY, S.C. 29560

HOWARD BURROUGHS
511 PALM CIR. R4 E.
LAKE CITY, S.C. 29560

LILA R. BURROUGHS
R3 BX. 56F
LAKE CITY, S.C. 29560

WOODROW W. BURROUGHS
122 THOMAS ST. W. APT. A
LAKE CITY, S.C. 29560

A. BURROUGHS
R4 BX. 31
LAKE CITY, S.C. 29560

COURTNEY BURROUGHS
R2 BX. 345A
LAKE CITY, S.C. 29560

M. BURROUGHS
R2 BX. 64
LANE, S.C. 29564

RAYMOND BURROUGHS
R1 BX. 166
LANE, S.C. 29564

JUANITA BURROUGHS
R2 BX. 348
LATTA, S.C. 29565

ELROY D. BURROUGHS
R1 BX. 303
LORIS, S.C. 29569

C. E. BURROUGHS
BX. 776
LORIS, S.C. 29569

D. BURROUGHS
R1
LORIS, S.C. 29569

WILLIE M. BURROUGHS
R1 BX. 148
MC COLL, S.C. 29570

CLARENCE E. BURROUGHS
608 GIBSON AV. E.
MC COLL, S.C. 29570

ALGER BURROUGHS
214 WALTERS ST.
MC COLL, S.C. 29570

LONNIE E. BURROUGHS
704 MAIN ST. N.
MC COLL, S.C. 29570

LEROY BURROUGHS
R3 BX. 17M
MARION, S.C. 29571

JIMMY BURROUGHS
CONTY CLB RD. R1
MARION, S.C. 29571

FRANKLIN J. BURROUGHS
BX. 612
MARION, S.C. 29571

CALVIN J. BURROUGHS
505 WILFORD CT.
MARION, S.C. 29571

FRANKLIN J. BURROUGHS, JR.
BX. 531
MARION, S.C. 29571

STACY J. BURROUGHS
R4 BX. 362
MARION, S.C. 29571

LILLIAN R. BURROUGHS
910 WATSONIA DR. APT. A.
MARION, S.C. 29571

ESTHER L. BURROUGHS
GILCHRIST ST. R2
MARION, S.C. 29571

LOUIS BURROUGHS
501 FRONT ST. R2 E.
MULLINS, S.C. 29574

EAUGIE BURROUGHS
421 JAMES ST. W.
MULLINS, S.C. 29574

ANNABELLE BURROUGHS
BX. 418
MURRELLS INLT, S.C. 29576

EDWARD E. BURROUGHS
4809 BURCHAP DR.
MYRTLE BEACH, S.C. 29577

CHARLES B. BURROUGHS
STARFSH CT. SR. 2 BX. 22
MYRTLE BEACH, S.C. 29577

BENJAMIN BURROUGHS
7100 PORCHER AV. N. APT.
MYRTLE BEACH, S.C. 29577

RONALD BURROUGHS
R3 BX. 414H
MYRTLE BEACH, S.C. 29577

CASSIE R. BURROUGHS
BX. 1701
MYRTLE BEACH, S.C. 29577

RONALD E. BURROUGHS
R2 BX. 414H
MYRTLE BEACH, S.C. 29577

EUNICE S. BURROUGHS
100 SUNRISE RD.
MYRTLE BEACH, S.C. 29577

HARRIET P. BURROUGHS
R1 BX. 64
NESMITH, S.C. 29580

JACK BURROUGHS, JR.
R1 BX. 346
NESMITH, S.C. 29580

AMELIA K. BURROUGHS
R1 BX. 136
NESMITH, S.C. 29580

RONALD D. BURROUGHS
R2 BX. 139A
SCRANTON, S.C. 29591

DAVID BURROUGHS
R2
SCRANTON, S.C. 29591

MICHAEL T. BURROUGHS
HAMBY DR. R6
GREENVILLE, S.C. 29607

WILLIS H. BURROUGHS
59 LONG FOREST DR.
GREENVILLE, S.C. 29609

JOHN BURROUGHS
117 CONE ST. LOT 6
GREENVILLE, S.C. 29609

L. M. BURROUGHS
PARKER RD. R7
GREENVILLE, S.C. 29609

ROBERT L. BURROUGHS
260 COLONY N. APT. R3 33
GREENVILLE, S.C. 29609

G. BURROUGHS
916 HUNTSBRIDGE RD. APT.
GREENVILLE, S.C. 29611

RAYMOND E. BURROUGHS
R11 BX. 122
ANDERSON, S.C. 29621

WILLIAM H. BURROUGHS
222 ROGERS ST.
ANDERSON, S.C. 29621

SAMUEL D. BURROUGHS
2602 CALROSSIE RD.
ANDERSON, S.C. 29621

TRESSIE BURROUGHS
R9 BX. 30A
ANDERSON, S.C. 29624

PRESTON B. BURROUGHS
135 GRIFFIN RD.
BELTON, S.C. 29627

JAMES R. BURROUGHS
BX. 262
DUE WEST, S.C. 29639

GEORGE BURROUGHS
103 HOLLINGSWRTH DR.
EASLEY, S.C. 29640

D. BURROUGHS, JR.
R2 BX. 384
GRAY COURT, S.C. 29645

LORENE E. BURROUGHS
215 CRESWELL ST. W.
GREENWOOD, S.C. 29646

DANNY B. BURROUGHS
28 WILDHOOD EST. R6
GREENWOOD, S.C. 29646

JAMES H. BURROUGHS
R1 BX. 164
HODGES, S.C. 29653

W. S. BURROUGHS
R1 BX. 98
HODGES, S.C. 29653

HELEN J. BURROUGHS
R1
HODGES, S.C. 29653

L. S. BURROUGHS
R2 BX. 503E
HODGES, S.C. 29653

R. A. BURROUGHS
R1
HODGES, S.C. 29653

ALTHEA J. BURROUGHS
BX. 297
NINETY SIX, S.C. 29666

ROCKY I. BURROUGHS
R2 BX. 289C
NINETY SIX, S.C. 29666

WILLIS H. BURROUGHS, JR.
R1 BX. 96A
NINETY SIX, S.C. 29666

PAUL H. BURROUGHS
221 SALUDA ST.
NINETY SIX, S.C. 29666

THOMAS R. BURROUGHS
R3 BX. 291A
PELZER, S.C. 29669

JAMES R. BURROUGHS
R1 BX. 40
SIMPSONVILLE, S.C. 29681

SARA P. BURROUGHS
200 OSMOND DR.
TAYLORS, S.C. 29687

MARC L. BURROUGHS
R1 BX. 423
WILLIAMSTON, S.C. 29697

W. B. BURROUGHS
R2 BX. 610K
WILLIAMSTON, S.C. 29697

C. P. BURROUGHS
2047 DOWNEY ST.
ROCK HILL, S.C. 29730

JAMES BURROUGHS
670 EDRIE ST.
AIKEN, S.C. 29801

ROBERT B. BURROUGHS
206 FAIRWAY DR. N.W.
NEW ELLENTON, S.C. 29809

VIRGINIA BURROUGHS
397 LITCHFLD APTS.
BARNWELL, S.C. 29812

EUGENE W. BURROUGHS
R1 BX. 12
EDGEFIELD, S.C. 29824

BARBARA BURROUGHS
R1 BX. 97RB
GRANITEVILLE, S.C. 29829

ROBERT B. BURROUGHS
R1
GRANITEVILLE, S.C. 29829

JOHN W. BURROUGHS
BX. 131
GRANITEVILLE, S.C. 29829

S. N. BURROUGHS
109 OAK HURST DR. R1
NORTH AUGUSTA, S.C. 29841

DAVID J. BURROUGHS
907 CAROLINA AV.
NORTH AUGUSTA, S.C. 29841

SANDRA N. BURROUGHS
109 OAKDALE AV.
NORTH AUGUSTA, S.C. 29841

CHARLIE BURROUGHS
R1 BX. 20
ULMER, S.C. 29849

LEMUEL BURROUGHS
303 BENNETT ST.
WILLISTON, S.C. 29853

RUBY M. BURROUGHS
BX. 6
BLUFFTON, S.C. 29910

JOHN H. BURROUGHS
1603 POST OAK RD. APT. D
CLARKSTON, GA. 30021

B. M. BURROUGHS
322 HILLDALE DR.
DECATUR, GA. 30030

ROBERT A. BURROUGHS
2740 SHELLBARK HWY.
DECATUR, GA. 30035

HELEN H. BURROUGHS
2004 ARTHURS CT. APT. B.
DECATUR, GA. 30035

LESTER D. BURROUGHS
2468 YOLONDA TR
ELLENWOOD, GA. 30049

WILLIAM T. BURROUGHS
2363 RANDALL RD.
LITHONIA, GA. 30058

J. M. BURROUGHS
4473 AMY DR. R6
LITHONIA, GA. 30058

T. M. BURROUGHS
227 LOG CABIN DR. R1
SMYRNA, GA. 30080

RALPH D. BURROUGHS
3247 FERN DR.
TUCKER, GA. 30084

WILLIAM A. BURROUGHS
490 KAREN DR.
ALPHARETTA, GA. 30201

H. E. BURROUGHS
225 MT. RAINER HWY. R6
ALPHARETTA, GA. 30201

THOMAS A. BURROUGHS
HOG MOUNTN RD.
AUBURN, GA. 30203

HAROLD BURROUGHS
3540 IRVINBRIDGE RD.
CONYERS, GA. 30207

DEBBIE BURROUGHS
WALNUT GROVE R3
COVINGTON, GA. 30209

JACK BURROUGHS
WALNUT GROVE R3
COVINGTON, GA. 30209

S. B. BURROUGHS, JR.
R4
COVINGTON, GA. 30209

H. G. BURROUGHS
64 PEARL ST.
FAIRBURN, GA. 30213

SANFORD BURROUGHS
HWY 81
HAMPTON, GA. 30228

ELLIS K. BURROUGHS
HIGHWAY N.
HOGANSVILLE, GA. 30230

MATTHEW H. BURROUGHS
8463 SHILOH CT.
JONESBORO, GA. 30236

JOE BURROUGHS
2733 HERITAGE LN.
MORROW, GA. 30260

FREDDIE BURROUGHS
161 WASHINGTON ST. W.
NEWNAN, GA. 30263

ROBERT W. BURROUGHS
11504 BUCKTHORNE DR.
NEWNAN, GA. 30263

EULA BURROUGHS
12 V. C. ST.
NEWNAN, GA. 30263

BRENDA BURROUGHS
R7 BX. 916
NEWNAN, GA. 30263

SAMUEL BURROUGHS
18 DUNCAN ST. APT. A.
NEWNAN, GA. 30263

ROBERT BURROUGHS
4 BUCKTHORNE DR.
NEWNAN, GA. 30263

DENNIS A. BURROUGHS
18 ELM CIR.
NEWNAN, GA. 30263

FANNIE B. BURROUGHS
48 BOONE DR.
NEWNAN, GA. 30263

EUGENE A. BURROUGHS
7545 MONTEGO CT.
RIVERDALE, GA. 30274

BEVERLY J. BURROUGHS
1138 VILLA DR. N.E. APT.
ATLANTA, GA. 30306

SANDRA K. BURROUGHS
1300 UNIVERSTY DR. N.E.
ATLANTA, GA. 30306

CINDY BURROUGHS
26 15TH ST. N.E. APT. 2
ATLANTA, GA. 30309

KEITH J. BURROUGHS
716 BROOKLINE ST. S.W.
ATLANTA, GA. 30310

BALDWIN W. BURROUGHS
10 ANDERSON AV. S.W.
ATLANTA, GA. 30314

BARBARA T. BURROUGHS
538 BECKWITH CT. S.W.
ATLANTA, GA. 30314

BALDWIN W. BURROUGHS
10 ANDERSON AV. N.W.
ATLANTA, GA. 30314

PATRICIA BURROUGHS
147 HILLTOP CIR. N.W. AP
ATLANTA, GA. 30314

H. J. BURROUGHS
2499 BAXTER RD. S.W.
ATLANTA, GA. 30315

FOSTER C. BURROUGHS
2153 BURROUGHS AV. S.E.
ATLANTA, GA. 30315

THELMA F. BURROUGHS
2254 SWALLOW CIR. S.E.
ATLANTA, GA. 30315

MAXIMILLIA A BURROUGHS
268 LYDIA DR. S.E.
ATLANTA, GA. 30315

LILLIE BURROUGHS
2851 BOULEVARD DR. S.E.
ATLANTA, GA. 30317

EDNA V. BURROUGHS
814 ANTONE ST. N.W.
ATLANTA, GA. 30318

LUTHER P. BURROUGHS
6306 VRNON WDS DR. N.E.
ATLANTA, GA. 30328

JOHN BURROUGHS
3656 BOLFAIR DR. N.W.
ATLANTA, GA. 30331

LILLIE BURROUGHS
400 FAIRBURN RD. S.W. AP
ATLANTA, GA. 30331

JAMES D. BURROUGHS
4620 BUCKLINE CT.
ATLANTA, GA. 30338

CLARA J. BURROUGHS
2925 ARLINGTON RD.
ATLANTA, GA. 30344

EDGAR BURROUGHS
2918 BRANCHWOOD DR.
ATLANTA, GA. 30344

DIANA BURROUGHS
COLLINS, GA. 30421

JEWELL BURROUGHS
R1 BX. 225
COLLINS, GA. 30421

B. BURROUGHS
402 BARNARD ST. E.
GLENNVILLE, GA. 30427

SPENCER BURROUGHS
BUCKHEAD RD. R. 2
MILLEN, GA. 30442

HATTIE M. BURROUGHS
BOY SCOUT RD. R2
MILLEN, GA. 30442

MARIE BURROUGHS
R.R. 4
MILLEN, GA. 30442

LOIS BURROUGHS
SCOUT HUT RD. R2
MILLEN, GA. 30442

S. V. BURROUGHS
SR. BOX 156
REIDSVILLE, GA. 30453

T. F. BURROUGHS
MILLEN RD.
SARDIS, GA. 30456

TOMMIE BURROUGHS
R.R. 3
STATESBORO, GA. 30458

DELOIS BURROUGHS
R.R. 7
SYLVANIA, GA. 30467

C. W. BURROUGHS, SR.
328 SINGLETON AV.
SYLVANIA, GA. 30467

EMMA L. BURROUGHS
LAVONIA HWY
CARNESVILLE, GA. 30521

MACK BURROUGHS
HWY 106
CARNESVILLE, GA. 30521

ROBERT A. BURROUGHS
HWY 145
CARNESVILLE, GA. 30521

HAROLD BURROUGHS
HWY 106 EXT.
CARNESVILLE, GA. 30521

J. E. BURROUGHS
WILSON JR. HI R4
COMMERCE, GA. 30529

GRACE BURROUGHS
GILMER ST.
LAVONIA, GA. 30553

F. R. BURROUGHS
CARNESVL HWY R1
LAVONIA, GA. 30553

MARVIN BURROUGHS
NICHOLSON, GA. 30565

J. B. BURROUGHS
SANFORD RD.
NICHOLSON, GA. 30565

LEE W. BURROUGHS
R. 1
SAUTE NACOCHE, GA. 30571

DANNY BURROUGHS
2162 WHITE OAK DR.
ATHENS, GA. 30606

WILLIAM R. BURROUGHS
275 RIVERHILL DR.
ATHENS, GA. 30606

CHARLES A. BURROUGHS
2158 MACON HWY
ATHENS, GA. 30606

J. F. BURROUGHS
8TH
CARLTON, GA. 30627

MATTIE BURROUGHS
R. 1
COLBERT, GA. 30628

PAUL BURROUGHS
DANVL RD.
COLBERT, GA. 30628

JACK A. BURROUGHS
2 AV.
COLBERT, GA. 30628

CARL T. BURROUGHS
POST RD.
COMER, GA. 30629

C. J. BURROUGHS
232 WILLOW
COMER, GA. 30629

BILLY T. BURROUGHS
DANIELSVILLE, GA. 30633

GREG J. BURROUGHS
R. 2
DANIELSVILLE, GA. 30633

JOE W. BURROUGHS
R2
DANIELSVILLE, GA. 30633

PAUL A. BURROUGHS
GEN DANL AV.
DANIELSVILLE, GA. 30633

RALPH H. BURROUGHS
R.R. 2
HARTWELL, GA. 30643

BRIAN BURROUGHS
105 VICKERY ST.
HARTWELL, GA. 30643

CHARLES T. BURROUGHS
R. 1
HULL, GA. 30646

DONALD BURROUGHS
HULL, GA. 30646

CHRIS D. BURROUGHS
BURROUGHS RD.
HULL, GA. 30646

A. D. BURROUGHS
R.R. 1
ROCK SPRING, GA. 30739

ELLIS E. BURROUGHS, SR.
631 GREENSLAKE CIR.
ROSSVILLE, GA. 30741

FRANK T. BURROUGHS
R1 BX. 229C
EVANS, GA. 30809

DOUG BURROUGHS
2ND AV.
GROVETOWN, GA. 30813

O. L. BURROUGHS
175 TRIPPE E.
HARLEM, GA. 30814

WALTER R. BURROUGHS
BX. 235
HARLEM, GA. 30814

OLIVER B. BURROUGHS, 3D
1845 OHIO AV.
AUGUSTA, GA. 30904

JOSEPH J. BURROUGHS
2013 1/2 MARYLAND AV.
AUGUSTA, GA. 30904

JIM W. BURROUGHS
1723 KISSINGBOWER RD.
AUGUSTA, GA. 30904

REBECCA G. BURROUGHS
2137 WALTON WY.
AUGUSTA, GA. 30904

WILLARD BURROUGHS
2518 WRIGHTSBORO RD.
AUGUSTA, GA. 30904

WILLIAM L. BURROUGHS
2148 EASTSIDE CT.
AUGUSTA, GA. 30906

MIKE BURROUGHS
2537 1/2 DEANS BRIDGE RD
AUGUSTA, GA. 30906

HARRY BURROUGHS
3018 EAGLE DR.
AUGUSTA, GA. 30906

MILTON G. BURROUGHS
2709 BOLLING RD.
AUGUSTA, GA. 30909

GERALD W. BURROUGHS
741 OXFORD RD.
AUGUSTA, GA. 30909

SUE W. BURROUGHS
1702 VALLEY PARK ST. W.
AUGUSTA, GA. 30909

MELVIN BURROUGHS
SOPERTON RD. R. 4
EASTMAN, GA. 31023

CULLEN BURROUGHS
DUBLIN RD. R. 5
EASTMAN, GA. 31023

HENRY BURROUGHS
304 TORTOISE DR.
WARNER ROBINS, GA. 31093

BILLY W. BURROUGHS
2020 MOODY RD.
WARNER ROBINS, GA. 31093

JOHN E. BURROUGHS
1721 EVELINE AV. APT. B.
MACON, GA. 31204

CAROLYN BURROUGHS
1221 CREEKWOOD DR. APT.
MACON, GA. 31211

BLAND BURROUGHS, SR.
RFD 1 BX. 75
PEMBROKE, GA. 31321

FREDDIE BURROUGHS
311 DUFFY ST. E.
SAVANNAH, GA. 31401

HAROLD BURROUGHS
670 FELLWOOD HOMES
SAVANNAH, GA. 31401

ALFRED BURROUGHS
35 CORNWALL ST.
SAVANNAH, GA. 31401

D. BURROUGHS
214 1/2 PARK AV. E.
SAVANNAH, GA. 31401

FRANK BURROUGHS
1213 41ST ST. W.
SAVANNAH, GA. 31401

M. L. BURROUGHS
204 TREADWAY DR. R1
SAVANNAH, GA. 31401

JOHN H. BURROUGHS, JR.
2119 WALZ DR.
SAVANNAH, GA. 31404

JOSEPH L. BURROUGHS
1208 ANDERSON ST. E.
SAVANNAH, GA. 31404

LEWIS BURROUGHS
2244 CAPITAL ST.
SAVANNAH, GA. 31404

SIMON H. BURROUGHS
2310 NEW YORK AV.
SAVANNAH, GA. 31404

WILLIAM S. BURROUGHS
10 ST. JOHNS AV.
SAVANNAH, GA. 31404

RANGE BURROUGHS
1015 SCOTT ST.
SAVANNAH, GA. 31405

ALFRED BURROUGHS
1605 1/2 STALEY AV. APT.
SAVANNAH, GA. 31405

WILLIAM H. BURROUGHS
112 ANDOVER DR.
SAVANNAH, GA. 31405

AARON C. BURROUGHS
403 61ST ST. E.
SAVANNAH, GA. 31405

VIOLA E. BURROUGHS
1611 AMHERST ST.
BRUNSWICK, GA. 31520

THOMAS BURROUGHS
118 ALDEN AV. W.
VALDOSTA, GA. 31601

JAMES R. BURROUGHS
403 MOORE ST. E.
VALDOSTA, GA. 31601

THOMAS W. BURROUGHS
1708 IOLA DR.
VALDOSTA, GA. 31601

RICHARD B. BURROUGHS
332 GONWOOD CIR.
VALDOSTA, GA. 31601

DAVID B. BURROUGHS
1859 CAROLINA AV. S. APT
ALBANY, GA. 31705

JIM BURROUGHS
125 TAYLOR ST.
AMERICUS, GA. 31709

EVERETT BURROUGHS
R1
CAIRO, GA. 31728

E. W. BURROUGHS
809 2ND AV. E.
DAWSON, GA. 31742

F. O. BURROUGHS
R.R. 3
DAWSON, GA. 31742

DAVID BURROUGHS
715 MAIN ST. N.
FITZGERALD, GA. 31750

R. W. BURROUGHS
1211 5TH ST. S.W.
MOULTRIE, GA. 31768

JEAN R. BURROUGHS
CLUBVIEW ST. R6
MOULTRIE, GA. 31768

FLEM BURROUGHS
307 MALAGA ST.
PELHAM, GA. 31779

OWEN BURROUGHS
106 LIBERIA ST.
PELHAM, GA. 31779

LEONA BURROUGHS
604 WHIDDON ST.
TIFTON, GA. 31794

EDNA BURROUGHS
1715 PICKARD AV.
TIFTON, GA. 31794

ROSETTA BURROUGHS
120 INDUSTRIAL DR.
TIFTON, GA. 31794

EDGAR S. BURROUGHS
6816 TRAPPER WY.
MIDLAND, GA. 31820

MANLEY M. BURROUGHS
1222 20TH ST.
COLUMBUS, GA. 31901

RICHARD A. BURROUGHS
3945 BILTMORE DR.
COLUMBUS, GA. 31904

ESTELLE L. BURROUGHS
1802 51ST ST.
COLUMBUS, GA. 31904

LINDA K. BURROUGHS
3405 GENTIAN BL APT. 205
COLUMBUS, GA. 31907

JAMES L. BURROUGHS
R1 BX. 31
DOCTORS INLET, FL. 32030

STEPHEN W. BURROUGHS
SR224 BX. 42
DOCTORS INLET, FL. 32030

HARRIS H. BURROUGHS
116 AVALON AV.
FLAGLER BEACH, FL. 32036

PAUL J. BURROUGHS
R2 BX. 104
GRN COVE SPG, FL. 32043

EUGENE BURROUGHS
STANTON ST.
HASTINGS, FL. 32045

LELAND BURROUGHS, JR.
R2 BX. 15A
INTERLACHEN, FL. 32048

TERRALENE BURROUGHS
HWY 315
INTERLACHEN, FL. 32048

LELAND BURROUGHS, SR.
MANNVILLE R1
INTERLACHEN, FL. 32048

SARA L. BURROUGHS
3 CAROLINE ST.
LAKE CITY, FL. 32055

LEON P. BURROUGHS
R4 BX. 173B
LIVE OAK, FL. 32060

ED BURROUGHS
SR21 BX. 181
MIDDLEBURG, FL. 32068

SHIRLEY S. BURROUGHS
125 BRICKYARD RD.
MIDDLEBURG, FL. 32068

JIM BURROUGHS
257 AQUARIUS CNCRSE
ORANGE PARK, FL. 32073

PHILLIP H. BURROUGHS
66 MELROSE AV.
ORMOND BEACH, FL. 32074

HAL J. BURROUGHS
453 WEST ST.
ORMOND BEACH, FL. 32074

DOROTHY L. BURROUGHS
2416 CRILL AV.
PALATKA, FL. 32077

DOROTHY BURROUGHS
401 IVY ST.
PALATKA, FL. 32077

DOROTHY L. BURROUGHS
1608 LAUREL ST.
PALATKA, FL. 32077

WILLIE D. BURROUGHS
56 SPRING ST. APT. B.
ST. AUGUSTINE, FL. 32084

EUGENE BURROUGHS
18 DAVIS ST.
ST. AUGUSTINE, FL. 32084

ETHEL BURROUGHS
734 DUVAL ST. W.
JACKSONVILLE, FL. 32202

JOSEPH H. BURROUGHS
6651 GRACE LN.
JACKSONVILLE, FL. 32205

LENWARD R. BURROUGHS
932 INGLESIDE AV.
JACKSONVILLE, FL. 32205

ELMER BURROUGHS
138 CARNEGIE ST.
JACKSONVILLE, FL. 32205

HOLLY BURROUGHS
910 LE BRUN ST.
JACKSONVILLE, FL. 32205

SUSAN G. BURROUGHS
5550 POTOMAC AV. APT. B.
JACKSONVILLE, FL. 32205

DAVID A. BURROUGHS
1824 PEARL ST. N.
JACKSONVILLE, FL. 32206

ROBERT C. BURROUGHS
1326 LAURA ST. N. APT. 4
JACKSONVILLE, FL. 32206

WILLIAM H. BURROUGHS
54 17TH ST. W.
JACKSONVILLE, FL. 32206

DAVID A. BURROUGHS
1834 PEARL ST. N.
JACKSONVILLE, FL. 32206

JAMES R. BURROUGHS
5051 WELBORN RD.
JACKSONVILLE, FL. 32207

TRUETT G. BURROUGHS
4715 SPRING PARK RD.
JACKSONVILLE, FL. 32207

HENRY BURROUGHS
9162 SIBBALD RD.
JACKSONVILLE, FL. 32208

JAMES H. BURROUGHS
9261 SIBBALD RD.
JACKSONVILLE, FL. 32208

PEGGY E. BURROUGHS
1411 JEFFERSON ST. N. AP
JACKSONVILLE, FL. 32209

EARL E. BURROUGHS
939 23RD ST. W.
JACKSONVILLE, FL. 32209

RUTH BURROUGHS
1537 7TH ST. W. APT. B.
JACKSONVILLE, FL. 32209

RICHARD B. BURROUGHS, JR.
2626 APACHE AV.
JACKSONVILLE, FL. 32210

GEORGE BURROUGHS
2308 LOOKING GLASS
JACKSONVILLE, FL. 32210

OSCAR C. BURROUGHS
355 MONUMENT RD. AP 23-E
JACKSONVILLE, FL. 32211

EMILY C. BURROUGHS
3414 JACQUELINE DR.
JACKSONVILLE, FL. 32211

RONALD A. BURROUGHS
7536 TRAIL ENDS
JACKSONVILLE, FL. 32211

ROBERT D. BURROUGHS
8227 BATEAU RD. S.
JACKSONVILLE, FL. 32216

SHERRY R. BURROUGHS
9930 COVE VIEW DR. E.
JACKSONVILLE, FL. 32217

SARAH S. BURROUGHS
6210 SAN JOSE BL
JACKSONVILLE, FL. 32217

REFORD J. BURROUGHS
37 SAN PEDRO RD.
JACKSONVILLE, FL. 32217

ORL BURROUGHS
8384 MONCRIEF DMR RD.
JACKSONVILLE, FL. 32219

LESTER L. BURROUGHS
9169 WOLLITZ PLZ
JACKSONVILLE, FL. 32220

JOHN W. BURROUGHS, 3D
3713 CEDAR POINT RD.
JACKSONVILLE, FL. 32226

F. D. BURROUGHS
766 HARVEL LN.
JACKSONVILLE, FL. 32233

ROBERT L. BURROUGHS
349 CHURCH RD.
JACKSONVILLE, FL. 32233

JESSIE L. BURROUGHS
R24 BX. 932
JACKSONVILLE, FL. 32234

JESSIE L. BURROUGHS
R15 BX. 128A
JACKSONVILLE, FL. 32234

JOHN A. BURROUGHS
1417 CONSTITUTION CT.
JACKSONVILLE, FL. 32250

CARLTON L. BURROUGHS
2004 ALBAN AV.
TALLAHASSEE, FL. 32301

WILLIAM W. BURROUGHS
805 BRIANDAV DR. R15
TALLAHASSEE, FL. 32301

RAY BURROUGHS
4333 OAKMONT ST.
TALLAHASSEE, FL. 32303

RAY W. BURROUGHS, II
8019 BLUE SMOKE R13
TALLAHASSEE, FL. 32312

JOSEPH E. BURROUGHS
R3 BX. 433
PERRY, FL. 32347

HERBERT W. BURROUGHS
R1 BX. 821
PERRY, FL. 32347

RALPH BURROUGHS
SMOKEY ST.
MALONE, FL. 32445

HERMAN R. BURROUGHS, JR.
SMOKEY ST.
MALONE, FL. 32445

WILLIAM B. BURROUGHS
1104 WATSON AV. N.
PENSACOLA, FL. 32503

VICTOR L. BURROUGHS
5410 HAVELAND ST. APT. A
PENSACOLA, FL. 32503

J. W. BURROUGHS
20 DEVANE ST. W.
PENSACOLA, FL. 32504

WILLIAM H. BURROUGHS
4521 LE MOYNE LN.
PENSACOLA, FL. 32505

ESCHOL D. BURROUGHS
415 SANDS PL.
PENSACOLA, FL. 32505

HAROLD B. BURROUGHS
6700 LILLIAN HWY
PENSACOLA, FL. 32506

JERROLD A. BURROUGHS
10010 SUNDAY RD. R7
CANTONMENT, FL. 32533

LOUVENIA J. BURROUGHS
373 WOODRUFF AV. W.
CRESTVIEW, FL. 32536

FRANKLIN D. BURROUGHS
R3 BX. 689A4
JAY, FL. 32565

LLOYD W. BURROUGHS
173 MIRAMAR DR.
MARY ESTHER, FL. 32569

JAMES A. BURROUGHS, JR.
1285 BAYSHORE DR.
VALPARAISO, FL. 32580

SHARON V. BURROUGHS
414 12TH TER. S.E.
GAINESVILLE, FL. 32601

I. A. BURROUGHS, SR.
R1 BX. 487J
BELL, FL. 32619

RALEIGH S. BURROUGHS
BX. 1597
CRYSTAL RIVER, FL. 32629

MARK A. BURROUGHS
SR484 BX. 1294
DUNNELLON, FL. 32630

MARK A. BURROUGHS
122 PALATKA DR.
DUNNELLON, FL. 32630

R. S. BURROUGHS
SR19 BX. 1086
HOMOSASSA SPG, FL. 32647

BRUCE A. BURROUGHS
1524 10TH ST. N.E.
OCALA, FL. 32670

JAMES R. BURROUGHS
701 52ND AV. S.E.
OCALA, FL. 32670

WAYNE A. BURROUGHS
630 ARNOLD LN.
CASSELBERRY, FL. 32707

GINGER BURROUGHS
41 JACKSON CT.
CASSELBERRY, FL. 32707

ROBERT C. BURROUGHS
253 MANSION BL
DE BARY, FL. 32713

GEORGE W. BURROUGHS
BX. 782
DE LAND, FL. 32720

ROBERT D. BURROUGHS
421 AIRPORT RD. R1
DE LAND, FL. 32720

CHARLES M. BURROUGHS
1449 FREEPORT DR.
ORANGE CITY, FL. 32725

CHARLES M. BURROUGHS
1950 OLD MILL RD.
ORANGE CITY, FL. 32725

ROBERT C. BURROUGHS
1326 PORTILLO ST.
ORANGE CITY, FL. 32725

CHARLES W. BURROUGHS
1718 NESBIT ST.
ORANGE CITY, FL. 32725

PAMELA S. BURROUGHS
1210 DE LEON AV.
LEESBURG, FL. 32748

ROBERT O. BURROUGHS
664 CHURCH AV. E.
LONGWOOD, FL. 32750

JANICE T. BURROUGHS
160 LAKEWIND TRL
MAITLAND, FL. 32751

JAMES C. BURROUGHS
116 LAKEWIND TRL
MAITLAND, FL. 32751

ISMAY H. BURROUGHS
1018 9TH AV. E.
MOUNT DORA, FL. 32757

EDNA M. BURROUGHS
2000 VOLUSIA AV. N. LOT
ORANGE CITY, FL. 32763

ALBERTA BURROUGHS
1028 CRAYFORD AV.
SAINT CLOUD, FL. 32769

RALPH BURROUGHS
21 EL RED DR. APT. D.
TAVARES, FL. 32778

MARIE B. BURROUGHS
R2 BX. 550
UMATILLA, FL. 32784

JAMES B. BURROUGHS
1301 INLAND SEAS BL
WINTER GARDEN, FL. 32787

JAMES B. BURROUGHS
BX. 1414
WINTER GARDEN, FL. 32787

JOHN P. BURROUGHS
325 ORLANDO ST. W. APT.
ORLANDO, FL. 32804

MERWYN G. BURROUGHS
6445 HOFFNER AV.
ORLANDO, FL. 32807

JOSEPH M. BURROUGHS
R5 BX. 127B
ORLANDO, FL. 32807

M. G. BURROUGHS
KIRBY SMITH R5
ORLANDO, FL. 32807

SWINTON BURROUGHS
1731 SHORE VIEW DR.
MELBOURNE, FL. 32903

S. M. BURROUGHS
1737 SHORE VIEW DR.
MELBOURNE, FL. 32903

JOSEPH E. BURROUGHS
1093 BYWOOD DR.
MELBOURNE, FL. 32905

MICHAEL S. BURROUGHS
2203 DARTMOUTH DR.
COCOA, FL. 32922

TIMOTHY A. BURROUGHS
BX. 205
COCOA BEACH, FL. 32931

JACK H. BURROUGHS
1180 DUNES ST.
MERRITT IS, FL. 32952

H. R. BURROUGHS
2743 OCEAN DR. APT. 38
VERO BEACH, FL. 32960

LELAND C. BURROUGHS
7 SEA GULL AV.
VERO BEACH, FL. 32960

JAMES G. BURROUGHS
720 7TH ST. S.W.
DANIA, FL. 33004

RAYMOND B. BURROUGHS
2822 VAN BUREN ST. APT.
HOLLYWOOD, FL. 33020

STEPHEN E. BURROUGHS
7320 RAMONA ST. W.
HOLLYWOOD, FL. 33023

ALICE A. BURROUGHS
1111 FAIRWAY RD.
HOLLYWOOD, FL. 33026

JOHN H. BURROUGHS
611 17TH ST. N.W.
HOMESTEAD, FL. 33030

CHARLES C. BURROUGHS, JR.
R1 BX. 280
BIG PINE KEY, FL. 33043

CLARA L. BURROUGHS
16201 18TH CT. N.W.
OPA LOCKA, FL. 33054

GEORGE BURROUGHS
2370 RUTLAND ST.
OPA LOCKA, FL. 33054

DIANE BURROUGHS
4921 181ST TER. N.W.
OPA LOCKA, FL. 33055

EDWARD J. BURROUGHS
4511 169TH TER. N.W.
OPA LOCKA, FL. 33055

ROBERT H. BURROUGHS, JR.
106 5TH ST. N.E.
POMPANO BEACH, FL. 33060

KENNETH J. BURROUGHS
641 8TH ST. N.E.
POMPANO BEACH, FL. 33060

JAMES B. BURROUGHS
700 27TH AV. N.W. APT. 3
POMPANO BEACH, FL. 33060

EVERETT V. BURROUGHS
401 26TH AV. N.E.
POMPANO BEACH, FL. 33062

DONALD M. BURROUGHS
1111 27TH AV. N.E.
POMPANO BEACH, FL. 33062

S. R. BURROUGHS
405 49TH PL. N.W.
POMPANO BEACH, FL. 33064

WILBUR E. BURROUGHS, JR.
4401 6TH CT. N.W.
POMPANO BEACH, FL. 33066

SHARON BURROUGHS
8231 4TH ST. S.W.
POMPANO BEACH, FL. 33068

EDWARD BURROUGHS
5130 7TH ST. N.W.
MIAMI, FL. 33126

EDWARD BURROUGHS
5130 7TH AV. N.W.
MIAMI, FL. 33127

THELMA B. BURROUGHS
305 MADEIRA AV.
MIAMI, FL. 33134

WILLIAM D. BURROUGHS
515 VALENCIA AV.
MIAMI, FL. 33134

MAC H. BURROUGHS
4481 5TH ST. S.W.
MIAMI, FL. 33134

GLADYS M. BURROUGHS
341 35TH ST. N.E.
MIAMI, FL. 33137

JOHN BURROUGHS, 3D
20 71ST ST. N.E.
MIAMI, FL. 33138

NATHANIEL BURROUGHS
4113 13TH AV. N.W.
MIAMI, FL. 33142

NATHANIEL BURROUGHS
3189 59TH ST. N.W.
MIAMI, FL. 33142

DOUGLAS R. BURROUGHS
5868 COMMERCE LN.
MIAMI, FL. 33143

BETTY J. BURROUGHS
6330 58TH AV. S.W.
MIAMI, FL. 33143

WILLIAM A. BURROUGHS
7260 11TH ST. S.W.
MIAMI, FL. 33144

JOYCE C. BURROUGHS
6817 3RD AV. N.W.
MIAMI, FL. 33150

WILLIAM BURROUGHS, JR.
980 LITTLE RIVER DR.
MIAMI, FL. 33150

WILLIAM E. BURROUGHS
8541 29TH ST. S.W.
MIAMI, FL. 33155

CHARLES C. BURROUGHS
4805 64TH PL. S.W.
MIAMI, FL. 33155

DONALD A. BURROUGHS
15425 PALMETTO LAKE
MIAMI, FL. 33157

WILLIAM E. BURROUGHS, JR.
9535 45TH TER. S.W.
MIAMI, FL. 33165

GLORIA J. BURROUGHS
711 ROYAL POINCNA S.
MIAMI, FL. 33166

WARD B. BURROUGHS
810 142ND ST. N.W.
MIAMI, FL. 33168

NATHANIEL BURROUGHS
10460 149TH ST. S.W.
MIAMI, FL. 33176

S. BURROUGHS
2805 212TH ST. N.E.
MIAMI, FL. 33180

RAQUEL Q. BURROUGHS
20021 112TH AV. S.W.
MIAMI, FL. 33189

DOUGLAS R. BURROUGHS
20031 112TH AV. S.W.
MIAMI, FL. 33189

RAQUEL Q. BURROUGHS
11221 203RD TER. S.W.
MIAMI, FL. 33189

ROBERT H. BURROUGHS
2710 OCEAN BL N.
FT LAUDERDALE, FL. 33308

ALFRED P. BURROUGHS, JR.
5407 31ST AV. N.E.
FT LAUDERDALE, FL. 33308

LINNIE BURROUGHS
429 9TH AV. N.W. APT. 2
FT LAUDERDALE, FL. 33311

BESSIE W. BURROUGHS
2740 21ST AV. N.W.
FT LAUDERDALE, FL. 33311

CATHERINE M. BURROUGHS
3291 14TH ST. N.W.
FT LAUDERDALE, FL. 33311

ARCHIBALD BURROUGHS
2216 34TH TER. S.W.
FT LAUDERDALE, FL. 33312

SAMUEL T. BURROUGHS
101 29TH TER. S.W.
FT LAUDERDALE, FL. 33312

GRADY BURROUGHS
4401 10TH CT. N.W. APT.
FT LAUDERDALE, FL. 33313

ADALINE A. BURROUGHS
4530 13TH ST. N.W.
FT LAUDERDALE, FL. 33313

JOHN I. BURROUGHS
9201 54TH ST. S.W.
FT LAUDERDALE, FL. 33328

VIRGIL L. BURROUGHS
4200 102ND AV. S.W.
FT LAUDERDALE, FL. 33328

NILES P. BURROUGHS
5778 15TH AV. N.E.
FT LAUDERDALE, FL. 33334

ROY P. BURROUGHS
3100 LAKE DR.
W. PALM BEACH, FL. 33404

O. W. BURROUGHS
514 20TH ST.
W. PALM BEACH, FL. 33407

LYMAN N. BURROUGHS
1310 TAMARIND HY.
BOCA RATON, FL. 33432

WILLIAM F. BURROUGHS
BX. 45
BRYANT, FL. 33439

WILLIAM D. BURROUGHS
908 15TH CT. S.E.
DEERFIELD BCH, FL. 33441

LAUREL BURROUGHS
926 SAVANNAS PT RD. APT.
FORT PIERCE, FL. 33450

GENEVA G. BURROUGHS
MYRTLE LN.
LAKE HARBOR, FL. 33459

JOSEPH G. BURROUGHS
R1 BX. 370B
MOORE HAVEN, FL. 33471

GEORGE BURROUGHS
116 4TH ST. S.W.
OKEECHOBEE, FL. 33472

JOHNNY BURROUGHS
225 11TH AV. N.W.
SOUTH BAY, FL. 33493

PEARLIE M. BURROUGHS
1102 ILEX ST.
SOUTH BAY, FL. 33493

EDWIN E. BURROUGHS
1024 52ND AV. BL W.
BRADENTON, FL. 33507

ARTHUR BURROUGHS
4908 ORLANDO CIR. W.
BRADENTON, FL. 33507

PAUL P. BURROUGHS
1538 GENTRY ST.
CLEARWATER, FL. 33515

DONALD BURROUGHS
1910 UNION ST.
CLEARWATER, FL. 33515

JAMES L. BURROUGHS
1354 ESSEX DR.
CLEARWATER, FL. 33516

RICHARD BURROUGHS
2939 GULF TO BAY BL
CLEARWATER, FL. 33519

ARETHER BURROUGHS
511 5TH ST. N.
DADE CITY, FL. 33525

FRANK M. BURROUGHS
R4 BX. 265K
DADE CITY, FL. 33525

R. E. BURROUGHS, JR.
R2 BX. 285
DADE CITY, FL. 33525

ROBT. L. BURROUGHS
7 LAKEVIEW DR. R3
DADE CITY, FL. 33525

CLAUDE A. BURROUGHS
OX R1
LAND O LAKES, FL. 33539

STEPHEN F. BURROUGHS
2153 NELLIE ST.
LARGO, FL. 33540

JOHN D. BURROUGHS, JR.
13570 LAS PALMAS DR.
LARGO, FL. 33540

CAROLE J. BURROUGHS
1301 5TH TER. N.W.
LARGO, FL. 33540

DOUGLAS E. BURROUGHS
34 COUNTRY CLUB DR.
LARGO, FL. 33541

DAVID B. BURROUGHS
7600 137TH ST.
LARGO, FL. 33542

BERNARD B. BURROUGHS
R1 BX. 513A
LITHIA, FL. 33547

SANDRA L. BURROUGHS
2559 SEAFORD CIR. 4
LUTZ, FL. 33549

EUGENE E. BURROUGHS
1110 JAMES ST.
NEW PRT RICHY, FL. 33552

EDWIN C. BURROUGHS
35 SEAWAY DR.
NEW PRT RICHY, FL. 33552

OTTO A. BURROUGHS
1245 STRATFIELD CIR. W.
NEW PRT RICHY, FL. 33552

RICHARD BURROUGHS
406 CROSSWINDS DR.
PALM HARBOR, FL. 33563

HARRY E. BURROUGHS
301 CROSSWINDS DR.
PALM HARBOR, FL. 33563

SHIRLEY D. BURROUGHS
6917 HAINES RD.
PINELLAS PARK, FL. 33565

KENNETH L. BURROUGHS
4711 74TH AV.
PINELLAS PARK, FL. 33565

BUENITA E. BURROUGHS
4 A. ST.    TR SQ.
PLANT CITY, FL. 33566

THOMAS A. BURROUGHS
R1 BX. 196A
RIVERVIEW, FL. 33569

CHARLES H. BURROUGHS
622 PAYNE PKWY.
SARASOTA, FL. 33577

ERNEST H. BURROUGHS
380 MIDWEST PKWY.
SARASOTA, FL. 33582

OWEN R. BURROUGHS
110 FLORAL LA
THONOTOSASSA, FL. 33592

KENNETH BURROUGHS
2450 16TH ST. EXT. R6
ZEPHYRHILLS, FL. 33599

CHARLES M. BURROUGHS
BX. 1714
TAMPA, FL. 33601

JOHN W. BURROUGHS
1112 SCOTT ST. E.
TAMPA, FL. 33602

MAYME A. BURROUGHS
4911 SUWANEE AV.
TAMPA, FL. 33603

ADALPHUS BURROUGHS
2102 TWO LAKES RD. APT.
TAMPA, FL. 33604

DORMAN W. BURROUGHS
2001 OAKWOOD ST.
TAMPA, FL. 33605

CAROLYN D. BURROUGHS
1428 ESTELLE ST. E.
TAMPA, FL. 33605

DAVID S. BURROUGHS
1611 CAYUGA ST. E.
TAMPA, FL. 33610

THOMAS E. BURROUGHS
3009 EMMA ST. E.
TAMPA, FL. 33610

RICHARD BURROUGHS
6407 49TH ST. N.
TAMPA, FL. 33610

J. D. BURROUGHS
1703 HANNA AV. E.
TAMPA, FL. 33610

CLIFFORD S. BURROUGHS
12107 GOLFSIDE RD.
TAMPA, FL. 33612

JAMES D. BURROUGHS
14808 WEDGEWOOD DR.
TAMPA, FL. 33612

STEPHEN C. BURROUGHS
217 BYWATER DR.
TAMPA, FL. 33615

ROBERT E. BURROUGHS
7016 SANTA ANA PL. APT.
TAMPA, FL. 33617

PAUL E. BURROUGHS
2403 WISHING WELL WY.
TAMPA, FL. 33619

X. T. BURROUGHS
7016 PARLIAMENT DR.
TAMPA, FL. 33619

HARRY E. BURROUGHS
625 9TH ST. N.
ST PETERSBURG, FL. 33701

M. BURROUGHS
11401 3RD ST. N. APT. 2
ST PETERSBURG, FL. 33702

RAYMOND E. BURROUGHS
9367 1ST ST. N.
ST PETERSBURG, FL. 33702

KENNETH L. BURROUGHS
7267 ONYX DR. N.
ST PETERSBURG, FL. 33702

MICHAEL T. BURROUGHS
4001 BIRCH ST. N.E.
ST PETERSBURG, FL. 33703

JOHN D. BURROUGHS
1065 EDEN ISLE BL APT. 2
ST PETERSBURG, FL. 33704

ANN BURROUGHS
902 RAPHAEL BL N.E.
ST PETERSBURG, FL. 33704

WILLIE BURROUGHS
759 42ND AV. S.
ST PETERSBURG, FL. 33705

JAMES T. BURROUGHS
4700 5TH ST. S.
ST PETERSBURG, FL. 33705

ELIZABETH M. BURROUGHS
1110 RUE DES ROIS APT. 1
ST PETERSBURG, FL. 33707

THOMAS M. BURROUGHS
5665 40TH AV. N. APT. 30
ST PETERSBURG, FL. 33709

WILLIAM D. BURROUGHS
5428 BURLINGTON AV. N.
ST PETERSBURG, FL. 33710

WILLIAM D. BURROUGHS
6946 16TH PL. N. APT. 55
ST PETERSBURG, FL. 33710

EDGAR H. BURROUGHS, SR.
5327 18TH AV. N.
ST PETERSBURG, FL. 33710

HAROLD BURROUGHS
2575 18TH AV. S.
ST PETERSBURG, FL. 33712

PAULETTE BURROUGHS
1112 GOLDEN DR.
ARCADIA, FL. 33821

CHARLIE BURROUGHS
248 MONROE AV. S.
ARCADIA, FL. 33821

GEORGE A. BURROUGHS
R2 BX. 407
AVON PARK, FL. 33825

EDDIE BURROUGHS
605 5TH AV. S.
BARTOW, FL. 33830

MARY L. BURROUGHS
BX. 1084
DUNDEE, FL. 33838

B. BURROUGHS
56 MYRTLE ST.
DUNDEE, FL. 33838

BENJAMIN BURROUGHS
LOUISE AV.
DUNDEE, FL. 33838

DESSIE M. BURROUGHS
BX. 732
DUNDEE, FL. 33838

DAWN H. BURROUGHS
BX. 525
FORT MEADE, FL. 33841

ALVIS D. BURROUGHS
1112 VALENCIA AV.
HAINES CITY, FL. 33844

LENS BURROUGHS
350 HAINES BL
LAKE ALFRED, FL. 33850

ALBERTA L. BURROUGHS
439 D. ST.
LAKE WALES, FL. 33853

WILLIE J. BURROUGHS
HWY 17 SOUTH
NOCATEE, FL. 33864

ROSS D. BURROUGHS
MARANTHA VLG R2
SEBRING, FL. 33870

INEZ M. BURROUGHS
340 4TH ST. S.E.
WINTER HAVEN, FL. 33880

MARTHA A. BURROUGHS
646 CENTRAL AV. W.
WINTER HAVEN, FL. 33880

FRANKIE L. BURROUGHS
BX. 1094
WINTER HAVEN, FL. 33880

ALLAN F. BURROUGHS
VAUGHN RD. R2
WINTER HAVEN, FL. 33880

JAMES B. BURROUGHS
BX. 3571
WINTER HAVEN, FL. 33880

ROBERT F. BURROUGHS
VAUGHN RD. R2
WINTER HAVEN, FL. 33880

E. M. BURROUGHS
40 STIPE ST.
FORT MYERS, FL. 33903

RUTH V. BURROUGHS
951 ESTERO BL
FT MYERS BCH, FL. 33931

L. G. BURROUGHS
477 18TH AV. S.
NAPLES, FL. 33940

GORDON D. BURROUGHS
2 ROYAL CV DR. R2
NAPLES, FL. 33940

ALBERTA M. BURROUGHS
206 CHELSEA DR.
PUNTA GORDA, FL. 33950

NORMAN L. BURROUGHS
567 HERNANDO AV. N.E.
PUNTA GORDA, FL. 33952

RALPH BURROUGHS
R2 BOX 32
ADGER, AL. 35006

B. G. BURROUGHS
1441 LAVISTA DR. R6
ALEXANDER CY, AL. 35010

DAVID BURROUGHS
2107 18TH WY. N.
BESSEMER, AL. 35020

J. L. BURROUGHS
418 PERRY AV.
BESSEMER, AL. 35020

ROBT. O. BURROUGHS
BX115 CAFFEE ST. R8
BESSEMER, AL. 35020

MADISON C. BURROUGHS
631 GRAYS DR.
BESSEMER, AL. 35020

FRANCES T. BURROUGHS
3525 7TH AV.
BESSEMER, AL. 35020

HENRY E. BURROUGHS
5024 WEST ST.
BESSEMER, AL. 35020

DONALD R. BURROUGHS
236 WESTLAKE LDG
BESSEMER, AL. 35020

CORNELIUS E. BURROUGHS
2008 13TH PL.
BESSEMER, AL. 35020

JOSEPH BURROUGHS
R4 BX. 404
BESSEMER, AL. 35020

MERRINE BURROUGHS
4435 EDWARDS ST.
BESSEMER, AL. 35020

JUDGE BURROUGHS
2304 12TH AV.
BESSEMER, AL. 35020

MILDRED D. BURROUGHS
142 BAKER AV.
BESSEMER, AL. 35020

R. A. BURROUGHS
5 PATRICIA DR. R2
CHILDERSBURG, AL. 35044

HILTON BURROUGHS
1546 BARTON DR. N.E.
CULLMAN, AL. 35055

JOE N. BURROUGHS
526 5TH ST. S.W.
GRAYSVILLE, AL. 35073

DONALD BURROUGHS
GREEN POND, AL. 35074

M. BURROUGHS
GEN DEL
GREEN POND, AL. 35074

RICHARD BURROUGHS
R5 BX. 187
HANCEVILLE, AL. 35077

BILLY R. BURROUGHS
BX. 43
KELLYTON, AL. 35089

MARY T. BURROUGHS
BX. 297
ODENVILLE, AL. 35120

WALTER BURROUGHS
R2 BX. 46K
QUINTON, AL. 35130

H. C. BURROUGHS
R2 BX. 331
RAGLAND, AL. 35131

J. H. BURROUGHS
R1 BOX 354
SPRINGVILLE, AL. 35146

JOHN H. BURROUGHS
209 SAVERY ST.
TALLADEGA, AL. 35160

RUFUS BURROUGHS
718 K. AV.
TALLADEGA, AL. 35160

GEORGE E. BURROUGHS
317 TINNEY ST. N.
TALLADEGA, AL. 35160

GEORGE BURROUGHS
R1 BX. 159A
TALLADEGA, AL. 35160

RICHARD BURROUGHS
RFD
TALLADEGA, AL. 35160

RICHARD BURROUGHS
R2
UNION GROVE, AL. 35175

SHARON BURROUGHS
BX. 493
WEST BLOCTON, AL. 35184

MELVIN BURROUGHS
WEST BLOCTON, AL. 35184

DEBORAH BURROUGHS
324 1ST ST. W.
BIRMINGHAM, AL. 35204

JOHN R. BURROUGHS
1504 16TH AV. S.
BIRMINGHAM, AL. 35205

TOMMY BURROUGHS, JR.
633 IDLEWILD CIR. APT.
BIRMINGHAM, AL. 35205

JOAN H. BURROUGHS
1008 86TH HWY. N.
BIRMINGHAM, AL. 35206

WILLIAM B. BURROUGHS
1917 34TH AV. N.
BIRMINGHAM, AL. 35207

LOUIE A. BURROUGHS
3315 33RD PL. N.
BIRMINGHAM, AL. 35207

HAROLD E. BURROUGHS
1761 48TH ST.
BIRMINGHAM, AL. 35208

ARCHIE BURROUGHS
300 COLUMBIANA RD.
BIRMINGHAM, AL. 35209

JAMES BURROUGHS
300 STONRDG TRL R27
BIRMINGHAM, AL. 35210

CARL BURROUGHS
315 CLEVELAND LN.
BIRMINGHAM, AL. 35211

HENRY BURROUGHS
28 11TH AV. S.W.
BIRMINGHAM, AL. 35211

REMBERT BURROUGHS
1876 FRANCIS AV.
BIRMINGHAM, AL. 35211

RODERICK BURROUGHS
1027 17TH HY. S.W.
BIRMINGHAM, AL. 35211

T. L. BURROUGHS
803 19TH PL. S.W.
BIRMINGHAM, AL. 35211

RAYMOND D. BURROUGHS
966 53RD ST. N.
BIRMINGHAM, AL. 35212

JAMES S. BURROUGHS
2417 ARCADIA RD.
BIRMINGHAM, AL. 35214

TONY D. BURROUGHS
851 PARK BROOK TRL APT.
BIRMINGHAM, AL. 35215

M. S. BURROUGHS
615 WOODLAND VLG
BIRMINGHAM, AL. 35216

JAMES B. BURROUGHS
2032 22ND ST.
BIRMINGHAM, AL. 35218

LEONARD R. BURROUGHS
3828 VALLEY HEAD RD.
BIRMINGHAM, AL. 35223

JANET S. BURROUGHS
2524 RANDOLPH PL.
BIRMINGHAM, AL. 35223

ARCHIE L. BURROUGHS, JR.
3502 ATVONN DR.
BIRMINGHAM, AL. 35226

EDNA E. BURROUGHS
1033 57TH ST.
BIRMINGHAM, AL. 35228

ORA C. BURROUGHS
805 ALDEN AV.
BIRMINGHAM, AL. 35228

SAMUEL L. BURROUGHS
1928 15TH TER. N.
BIRMINGHAM, AL. 35234

ROBERT L. BURROUGHS
3908 BRIAROAK DR.
BIRMINGHAM, AL. 35243

JOHN E. BURROUGHS
R13 BX. 582
BIRMINGHAM, AL. 35243

CURTIS P. BURROUGHS
33 GREENVIEW
TUSCALOOSA, AL. 35401

EMORY M. BURROUGHS
2514 11TH AV.
TUSCALOOSA, AL. 35401

RUTH E. BURROUGHS
2215 HARRISON ST.
TUSCALOOSA, AL. 35401

JON F. BURROUGHS
1717 2ND AV.
TUSCALOOSA, AL. 35401

EMMECY BURROUGHS
2214 HERMAN AV.
TUSCALOOSA, AL. 35401

JOE L. BURROUGHS
3311 GLEN DR.
TUSCALOOSA, AL. 35401

BETTY BURROUGHS
7 SAHAMA VILLAGE APT. K.
TUSCALOOSA, AL. 35401

CARL F. BURROUGHS
1714 17TH ST.
TUSCALOOSA, AL. 35401

MICHAEL BURROUGHS
2414 PRINCE AV.
TUSCALOOSA, AL. 35401

GESSNER P. BURROUGHS
1637 43RD AV.
TUSCALOOSA, AL. 35401

JACQUELINE H BURROUGHS
1306 23RD AV. APT. 1B
TUSCALOOSA, AL. 35401

ROBERT E. BURROUGHS
1434 QUEEN CITY AV.
TUSCALOOSA, AL. 35401

JULIA BURROUGHS
1637 44TH AV. R3
TUSCALOOSA, AL. 35401

MARK G. BURROUGHS
1213 12TH ST. APT. 4
TUSCALOOSA, AL. 35401

JERALD S. BURROUGHS
3027 24TH AV.
TUSCALOOSA, AL. 35401

JAMES O. BURROUGHS
2015 20TH ST.
TUSCALOOSA, AL. 35401

MARY L. BURROUGHS
1208 26TH ST.
TUSCALOOSA, AL. 35401

KEN BURROUGHS
3027 GREENSBORO LOT 4
TUSCALOOSA, AL. 35401

MINNIE G. BURROUGHS
1822 QUEEN CITY AV.
TUSCALOOSA, AL. 35401

EARLENE BURROUGHS
1434 18TH AV.
TUSCALOOSA, AL. 35401

JACOB C. BURROUGHS
3 GRESHAM VILLAGE
TUSCALOOSA, AL. 35401

JOE L. BURROUGHS
3311 37TH AV.
TUSCALOOSA, AL. 35401

W. H. BURROUGHS
BX. 2492
TUSCALOOSA, AL. 35403

CHARLES E. BURROUGHS
3518 CAMP ST.
TUSCALOOSA, AL. 35404

ROBERT E. BURROUGHS
56 CUMBERLAND PK.
TUSCALOOSA, AL. 35404

DOUGLAS M. BURROUGHS
128 JUANITA DR.
TUSCALOOSA, AL. 35404

DANNY K. BURROUGHS
4311 HIGHPOINT DR.
TUSCALOOSA, AL. 35404

RUBY A. BURROUGHS
1411 19TH AV. E.
TUSCALOOSA, AL. 35404

W. H. BURROUGHS
BOX 3103
TUSCALOOSA, AL. 35404

WILLIAM L. BURROUGHS
1713 19TH AV. E.
TUSCALOOSA, AL. 35404

KEN F. BURROUGHS
1520 57TH AV. R2 E.
TUSCALOOSA, AL. 35404

ALFRED BURROUGHS
3722 1ST ST. E.
TUSCALOOSA, AL. 35404

WALLACE O. BURROUGHS
606 43RD AV. E.
TUSCALOOSA, AL. 35404

RAYBURN L. BURROUGHS
500 26TH AV. E.
TUSCALOOSA, AL. 35404

CHAP B. BURROUGHS, JR.
5 LONGVIEW RD.
TUSCALOOSA, AL. 35404

WILLIAM R. BURROUGHS
3515 1ST CT. E.
TUSCALOOSA, AL. 35405

DANIEL C. BURROUGHS
3516 5TH AV.
TUSCALOOSA, AL. 35405

E. D. BURROUGHS
2429 LOOP RD.
TUSCALOOSA, AL. 35405

JAMES R. BURROUGHS
215 41ST ST. E.
TUSCALOOSA, AL. 35405

LELAND BURROUGHS
20 WOODBINE RD.
TUSCALOOSA, AL. 35405

KITTIE N. BURROUGHS
71 CIRCLEWOOD ST.
TUSCALOOSA, AL. 35405

THOMAS E. BURROUGHS
923 CANTERBURY RD.
TUSCALOOSA, AL. 35405

CHARLES R. BURROUGHS
R4 BX. 556E
TUSCALOOSA, AL. 35405

WAYNELL G. BURROUGHS
26 FAIRWAY DR.
TUSCALOOSA, AL. 35405

JOHN W. BURROUGHS
3815 37TH ST. E.
TUSCALOOSA, AL. 35405

EMORY BURROUGHS
ROEBUCK L. R1
AKRON, AL. 35441

FORREST BURROUGHS
R1 BX. 72
BUHL, AL. 35446

ORELIA BURROUGHS
R1
BUHL, AL. 35446

ROY BURROUGHS
R1
BUHL, AL. 35446

ALTON T. BURROUGHS
R1 BX. 47
BUHL, AL. 35446

JESSIE BURROUGHS
R1 BX. 1368
BUHL, AL. 35446

GESNER BURROUGHS
R1 BX. 39B
BUHL, AL. 35446

WILLIAM C. BURROUGHS
BX. 13
BUHL, AL. 35446

THELMA BURROUGHS
R1
BUHL, AL. 35446

PAUL D. BURROUGHS
R1 BX. 421
COKER, AL. 35452

A. B. BURROUGHS
BX. 54
COKER, AL. 35452

RONNIE BURROUGHS
R1 BX. 579
COTTONDALE, AL. 35453

JAMES P. BURROUGHS
R1
COTTONDALE, AL. 35453

IVORY BURROUGHS
R1 BX. 20
COTTONDALE, AL. 35453

FLOYD BURROUGHS
R1 BX. 637
COTTONDALE, AL. 35453

HUBERT BURROUGHS
BX. 61
COTTONDALE, AL. 35453

H. O. BURROUGHS
R1 BX. 349
COTTONDALE, AL. 35453

HELEN BURROUGHS
9 GEER TRLPK
COTTONDALE, AL. 35453

SALLY BURROUGHS
61 LAKE WILDHOOD
COTTONDALE, AL. 35453

JAMES R. BURROUGHS
301 EUTAW AV. N.
EUTAW, AL. 35462

LEONARD BURROUGHS
R1 BX. 132
GORDO, AL. 35466

V. BURROUGHS
R1
GORDO, AL. 35466

J. G. BURROUGHS
R1 BX. 64
MOUNDVILLE, AL. 35474

SYLVESTER BURROUGHS
R2 BX. 205
MOUNDVILLE, AL. 35474

WILLIE BURROUGHS
MOUNDVILLE, AL. 35474

FLOYD J. BURROUGHS
R1 BX. 80
MOUNDVILLE, AL. 35474

MICHAEL BURROUGHS
R2 BX. 482
MOUNDVILLE, AL. 35474

MATHEH BURROUGHS
R1 BX. 538
MOUNDVILLE, AL. 35474

R. BURROUGHS
40 CAROLHD ESTS R4
NORTHPORT, AL. 35476

MICHAEL R. BURROUGHS
35 ELEANOR DR.
NORTHPORT, AL. 35476

R. C. BURROUGHS
5 CLEARWTR EST. R5
NORTHPORT, AL. 35476

M. S. BURROUGHS
38 FOREST MANOR ST.
NORTHPORT, AL. 35476

W. H. BURROUGHS
520 MAIN AV. APT. D7
NORTHPORT, AL. 35476

FANNIE G. BURROUGHS
3214 MAIN AV.
NORTHPORT, AL. 35476

MARTHA E. BURROUGHS
2421 5TH ST.
NORTHPORT, AL. 35476

ROBERT C. BURROUGHS
114 WEST CIR. APT. A1
NORTHPORT, AL. 35476

CLYDE H. BURROUGHS
2810 21ST AV.
NORTHPORT, AL. 35476

RAY BURROUGHS
R6 BX. 214
NORTHPORT, AL. 35476

RICHARD V. BURROUGHS
1209 NORTHWOOD LAKE
NORTHPORT, AL. 35476

JOSEPH B. BURROUGHS
2104 21ST AV.
NORTHPORT, AL. 35476

TERRY BURROUGHS
R1
RALPH, AL. 35480

NELSON BURROUGHS
R1
RALPH, AL. 35480

MONTGOMERY BURROUGHS
R1 BX. 87
RALPH, AL. 35480

JOE BURROUGHS
R1 BX. 90A
RALPH, AL. 35480

JAMES BURROUGHS
1201 CHEROKEE RD.
JASPER, AL. 35501

JIMMY O. BURROUGHS
1708 GRAY AV.
JASPER, AL. 35501

R. T. BURROUGHS
401 16TH AV.
JASPER, AL. 35501

W. B. BURROUGHS
R5 BX. 81
FAYETTE, AL. 35555

JERRY W. BURROUGHS
R10
ATHENS, AL. 35611

TONI D. BURROUGHS
R1 BX. 2A
HARTSELLE, AL. 35640

ORA L. BURROUGHS
R1 BX. 8
ROGERSVILLE, AL. 35652

OLIN BURROUGHS
R2
GRANT, AL. 35747

J. B. BURROUGHS
BX. 22
GRANT, AL. 35747

CARL D. BURROUGHS
R1
NEW HOPE, AL. 35760

OLLIE BURROUGHS
R3
SCOTTSBORO, AL. 35768

BILLIE BURROUGHS
3116 HOLMES AV. N.W.
HUNTSVILLE, AL. 35805

J. H. BURROUGHS
417 EDGEMT CIR. N.W. S.
HUNTSVILLE, AL. 35811

BERTHA D. BURROUGHS
102 6TH ST.   EG N.
GADSDEN, AL. 35903

DANNY BURROUGHS
197 HIGHLAND MBL HM
BOAZ, AL. 35957

JIMMY S. BURROUGHS
R6 BOX 216A
GUNTERSVILLE, AL. 35976

CLIFFORD BURROUGHS
R2 BX. 916
MILLBROOK, AL. 36054

CLYDE E. BURROUGHS
625 WILLIAMSON RD.
MONTGOMERY, AL. 36109

JAMES BURROUGHS
3905 CHOCOLOCC RD. R6
ANNISTON, AL. 36203

E. G. BURROUGHS
R1
ASHLAND, AL. 36251

JOHN R. BURROUGHS
R1 BX. 114
WADLEY, AL. 36276

PHYLLIS BURROUGHS
R2
ENTERPRISE, AL. 36330

VERTICE BURROUGHS
BX. 133
GROVE HILL, AL. 36451

PHYDLIA BURROUGHS
WHATLEY, AL. 36482

EDDIE J. BURROUGHS
R1
WHATLEY, AL. 36482

RICHARD BURROUGHS
R2 BX. 323B
DAPHNE, AL. 36526

L. H. BURROUGHS
BX. 85
LOXLEY, AL. 36551

G. J. BURROUGHS
BX. 203
STAPLETON, AL. 36578

TAYLOR BURROUGHS
254 FRANKLIN ST. N.
MOBILE, AL. 36603

GEORGE BURROUGHS
860 SHORT MAHASSAS APT.
MOBILE, AL. 36603

SAM A. BURROUGHS
1675 WARBLER DR.
MOBILE, AL. 36605

VELMA G. BURROUGHS
903 ROWELL ST.
MOBILE, AL. 36606

F. L. BURROUGHS
R11 BX. 261B
MOBILE, AL. 36608

ANNE BURROUGHS
206 8TH ST. S.W.
DECATUR, AL. 35601

RICKY M. BURROUGHS
307 3RD AV.
ATHENS, AL. 35611

CARSON BURROUGHS
R3 BX. 323
KILLEN, AL. 35645

ELVIN BURROUGHS
R2
ROGERSVILLE, AL. 35652

STANLEY BURROUGHS
R2
GRANT, AL. 35747

IVAN BURROUGHS
R1 BX. 177
GURLEY, AL. 35748

OLIVER BURROUGHS
R1
OWENS XRDS, AL. 35763

MIKE BURROUGHS
R3
SCOTTSBORO, AL. 35768

MICHAEL H. BURROUGHS
403 JACK CLMN DR. N.W.
HUNTSVILLE, AL. 35805

LEONARD BURROUGHS
603 GLASGOW RD. N.W.
HUNTSVILLE, AL. 35811

EVA A. BURROUGHS
617 BLYTHE ST.
GADSDEN, AL. 35903

SUSAN BURROUGHS
33 COOPER CTS
BOAZ, AL. 35957

JAMES H. BURROUGHS
3609 PERRY ST.
GUNTERSVILLE, AL. 35976

JOEL BURROUGHS
3812 MEADOWVIEW ST. APT.
MONTGOMERY, AL. 36105

IVY H. BURROUGHS
637 WESLEY DR.
MONTGOMERY, AL. 36111

CAROLYN BURROUGHS
ASHLAND, AL. 36251

MAZIE BURROUGHS
R1
ASHLAND, AL. 36251

BOBBY BURROUGHS
R2 BX. 85A
WEDOWEE, AL. 36278

GEORGE BURROUGHS
R1
SLOCOMB, AL. 36375

DELEAN BURROUGHS
BX. 179
GROVE HILL, AL. 36451

WILLIE BURROUGHS
R1 BX. 227
WHATLEY, AL. 36482

WILMER BURROUGHS
WHATLEY, AL. 36482

DON BURROUGHS
BX. 432
DAUPHIN IS, AL. 36528

RODNEY BURROUGHS
BX. 606
LOXLEY, AL. 36551

HERBERT BURROUGHS
R1 BX. 44A
THEODORE, AL. 36582

ESSIE M. BURROUGHS
911 LYONS ST.
MOBILE, AL. 36603

ELOUISE E. BURROUGHS
460 CHARLES ST. APT. A.
MOBILE, AL. 36604

DAMON BURROUGHS
20 DAUPHINWOOD DR. APT.
MOBILE, AL. 36606

ROBERT BURROUGHS
2668 NALL ST.
MOBILE, AL. 36607

EMILY T. BURROUGHS
R12 BX. 486
MOBILE, AL. 36609

EDWARD BURROUGHS
R9 BX. 420
ATHENS, AL. 35611

DAVID BURROUGHS
1602 COFFMAN DR.
ATHENS, AL. 35611

E. BURROUGHS
R2 BX. 234
ROGERSVILLE, AL. 35652

LESTER BURROUGHS
R2 BX. 32A
ROGERSVILLE, AL. 35652

JIMMY BURROUGHS
R1
GRANT, AL. 35747

JIMMY S. BURROUGHS
R6 BOX 216A
GURLEY, AL. 35748

MARY S. BURROUGHS
R10
OWENS XRDS, AL. 35763

MARVIN L. BURROUGHS
423 HOMEWOOD DR. S.W.
HUNTSVILLE, AL. 35801

DONALD BURROUGHS
1102 TYLER RD. N.W.
HUNTSVILLE, AL. 35805

TILMAN V. BURROUGHS
4017 RAINBOW DR.
GADSDEN, AL. 35901

LEROY BURROUGHS
1008 3RD ST. N.W.
ATTALLA, AL. 35954

GEORGE BURROUGHS
CEDAR BLUFF, AL. 35959

MARY BURROUGHS
SR. 6
GUNTERSVILLE, AL. 35976

F. C. BURROUGHS
2465 CARTER HILL RD.
MONTGOMERY, AL. 36106

HARLAND BURROUGHS
5011 LONG LEAF PN DR.
MONTGOMERY, AL. 36116

SARAH BURROUGHS
R1
ASHLAND, AL. 36251

LEVELL BURROUGHS
R3
LINEVILLE, AL. 36266

WYBURN BURROUGHS
R2 BX. 276
ENTERPRISE, AL. 36330

BEN BURROUGHS
R1 BX. 170
FRISCO CITY, AL. 36445

LELAND BURROUGHS
121 MORRIS ST.
GROVE HILL, AL. 36451

MATHEW BURROUGHS
R1 BX. 53
WHATLEY, AL. 36482

ROY B. BURROUGHS
R3 BX. 317A
BAY MINETTE, AL. 36507

SHIRLEY BURROUGHS
R2 BX. 134
GRAND BAY, AL. 36541

B. L. BURROUGHS
BX. 11
LOXLEY, AL. 36551

STROTHER BURROUGHS
455 PLUM ST.
MOBILE, AL. 36603

LOVARN BURROUGHS
1315 CHINQUEPIN ST.
MOBILE, AL. 36603

JAN S. BURROUGHS
1605 PENICAULT DR.
MOBILE, AL. 36605

WALTER D. BURROUGHS
2401 SALVIA ST. N.
MOBILE, AL. 36606

C. K. BURROUGHS
1121 WALLEN ST.
MOBILE, AL. 36608

RONNIE D. BURROUGHS
2713 DEMETROPOLIS RD.
MOBILE, AL. 36609

WILLIAM BURROUGHS
R1
ATHENS, AL. 35611

W. A. BURROUGHS, JR.
R1 BX. 294
ELKMONT, AL. 35620

EDGAR J. BURROUGHS
R1 BX. 252
ROGERSVILLE, AL. 35652

MIMI M. BURROUGHS
107 EMERALD DR.
TUSCUMBIA, AL. 35674

GLADYS BURROUGHS
R2
GRANT, AL. 35747

JAMES H. BURROUGHS
R1 BX. 201
LACEYS SPRING, AL. 35754

WILLIAM M. BURROUGHS
R3 BX. 345
SCOTTSBORO, AL. 35768

CARTER BURROUGHS
12809 MEMORIAL S.W. R4
HUNTSVILLE, AL. 35803

HENRY W. BURROUGHS
3214 YALE CIR. N.W.
HUNTSVILLE, AL. 35810

EARL G. BURROUGHS
1510 TUSCALOOSA AV.
GADSDEN, AL. 35901

ELMUS L. BURROUGHS
R2 BX. 359
ATTALLA, AL. 35954

LEONARD BURROUGHS
R2
FORT PAYNE, AL. 35967

DALLAS BURROUGHS
SR. 6
GUNTERSVILLE, AL. 35976

HARLAND BURROUGHS
5011 LONG LEAF DR. R8
MONTGOMERY, AL. 36108

THOS D. BURROUGHS
3820 KNOLLWOOD DR. R8
ANNISTON, AL. 36201

W. D. BURROUGHS
R1 BOX 456
ASHLAND, AL. 36251

LIZZIE BURROUGHS
R1
NEWELL, AL. 36270

WILLIAM T. BURROUGHS
132 HOLIDAY VLG R3
ENTERPRISE, AL. 36330

LELAND BURROUGHS
GROVE HILL, AL. 36451

MARION BURROUGHS
GROVE HILL, AL. 36451

C. L. BURROUGHS
WHATLEY, AL. 36482

CECIL BURROUGHS
BX. 196
CODEN, AL. 36523

L. H. BURROUGHS
R1
LOXLEY, AL. 36551

R. T. BURROUGHS
1226 MARTHA ALLEN R1
SARALAND, AL. 36571

JOHN T. BURROUGHS
751 WARREN ST. S.
MOBILE, AL. 36603

DAMON B. BURROUGHS
1156 HERCULES ST. APT. A
MOBILE, AL. 36603

CLYDE A. BURROUGHS
2604 MURWOOD DR.
MOBILE, AL. 36605

RICHARD A. BURROUGHS
205 PINEHILL DR.
MOBILE, AL. 36606

ANNIE BURROUGHS
3771 SHEIPS LN.
MOBILE, AL. 36608

BILL BURROUGHS
4354 HALLS ML RD. R10
MOBILE, AL. 36609

CURTIS P. BURROUGHS
1917 MC ARTHUR AV.
MOBILE, AL. 36610

VELMA BURROUGHS
1016 THOMAS AV. S.
MOBILE, AL. 36610

GERTRUDE I. BURROUGHS
914 PARSONS DR.
MOBILE, AL. 36610

JOE E. BURROUGHS
124 SANDERS RD.
MOBILE, AL. 36610

KENNETH R. BURROUGHS
214 ALPINE DR.
MOBILE, AL. 36611

JESSIE L. BURROUGHS
206 AUTUMNDALE CIR.
MOBILE, AL. 36611

ZOIE G. BURROUGHS
2856 WHISTLER ST.
MOBILE, AL. 36612

BRENDA L. BURROUGHS
850 ALVAREZ AV.
MOBILE, AL. 36612

ARMATHA C. BURROUGHS
2957 WHISTLER ST.
MOBILE, AL. 36612

DANIEL BURROUGHS
4920 MYERS RD. W.
MOBILE, AL. 36613

JOSEPH T. BURROUGHS
2151 BARLOW ST.
MOBILE, AL. 36617

MONICA L. BURROUGHS
2620 BANKS AV.
MOBILE, AL. 36617

LEON BURROUGHS
506 STANTON RD.
MOBILE, AL. 36617

JOHN D. BURROUGHS
558 KENT ST.
MOBILE, AL. 36617

MATTHEW BURROUGHS
501 ST. CHARLES AV. APT.
MOBILE, AL. 36617

MACINE BURROUGHS
2418 DENMARK ST.
MOBILE, AL. 36617

CHARLIE BURROUGHS
2442 OAKLEIGH DR.
MOBILE, AL. 36617

JOHN L. BURROUGHS
500 ST. CHARLES AV. APT.
MOBILE, AL. 36617

COLLIE BURROUGHS
2307 RUSHING DR.
MOBILE, AL. 36617

DELBERT A. BURROUGHS
4925 AUBURN DR. S.
MOBILE, AL. 36618

ARTHUR E. BURROUGHS
1550 LARKWOOD DR.
MOBILE, AL. 36618

ARTHUR BURROUGHS
1530 LARKWOOD DR.
MOBILE, AL. 36618

GORDON T. BURROUGHS
7173 THREE NOTCH RD.
MOBILE, AL. 36619

JOE H. BURROUGHS
6652 SANTOS DR. E.
MOBILE, AL. 36619

TERRY E. BURROUGHS
7129 EMERALD DR.
MOBILE, AL. 36619

MORRIS BURROUGHS
301 DRAYTON DR.
SELMA, AL. 36701

LEO BURROUGHS
R1 BX. 546
GREENSBORO, AL. 36744

JERRY BURROUGHS
R1 BX. 145
PINE APPLE, AL. 36768

J. J. BURROUGHS
PINE APPLE, AL. 36768

FREDDIE BURROUGHS
445 5TH W.
THOMASVILLE, AL. 36784

LEONARD BURROUGHS
1145 SPINKS DR.
THOMASVILLE, AL. 36784

FRAZIER BURROUGHS
619 TRAWICK
THOMASVILLE, AL. 36784

ALPHONSO BURROUGHS
BX. 634
THOMASVILLE, AL. 36784

JAMES O. BURROUGHS
1312 GLENN CIR.
OPELIKA, AL. 36801

BUREN BURROUGHS
BX. 68
LAFAYETTE, AL. 36862

JOE D. BURROUGHS
R1 BX. 582
SMITHS, AL. 36877

BOB BURROUGHS, JR.
R1
GILBERTOWN, AL. 36908

BARBARA S. BURROUGHS
4864 SHIHMAN DR. R7
ANTIOCH, TN. 37013

BILLY H. BURROUGHS
R2 BX. 14
BETHPAGE, TN. 37022

BETTY C. BURROUGHS
R2
BETHPAGE, TN. 37022

CLAUDE W. BURROUGHS
R1 BX. 330
COTTONTOWN, TN. 37048

J. E. BURROUGHS
100 MAPLE ST. W. LOT 10
GALLATIN, TN. 37066

TIMOTHY BURROUGHS
121 HAZELWOOD DR. APT. 1
HENDERSONVL, TN. 37075

ROY BURROUGHS
R2
KINGSTON SPG, TN. 37082

L. BURROUGHS
300 HIAWATHA DR.
LEBANON, TN. 37087

THOMAS F. BURROUGHS
501 MAIN ST. W.
MC MINNVILLE, TN. 37110

ROSS C. BURROUGHS
BX. 610
MC MINNVILLE, TN. 37110

JEAN S. BURROUGHS
QUEENS DR. R5
MOUNT JULIET, TN. 37122

JAMES F. BURROUGHS
502 HADLEY BEND RD.
OLD HICKORY, TN. 37138

JACK W. BURROUGHS
BX. 23781
NASHVILLE, TN. 37202

BEATRICE L. BURROUGHS
905 16TH ST. N.
NASHVILLE, TN. 37206

L. A. BURROUGHS
1111 SHARPE AV.
NASHVILLE, TN. 37206

JEAN BURROUGHS
435 TRINITY LN. E.
NASHVILLE, TN. 37207

CHARLES BURROUGHS
146 OAK VALLEY DR.
NASHVILLE, TN. 37207

BOBBY J. BURROUGHS
411 CAPRI CT.
NASHVILLE, TN. 37209

CLYDE BURROUGHS
576 ANNEX CT.
NASHVILLE, TN. 37209

ROGER L. BURROUGHS
205 NORWAY TER.
NASHVILLE, TN. 37211

JAMES H. BURROUGHS
922 VIRGINIA AV.
NASHVILLE, TN. 37216

JOHNNY BURROUGHS
2411 LLOYD ST.
NASHVILLE, TN. 37218

EVELYN BURROUGHS
4048 BOYD DR.
NASHVILLE, TN. 37218

LARRY J. BURROUGHS
2409 LLOYD ST.
NASHVILLE, TN. 37218

ELBERT E. BURROUGHS
3215 LINCOLN AV.
NASHVILLE, TN. 37218

JOHNNY BURROUGHS
3718 FAIRVIEW DR. LOWER
NASHVILLE, TN. 37218

J. B. BURROUGHS
929 ROBTSN ACDMY RD.
NASHVILLE, TN. 37220

KENNY BURROUGHS
R5
NASHVILLE, TN. 37221

CHARLES BURROUGHS
8504 DAYTON PKE.
DAISY, TN. 37319

EDWARD BURROUGHS
MORTON DR. R1
FAYETTEVILLE, TN. 37334

ROBERT H. BURROUGHS
COLONY RD.
GRUETLI, TN. 37339

JOYCEDEEN BURROUGHS
9002 WACONDA CIR.
HARRISON, TN. 37341

ETHEL A. BURROUGHS
R2 BX. 165C
JASPER, TN. 37347

MARY S. BURROUGHS
BX. 38
KELSO, TN. 37348

BOBBY BURROUGHS
RIGNEY RD. R2
MANCHESTER, TN. 37355

BILLY E. BURROUGHS
LEE PKE.
SODDY-DAISY, TN. 37379

LYNDA V. BURROUGHS
R1
SODDY-DAISY, TN. 37379

ROBERT C. BURROUGHS
317 WISEMAN RD. R4
TULLAHOMA, TN. 37388

ELLIS BURROUGHS
1817 BAILEY AV.
CHATTANOOGA, TN. 37404

VELMA D. BURROUGHS
1811 TAYLOR ST.
CHATTANOOGA, TN. 37406

MARY F. BURROUGHS
4520 LOCKINGTON LN.
CHATTANOOGA, TN. 37416

COLEMAN BURROUGHS
9011 WACONDA SHR DR.
CHATTANOOGA, TN. 37416

C. F. BURROUGHS
9011 WACONDA RD. R2
CHATTANOOGA, TN. 37416

BILLY W. BURROUGHS
9002 WACONDA SHR DR.
CHATTANOOGA, TN. 37416

ROBERT BURROUGHS
4626 TARPON TRL
CHATTANOOGA, TN. 37416

T. K. BURROUGHS
2827 ST. LAWRENCE RD.
CHATTANOOGA, TN. 37421

FRANK BURROUGHS
308 LAMONT ST. APT. 2
JOHNSON CITY, TN. 37601

CHARLES E. BURROUGHS
428 BROOKWOOD DR.
BRISTOL, TN. 37620

HENRY J. BURROUGHS
2454 BROAD ST.
BRISTOL, TN. 37620

JULIAN L. BURROUGHS
BX. 144
BRISTOL, TN. 37620

JULIAN L. BURROUGHS
214 EDGEWOOD RD.
BRISTOL, TN. 37620

JAMES N. BURROUGHS
709 SANTA FE DR.
BRISTOL, TN. 37620

DENNIS BURROUGHS
R3
JONESBORO, TN. 37659

H. P. BURROUGHS
R5 BX. 90
CLINTON, TN. 37716

KATHLEEN B. BURROUGHS
R1
MASCOT, TN. 37806

RICKY BURROUGHS
125 BROWN AV.
MORRISTOWN, TN. 37814

RICKEY D. BURROUGHS
LINCOLN MANOR B7
MORRISTOWN, TN. 37814

MONTIE BURROUGHS
R2
MOSHEIM, TN. 37818

EDWARD BURROUGHS
THRN GRV PKE. S.E.
KNOXVILLE, TN. 37914

BOB BURROUGHS
RUGGLES FRY PKE. S.E.
KNOXVILLE, TN. 37914

WALLACE F. BURROUGHS
R4
KNOXVILLE, TN. 37914

PAUL M. BURROUGHS
R4
KNOXVILLE, TN. 37914

MAURICE M. BURROUGHS
CASH RD. S.E.
KNOXVILLE, TN. 37914

JANE BURROUGHS
CLOWERS DR. S.E.
KNOXVILLE, TN. 37914

I. L. BURROUGHS
337 CROSSFIELD DR. S.E.
KNOXVILLE, TN. 37920

DOYLE BURROUGHS
110 WEAVER LN.
BOLIVAR, TN. 38008

BILLY BURROUGHS
R5
BROWNSVILLE, TN. 38012

ROYCE B. BURROUGHS
R5
BROWNSVILLE, TN. 38012

DOYLE BURROUGHS
504 MAGNOLIA ST.
BROWNSVILLE, TN. 38012

HAROLD BURROUGHS
R1
HALLS, TN. 38040

J. H. BURROUGHS
R1
HALLS, TN. 38040

JAMES E. BURROUGHS
6401 VENTURA RD. APT. B.
MILLINGTON, TN. 38053

J. L. BURROUGHS
R2
RIPLEY, TN. 38063

JERRY L. BURROUGHS
R2E
RIPLEY, TN. 38063

JERRY L. BURROUGHS
R2
RIPLEY, TN. 38063

BILLY R. BURROUGHS
R5
ROSSVILLE, TN. 38066

ORA B. BURROUGHS
1335 WASHINGTON AV.
MEMPHIS, TN. 38104

WILLIAM D. BURROUGHS
1763 GLENWOOD PL.
MEMPHIS, TN. 38104

RACHEL C. BURROUGHS
35 MC LEAN BL N. APT. 14
MEMPHIS, TN. 38104

GLORIA J. BURROUGHS
1430 GREENWOOD ST.
MEMPHIS, TN. 38106

VELMA BURROUGHS
674 MANASSAS ST. N.
MEMPHIS, TN. 38107

FRANK BURROUGHS
2112 FARRINGTON ST.
MEMPHIS, TN. 38109

FRANK BURROUGHS, JR.
4172 HANATAH ST.
MEMPHIS, TN. 38109

JOHN A. BURROUGHS
1515 HOPE ST.
MEMPHIS, TN. 38111

JAMES A. BURROUGHS
1939 GOODLETT ST. S.
MEMPHIS, TN. 38111

JOHN W. BURROUGHS
1397 ESTATE DR.
MEMPHIS, TN. 38117

JOHN L. BURROUGHS
3675 OAKLAKE LN.
MEMPHIS, TN. 38118

ALLEN C. BURROUGHS
4632 CHUCK AV.
MEMPHIS, TN. 38118

BARBARA BURROUGHS
4431 PINE RIDGE CV
MEMPHIS, TN. 38118

SPURGEON BURROUGHS
3977 KINGSBURY RD.
MEMPHIS, TN. 38122

WILLIE T. BURROUGHS
4143 OVERTON CROSSNG
MEMPHIS, TN. 38127

RAYMON BURROUGHS
219 MAGNOLIA AV. W.
MC KENZIE, TN. 38201

BERNICE BURROUGHS
R1 BX. 94
HENDERSON, TN. 38340

JESSE L. BURROUGHS
R1
HENDERSON, TN. 38340

O. J. BURROUGHS
R5 BX. 86
LEXINGTON, TN. 38351

JAMES BURROUGHS
R5
LEXINGTON, TN. 38351

JIMMY BURROUGHS
544 MAYHOOD
LEXINGTON, TN. 38351

ROBERT A. BURROUGHS
R2 BX. 315
MEDON, TN. 38356

LANKFORD BURROUGHS
327 MILITARY AV. S.
LAWRENCEBURG, TN. 38464

JERRY BURROUGHS
310 MILITARY AV. S.
LAWRENCEBURG, TN. 38464

DONALD BURROUGHS
R6 BX. 21A
COOKEVILLE, TN. 38501

CLYDE M. BURROUGHS
209 DRY VLLY RD.
COOKEVILLE, TN. 38501

WILLIAM F. BURROUGHS
R10 BX. 264
COOKEVILLE, TN. 38501

WALTER BURROUGHS
R7 BX. 254B
COOKEVILLE, TN. 38501

IRENE BURROUGHS
R7
COOKEVILLE, TN. 38501

THURMAN BURROUGHS
R3 BX. 309
BAXTER, TN. 38544

W. G. BURROUGHS
R1 BX. 74
BLMNGTN SPG, TN. 38545

RALPH BURROUGHS
R3
GAINESBORO, TN. 38562

TOMMY E. BURROUGHS
R2 BX. 188M
ASHLAND, MS. 38603

MARY H. BURROUGHS
R2
ASHLAND, MS. 38603

VIOLA BURROUGHS
516 SUNFLOWER AV.
CLARKSDALE, MS. 38614

WELDON L. BURROUGHS
BX. 82
BENOIT, MS. 38725

RUSTY BURROUGHS
R1 BX. 217A
SHELBY, MS. 38774

OLA M. BURROUGHS
205 MONUMENT DR.
TUPELO, MS. 38801

DANIEL H. BURROUGHS
640 MADISON AV. N.
TUPELO, MS. 38801

OLA M. BURROUGHS
205 MOUNMENT DR.
TUPELO, MS. 38801

O. W. BURROUGHS
1611 CHEROKEE ST.
AMORY, MS. 38821

VANCE BURROUGHS
108 PECAN ORCHRD ST.
AMORY, MS. 38821

VAN L. BURROUGHS
3 GREEN COVE
AMORY, MS. 38821

RUBLE BURROUGHS
R2 BX. 110I
NETTLETON, MS. 38858

ALVIE R. BURROUGHS
R2
NETTLETON, MS. 38858

L. L. BURROUGHS
R1
SMITHVILLE, MS. 38870

HENRY BURROUGHS
509 3RD ST.
GRENADA, MS. 38901

WILLIE BURROUGHS
R2
CHARLESTON, MS. 38921

JOHN BURROUGHS
BX. 415
SIDON, MS. 38954

GARY C. BURROUGHS
415 WAYNE ST.
CLINTON, MS. 39056

H. C. BURROUGHS, JR.
R4 BX. 25
FLORENCE, MS. 39073

KAY J. BURROUGHS
115 PINE RIDGE ST. N.
FOREST, MS. 39074

R. K. BURROUGHS
BX. 516
KOSCIUSKO, MS. 39090

JOHN BURROUGHS
R1 BX. 44
KOSCIUSKO, MS. 39090

ROY S. BURROUGHS
207 WELLS ST. S.
KOSCIUSKO, MS. 39090

KENNETH BURROUGHS
R4
MORTON, MS. 39117

CHARLES W. BURROUGHS
BOX 263
REDWOOD, MS. 39156

CLIFF BURROUGHS
R6 BX. 2
REDWOOD, MS. 39156

WILLARD BURROUGHS
REDWOOD, MS. 39156

LARRY E. BURROUGHS
BX. 174
REDWOOD, MS. 39156

A. E. BURROUGHS
R6 BX. 9
REDWOOD, MS. 39156

GUY BURROUGHS
R1 BX. 108H
TERRY, MS. 39170

JUDY F. BURROUGHS
6306 INDIANA AV. E.
VICKSBURG, MS. 39180

JUDY F. BURROUGHS
6303 INDIANA AV. E.
VICKSBURG, MS. 39180

RALPH BURROUGHS
504 ALVERTON CT. R4
JACKSON, MS. 39208

NADINE BURROUGHS
5025 WAYNELAND DR. APT.
JACKSON, MS. 39211

T. L. BURROUGHS
3414 HIGHLAND AV.
MERIDIAN, MS. 39301

ROY T. BURROUGHS
R3 BX. 235A
COLLINSVILLE, MS. 39325

KENT BURROUGHS
R1 BX. 78
DECATUR, MS. 39327

MARIE E. BURROUGHS
R1 BX. 12
DECATUR, MS. 39327

CARL H. BURROUGHS
R1
DECATUR, MS. 39327

JAMES L. BURROUGHS
BX. 301
DE KALB, MS. 39328

DENNIS T. BURROUGHS
R6 BX. 294
LOUISVILLE, MS. 39339

COYTLEY BURROUGHS
R9 BX. 193
PHILADELPHIA, MS. 39350

EDWARD BURROUGHS
R1 BX. 38
SCOOBA, MS. 39358

BETTY L. BURROUGHS
SCOOBA, MS. 39358

HAZEL E. BURROUGHS
R2 BX. 173
UNION, MS. 39365

ARTHUR BURROUGHS
R8 BX. 273
LAUREL, MS. 39440

BUDDY M. BURROUGHS
R4 BX. 268
LUMBERTON, MS. 39455

ALVIN C. BURROUGHS
24 PRADO RD.
OCEAN SPRINGS, MS. 39564

KENNY BURROUGHS
3311 MORELAND ST.
PASCAGOULA, MS. 39567

ROLAND W. BURROUGHS
702 LAKE AV.
PASCAGOULA, MS. 39567

LEO F. BURROUGHS
3108 MARTIN ST.
PASCAGOULA, MS. 39567

JERRY BURROUGHS
1605 POITEVAN DR.
PASCAGOULA, MS. 39567

JAMES BURROUGHS, JR.
3517 BURROUGHS AV.
PASCAGOULA, MS. 39567

EDDIE L. BURROUGHS
4215 ORCHARD RD.
PASCAGOULA, MS. 39567

RAYMOND E. BURROUGHS
2722 CHICO ST.
PASCAGOULA, MS. 39567

GLADYS BURROUGHS
R1 BX. 1157
PASCAGOULA, MS. 39567

H. E. BURROUGHS, JR.
R3 BX. 15JK
PASCAGOULA, MS. 39567

PERCY L. BURROUGHS
R2 BOX 230A
MC COMB, MS. 39648

HAL D. BURROUGHS
709 MERIDIAN ST. S.
ABERDEEN, MS. 39730

SAMMIE L. BURROUGHS
208 PARK ST.
ABERDEEN, MS. 39730

MELINDA BURROUGHS
523 ORANGE ST. R1
ABERDEEN, MS. 39730

WILLIAM H. BURROUGHS
303 CHERYL ST.
VINE GROVE, KY. 40175

GARY BURROUGHS
1323 GILMORE LN.
LOUISVILLE, KY. 40213

CLINTON R. BURROUGHS
2814 BROOKDALE AV.
LOUISVILLE, KY. 40220

CLAUDE E. BURROUGHS
6805 WATTERSN TRL R5 S.
LOUISVILLE, KY. 40291

WILLIAM BURROUGHS
8TH
MILLERSBURG, KY. 40348

C. K. BURROUGHS
1929 CAMBRIDGE DR. APT.
LEXINGTON, KY. 40504

E. M. BURROUGHS
2475 THORNBERRY CT.
LEXINGTON, KY. 40509

HESTON BURROUGHS
1401 MAPLE LN. APT. 5
CORBIN, KY. 40701

BETTY BURROUGHS
5 TRIANGLE CT.
NEWPORT, KY. 41071

GEORGE W. BURROUGHS
500 7TH AV.
NEWPORT, KY. 41074

M. M. BURROUGHS
201 CARLISLE ST.
WARSAW, KY. 41095

JOHN W. BURROUGHS
1414 PROSPECT AV.
ASHLAND, KY. 41101

PAUL C. BURROUGHS
441 RIVERSIDE DR.
RUSSELL, KY. 41169

JOHN BURROUGHS
BOONEVILLE, KY. 41314

BUENITA BURROUGHS
R.R. 5
BENTON, KY. 42025

ROBERT BURROUGHS
R1 BX. 361
HARDIN, KY. 42048

JEANNE M. BURROUGHS
R. 6
CADIZ, KY. 42211

CARROLL L. BURROUGHS
3000 YOSEMITE DR.
OWENSBORO, KY. 42301

CARROLL L. BURROUGHS
3000 YELLOWSTONE DR. E.
OWENSBORO, KY. 42301

BRENDA BURROUGHS
1218 7TH ST. W.
OWENSBORO, KY. 42301

PEARL BURROUGHS
907 4TH ST. W.
OWENSBORO, KY. 42301

JIMMY L. BURROUGHS
3285 6TH ST. E. APT. 14
OWENSBORO, KY. 42301

CLIFFORD A. BURROUGHS
R2
CECILIA, KY. 42724

THOMAS W. BURROUGHS
272 CURTIS ST.
DELAWARE, OH. 43015

ROBERT E. BURROUGHS
139 CURTIS ST.
DELAWARE, OH. 43015

VIVIAN BURROUGHS
100 GEORGETOWN DR. APT.
DELAWARE, OH. 43015

EUGENE P. BURROUGHS
612 MAGNOLIA DR.
DELAWARE, OH. 43015

DANIEL W. BURROUGHS
10000 HORSESHOE RD.
DELAWARE, OH. 43015

DANIEL W. BURROUGHS
1000 HORSESHOE RD. R5
DELAWARE, OH. 43015

PETER W. BURROUGHS
112 MEADOW LN.
GAMBIER, OH. 43022

LINDA BURROUGHS
JAMES RD. R1
GRANVILLE, OH. 43023

FRANK BURROUGHS
JAMES RD. R1
GRANVILLE, OH. 43023

CARL R. BURROUGHS
530 LAKESHORE W.
HEBRON, OH. 43025

DALTON BURROUGHS
942 VAN KIRK DR.
MARYSVILLE, OH. 43040

| | | | |
|---|---|---|---|
| CARROLL W. BURROUGHS<br>948 VAN KIRK DR.<br>MARYSVILLE, OH. 43040 | DONALD E. BURROUGHS<br>17289 WALDO RD. R3<br>MARYSVILLE, OH. 43040 | BRUCE A. BURROUGHS<br>1111 1/2 CHESTNUT ST. W.<br>MOUNT VERNON, OH. 43050 | ILDA M. BURROUGHS<br>94 ELMWOOD AV.<br>NEWARK, OH. 43055 |
| DAVID E. BURROUGHS<br>280 10TH ST. APT. B.<br>NEWARK, OH. 43055 | WILLIAM C. BURROUGHS<br>120 SYCAMORE ST. S.<br>N. LEWISBURG, OH. 43060 | WILLIAM C. BURROUGHS<br>130 SYCAMORE S.<br>N. LEWISBURG, OH. 43060 | JAMES L. BURROUGHS<br>128 BURR OAK DR.<br>PATASKALA, OH. 43062 |
| ROBERT H. BURROUGHS<br>1569 ST. PARIS JACKSO<br>SAINT PARIS, OH. 43072 | JEFF BURROUGHS<br>118 MAIN ST. E.<br>SAINT PARIS, OH. 43072 | JAMES BURROUGHS<br>ST. PARIS JACK<br>SAINT PARIS, OH. 43072 | ROBERT BURROUGHS<br>ST. PARIS JACK<br>SAINT PARIS, OH. 43072 |
| GREG BURROUGHS<br>1658 ST. PARIS JACK<br>SAINT PARIS, OH. 43072 | G. BURROUGHS<br>10257 RUNKLE RD.<br>SAINT PARIS, OH. 43072 | KRISTIN A. BURROUGHS<br>10117 RUNKLE RD.<br>SAINT PARIS, OH. 43072 | JOYCE C. BURROUGHS<br>1681 ST. PARIS JACKSO<br>SAINT PARIS, OH. 43072 |
| MICHAEL BURROUGHS<br>1060 HIGH ST. S. APT. 17<br>URBANA, OH. 43078 | DONALD H. BURROUGHS<br>5615 COPENHAGEN DR.<br>WESTERVILLE, OH. 43081 | V. C. BURROUGHS<br>11511 WOOD BRDG LN. R2<br>BALTIMORE, OH. 43105 | PRENTIS E. BURROUGHS<br>11511 WOODBRDGE LN. R3<br>BALTIMORE, OH. 43105 |
| G. L. BURROUGHS<br>9616 TAYLOR CT. R2<br>PICKERINGTON, OH. 43147 | CHARLES R. BURROUGHS<br>8803 FOSNAUGH SCHOOL<br>STOUTSVILLE, OH. 43154 | MICHAEL H. BURROUGHS<br>2874 EAST AV.<br>COLUMBUS, OH. 43202 | RAYMOND R. BURROUGHS<br>73 WEBER RD. W.<br>COLUMBUS, OH. 43202 |
| LEROY BURROUGHS<br>39 GARFIELD AV. S.<br>COLUMBUS, OH. 43205 | LEROY BURROUGHS<br>902 CHAMPION AV. S.<br>COLUMBUS, OH. 43206 | JUNIOUS L. BURROUGHS<br>1329 LOCKBERRY AV.<br>COLUMBUS, OH. 43207 | OLIVER C. BURROUGHS<br>4049 GARRETT DR. W.<br>COLUMBUS, OH. 43214 |
| ROBERT BURROUGHS<br>4900 OLDBRIDGE RD.<br>COLUMBUS, OH. 43220 | FRANCES M. BURROUGHS<br>4499 WESTBOROUGH DR. W.<br>COLUMBUS, OH. 43220 | HOWARD C. BURROUGHS<br>3665 SUNSET DR.<br>COLUMBUS, OH. 43221 | LEROY BURROUGHS<br>2720 WOODCUTTER AV.<br>COLUMBUS, OH. 43224 |
| JUNIOUS S. BURROUGHS<br>3422 BURBANK RD.<br>COLUMBUS, OH. 43227 | HARRISON BURROUGHS<br>3419 CLARKSTON AV.<br>COLUMBUS, OH. 43227 | JOHN BURROUGHS<br>3599 RODELL RD.<br>COLUMBUS, OH. 43227 | DAVID C. BURROUGHS<br>4342 CHATEAU MRSE DR.<br>COLUMBUS, OH. 43229 |
| PAULA BURROUGHS<br>790 GROVE ST.<br>MARION, OH. 43302 | LAWRENCE H. BURROUGHS<br>700 DETROIT ST. S.<br>BELLEFONTAINE, OH. 43311 | EVELYN M. BURROUGHS<br>317 GRANT ST. E.<br>CLYDE, OH. 43410 | RANDALL L. BURROUGHS<br>2812 CNTY RD. 185 R2<br>CLYDE, OH. 43410 |
| DOUGLAS BURROUGHS<br>121 MASON ST. E.<br>CLYDE, OH. 43410 | D. E. BURROUGHS, JR.<br>418 WOODLAND AV.<br>CLYDE, OH. 43410 | BRADLEY R. BURROUGHS<br>442 WOODLAND AV.<br>CLYDE, OH. 43410 | JAMES R. BURROUGHS<br>708 OHIO AV. N.<br>FREMONT, OH. 43420 |
| BRIAN L. BURROUGHS<br>1020 MILLER ST.<br>FREMONT, OH. 43420 | MARGE BURROUGHS<br>809 UPTON RD.<br>FREMONT, OH. 43420 | HARRY E. BURROUGHS<br>668 COUNTY R232 R6<br>FREMONT, OH. 43420 | CYNTHIA L. BURROUGHS<br>1057 SHOREWOOD DR. R5<br>FREMONT, OH. 43420 |
| LARRY BURROUGHS<br>STATE RT. 281 R6<br>DEFIANCE, OH. 43512 | LARRY BURROUGHS<br>CARPENTER RD. R2<br>DEFIANCE, OH. 43512 | BEULAH BURROUGHS<br>23919 BO GREEN RD. WE<br>GRAND RAPIDS, OH. 43522 | ROBERT J. BURROUGHS<br>R1 BX. 157<br>LYONS, OH. 43533 |
| W. R. BURROUGHS<br>1 13899<br>LYONS, OH. 43533 | WILLIAM G. BURROUGHS<br>R1<br>LYONS, OH. 43533 | ELDON BURROUGHS<br>R1<br>METAMORA, OH. 43540 | C. BURROUGHS<br>210 MAIN ST. E.<br>METAMORA, OH. 43540 |
| JANICE G. BURROUGHS<br>303 DODGE ST. APT. 8<br>SWANTON, OH. 43558 | CHARLES R. BURROUGHS<br>1 HOLIDAY DR. R1<br>SWANTON, OH. 43558 | JOHN B. BURROUGHS<br>1621 CENTRAL AV. W.<br>TOLEDO, OH. 43606 | MARLAN BURROUGHS<br>125 CENTRAL AV. W.<br>TOLEDO, OH. 43608 |
| CECIL H. BURROUGHS<br>6666 SANDYWELL DR.<br>TOLEDO, OH. 43613 | ROBERT O. BURROUGHS<br>3633 LYNBROOK DR.<br>TOLEDO, OH. 43614 | JERRY J. BURROUGHS<br>2106 HARLAN RD.<br>TOLEDO, OH. 43615 | KENNETH R. BURROUGHS<br>2750 PICKLE RD. APT. 81<br>TOLEDO, OH. 43616 |
| J. BURROUGHS<br>2105 WARREN ST.<br>TOLEDO, OH. 43620 | CLAYTON B. BURROUGHS<br>274 BLACKWOOD DR. N.<br>ZANESVILLE, OH. 43701 | MARVIN BURROUGHS<br>135 7TH ST. S.<br>ZANESVILLE, OH. 43701 | THOMAS L. BURROUGHS<br>R1 BX. 350<br>BELMONT, OH. 43718 |
| FOSTER R. BURROUGHS<br>1354 ELM ST.<br>CAMBRIDGE, OH. 43725 | FOSTER R. BURROUGHS<br>R1<br>LORE CITY, OH. 43755 | GARRY R. BURROUGHS<br>R1<br>LORE CITY, OH. 43755 | MARTHA BURROUGHS<br>3739 NOBLE ST.<br>BELLAIRE, OH. 43906 |
| MARVIN D. BURROUGHS<br>BEAVR CST ET R3<br>E. LIVERPOOL, OH. 43920 | THOMAS L. BURROUGHS<br>R1 BX. 177<br>SHADYSIDE, OH. 43947 | DAVID T. BURROUGHS<br>121 HUTCHINSON DR.<br>ST. CLAIRSVL. OH. 43950 | MERLE BURROUGHS<br>134 WOODROW AV.<br>ST. CLAIRSVL. OH. 43950 |
| DAVID L. BURROUGHS<br>410 4TH ST.<br>WELLSVILLE, OH. 43968 | JANICE M. BURROUGHS<br>R1<br>FREEPORT, OH. 43973 | S. A. BURROUGHS<br>1272 GARRISON RD. R5<br>ASHTABULA, OH. 44004 | JOHN L. BURROUGHS<br>324 CONCORD AV.<br>ELYRIA, OH. 44035 |
| JAMES A. BURROUGHS<br>38741 EAST RIVER R3<br>ELYRIA, OH. 44035 | CHARLES BURROUGHS<br>415 15TH ST. W.<br>LORAIN, OH. 44052 | ROBERT L. BURROUGHS<br>4745 OBERLIN AV. APT. 4C<br>LORAIN, OH. 44053 | BENTON L. BURROUGHS<br>1164 THINSBURG RD. E.<br>MACEDONIA, OH. 44056 |
| THOMAS B. BURROUGHS<br>1144 THINSBURG RD. E.<br>MACEDONIA, OH. 44056 | HOWARD T. BURROUGHS<br>37424 ARTHUR ST.<br>WILLOUGHBY, OH. 44094 | ERNEST R. BURROUGHS<br>1330 91ST ST. W.<br>CLEVELAND, OH. 44102 | WILLIAM P. BURROUGHS<br>6719 EUCLID AV.<br>CLEVELAND, OH. 44103 |
| C. BURROUGHS<br>3403 103RD ST. E.<br>CLEVELAND, OH. 44104 | ALBERT C. BURROUGHS<br>12311 WADE PARK AV.<br>CLEVELAND, OH. 44106 | JONOTHAN H. BURROUGHS<br>2748 EUCLID HTS. BL<br>CLEVELAND, OH. 44106 | LUELLA BURROUGHS<br>741 PARKWOOD DR.<br>CLEVELAND, OH. 44108 |
| LOUIS B. BURROUGHS<br>903 123RD ST. E.<br>CLEVELAND, OH. 44108 | ROBERT BURROUGHS<br>3914 SACKETT AV.<br>CLEVELAND, OH. 44109 | KENNETH W. BURROUGHS<br>4214 42ND ST. W.<br>CLEVELAND, OH. 44109 | JAMES G. BURROUGHS<br>19009 FIRWOOD RD.<br>CLEVELAND, OH. 44110 |
| CLYDE BURROUGHS<br>1128 144TH ST. E.<br>CLEVELAND, OH. 44110 | VIRGINIA M. BURROUGHS<br>450 146TH ST. E.<br>CLEVELAND, OH. 44110 | B. J. BURROUGHS<br>14616 ALDER AV.<br>CLEVELAND, OH. 44112 | LOUIS B. BURROUGHS<br>1135 CARVER RD.<br>CLEVELAND, OH. 44112 |
| TIMOTHY BURROUGHS<br>1356 141ST ST. E.<br>CLEVELAND, OH. 44112 | J. E. BURROUGHS<br>2878 MAYFIELD RD. APT. 3<br>CLEVELAND, OH. 44118 | LORRAINE BURROUGHS<br>3957 BUSHNELL RD.<br>CLEVELAND, OH. 44118 | M. P. BURROUGHS<br>3068 HUNTINGTON RD.<br>CLEVELAND, OH. 44120 |
| WILLIAM R. BURROUGHS<br>3319 123RD ST. E.<br>CLEVELAND, OH. 44120 | FRED BURROUGHS<br>3995 154TH ST. E.<br>CLEVELAND, OH. 44128 | RONALD D. BURROUGHS<br>7209 BERESFORD AV.<br>CLEVELAND, OH. 44130 | THOMAS E. BURROUGHS<br>731 256TH ST. E.<br>CLEVELAND, OH. 44132 |
| DONALD R. BURROUGHS<br>3907 RUSSELL AV.<br>CLEVELAND, OH. 44134 | JEFFREY R. BURROUGHS<br>4512 191ST ST. W.<br>CLEVELAND, OH. 44135 | ERNEST R. BURROUGHS, JR.<br>6496 LIBERTY BELL DR.<br>CLEVELAND, OH. 44142 | KENNETH BURROUGHS<br>355 FRANK ST.<br>BARBERTON, OH. 44203 |
| CLAUDIA J. BURROUGHS<br>517 ROBINSON AV.<br>BARBERTON, OH. 44203 | KENNETH BURROUGHS<br>4297 BENNINGTON BL<br>BRUNSWICK, OH. 44212 | ROLAND L. BURROUGHS<br>2203 ARNDALE RD.<br>CUYAHOGA FLS. OH. 44224 | JANELL BURROUGHS<br>4442 TIMBERDALE ST.<br>CUYAHOGA FLS. OH. 44224 |
| PRESTON BURROUGHS<br>3755 LOVERS LN. R7<br>RAVENNA, OH. 44266 | DONALD R. BURROUGHS<br>3941 BRECKSVILLE RD.<br>RICHFIELD, OH. 44286 | RICHARD E. BURROUGHS<br>1052 LA CROIX AV.<br>AKRON, OH. 44307 | EDWARD BURROUGHS<br>1101 DAYTON ST.<br>AKRON, OH. 44310 |

ALVIN BURROUGHS
1431 BYE ST.
AKRON, OH. 44320

CHARLES E. BURROUGHS
1096 GREENWOOD AV.
AKRON, OH. 44320

KENNETH K. BURROUGHS
11603 MARKET ST.
NORTH LIMA, OH. 44452

JAMES E. BURROUGHS
2275 NORTHWEST BL N.W.
WARREN, OH. 44485

WILLIAM A. BURROUGHS
508 CARROLL ST.
YOUNGSTOWN, OH. 44502

JAMES BURROUGHS
1404 FLORENCEDALE AV.
YOUNGSTOWN, OH. 44505

THELMA BURROUGHS
448 HILLTOP ST.
YOUNGSTOWN, OH. 44506

WALTER BURROUGHS
349 TRUESDALE AV. N.
YOUNGSTOWN, OH. 44506

ROBERT BURROUGHS
2408 CHERRY AV.
ALLIANCE, OH. 44601

LELAND B. BURROUGHS, JR.
731 DAN ST.
CANAL FULTON, OH. 44614

BESSIE M. BURROUGHS
20 GROOSE AV. N.W.
MASSILLON, OH. 44646

ROBERT R. BURROUGHS
2473 LIST RD. R7 N.W.
MASSILLON, OH. 44646

J. BURROUGHS
118 MAIN ST. E.
PARIS, OH. 44669

TERRY BURROUGHS
225 OHIO ST.
ASHLAND, OH. 44805

SUSAN H. BURROUGHS
10 EARL AV.
BLOOMVILLE, OH. 44818

ROBBI A. BURROUGHS
7091 COUNTY RD. 12 R1 E.
BLOOMVILLE, OH. 44818

DEBRA A. BURROUGHS
LIBERTY HILL APTS.
BLOOMVILLE, OH. 44818

RICKY E. BURROUGHS
9025 COUNTY R6 E.
BLOOMVILLE, OH. 44818

DORCAS J. BURROUGHS
153 SHOREWAY DR.
SANDUSKY, OH. 44870

CHARLES E. BURROUGHS
6706 LOSS CREEK RD.
TIRO, OH. 44887

WILLIAM BURROUGHS
1219 1 AV.
ADDYSTON, OH. 45001

ROY S. BURROUGHS
608 4TH ST. E.
FRANKLIN, OH. 45005

CHARLES A. BURROUGHS
7157 IRON KETTLE DR.
HAMILTON, OH. 45011

JOHN W. BURROUGHS
5604 CHATEAU HY.
HAMILTON, OH. 45014

E. BURROUGHS
6123 STATE RT. 48 R1 N.
LEBANON, OH. 45036

JOHN W. BURROUGHS, JR.
201 WASHINGTON HY.
MASON, OH. 45040

JOHN BURROUGHS
2408 EASTON AV.
MIDDLETOWN, OH. 45042

HUBERT BURROUGHS
2112 MAIN ST. S.
MIDDLETOWN, OH. 45042

OSCAR BURROUGHS
60 OHIO AV.
NORTH BEND, OH. 45052

VAUGHN L. BURROUGHS
40 HOME AV.
SPRINGBORO, OH. 45066

GUY E. BURROUGHS
3384 LYTLE RD.
WAYNESVILLE, OH. 45068

ROBERT K. BURROUGHS
R3 BX. 1674
BATAVIA, OH. 45103

RALPH A. BURROUGHS
223 BALDWIN ST. W.
BLANCHESTER, OH. 45107

RALPH V. BURROUGHS
136 NORTHVIEW ST. R2
BLANCHESTER, OH. 45107

ADAM P. BURROUGHS
232 BLAND AV.
BLANCHESTER, OH. 45107

DALE BURROUGHS
R1
FAYETTEVILLE, OH. 45118

THOMAS T. BURROUGHS
STATE HY 753 R1 S.
HILLSBORO, OH. 45133

GARY W. BURROUGHS
231 HEIDELBERG DR.
LOVELAND, OH. 45140

TERRENCE R. BURROUGHS
234 MINDY DR. R2
LOVELAND, OH. 45140

ELZA BURROUGHS
815 DOAK RD.
MIDLAND, OH. 45148

EDWARD BURROUGHS
5657 LOCUST DR.
MILFORD, OH. 45150

CHARLES W. BURROUGHS
1925 VERA CRUZ PKE.
MILFORD, OH. 45150

CHARLES A. BURROUGHS
7608 OHARA DR. R3
MORROW, OH. 45152

D. BURROUGHS
6629 STROUT RD. R1
MORROW, OH. 45152

LAUREEN BURROUGHS
DOROTHY LN. R1
NEW VIENNA, OH. 45159

LINDA S. BURROUGHS
136 3RD ST. S.
WILLIAMSBURG, OH. 45176

DONALD W. BURROUGHS
1443 ZIMMERER RD. R2
WILLIAMSBURG, OH. 45176

RONALD BURROUGHS
HIGHWAY 133 R1
WILLIAMSBURG, OH. 45176

MARGARET BURROUGHS
3055 HACKBERRY ST.
CINCINNATI, OH. 45206

ALEXANDER BURROUGHS
1217 HALPIN AV.
CINCINNATI, OH. 45208

R. BURROUGHS
3516 STETTINIUS AV. APT.
CINCINNATI, OH. 45208

EDWARD M. BURROUGHS
4019 LEESBURG LN. APT. 2
CINCINNATI, OH. 45209

LAURA A. BURROUGHS
2723 EDROY CT. APT. 70
CINCINNATI, OH. 45209

MILDRED V. BURROUGHS
4040 LEESBURG LN. APT. 7
CINCINNATI, OH. 45209

FRANCIS BURROUGHS
3093 GODA AV.
CINCINNATI, OH. 45211

CALVIN BURROUGHS
3521 ZINSLE AV.
CINCINNATI, OH. 45213

WILLIAM E. BURROUGHS
208 VINE ST. W.
CINCINNATI, OH. 45215

ALBERT S. BURROUGHS
17 WILMUTH AV.
CINCINNATI, OH. 45215

W. BURROUGHS
25 UNIVERSITY AV. W.
CINCINNATI, OH. 45219

DON A. BURROUGHS
3315 JEFFERSON AV.
CINCINNATI, OH. 45220

EDGAR H. BURROUGHS
5135 HAWAIIAN TER. APT.
CINCINNATI, OH. 45223

B. M. BURROUGHS
6828 PARKLAND AV.
CINCINNATI, OH. 45233

MAGGIE B. BURROUGHS
1219 FRANKLIN AV. APT. B
CINCINNATI, OH. 45237

JOSEPH BURROUGHS
1918 LANGDON FARM RD.
CINCINNATI, OH. 45237

LEE F. BURROUGHS
2504 DUNAWAY CT.
CINCINNATI, OH. 45238

EDWARD T. BURROUGHS
6938 DIANA DR.
CINCINNATI, OH. 45239

DAVID N. BURROUGHS
3210 LAPLAND DR.
CINCINNATI, OH. 45239

MICHAEL G. BURROUGHS
8967 ARABIAN CT.
CINCINNATI, OH. 45242

FRANK G. BURROUGHS
7001 FOWLER ST.
CINCINNATI, OH. 45243

TED T. BURROUGHS
7120 WALLACE ST.
CINCINNATI, OH. 45243

MABEL F. BURROUGHS
7112 WALLACE ST.
CINCINNATI, OH. 45243

VIRGIL L. BURROUGHS
803 DIANE DR.
CINCINNATI, OH. 45245

L. J. BURROUGHS
252 HOLMES DR.
FAIRBORN, OH. 45324

JAMES T. BURROUGHS
5800 DIAMOND MILL R2
GERMANTOWN, OH. 45327

JOHN W. BURROUGHS
833 COTTAGE AV.
MIAMISBURG, OH. 45342

JOHN W. BURROUGHS
733 LOOP ST.
MIAMISBURG, OH. 45342

R. E. BURROUGHS
1658 DORSEY HG ST. R3
SIDNEY, OH. 45365

MICHAEL BURROUGHS
610 MAIN AV. S.
SIDNEY, OH. 45365

DALE W. BURROUGHS
560 FOREST AV. APT. 4
DAYTON, OH. 45405

HERBERT BURROUGHS
2909 HARVARD BL
DAYTON, OH. 45406

KAREN E. BURROUGHS
2767 TRIANGLE VW DR.
DAYTON, OH. 45414

EDWARD R. BURROUGHS
630 BURGESS AV.
DAYTON, OH. 45415

L. BURROUGHS
3030 HOME AV. APT. 3
DAYTON, OH. 45417

WILLIAM P. BURROUGHS, JR
4639 OAKRIDGE DR.
DAYTON, OH. 45417

E. M. BURROUGHS
1101 WILMINGTON PKE. APT
DAYTON, OH. 45420

CLARENCE A. BURROUGHS, JR.
1540 WATERVLIET AV.
DAYTON, OH. 45420

IRMA L. BURROUGHS
143 BILLWOOD RD.
DAYTON, OH. 45431

CECIL C. BURROUGHS
R1
CREOLA, OH. 45622

TIMOTHY BURROUGHS
21 WISCONSIN AV. N.
WELLSTON, OH. 45692

JANE BURROUGHS
R2 BX. 16
WEST UNION, OH. 45693

STEVE BURROUGHS
STATE RT. 247 R1 N.
WEST UNION, OH. 45693

THOMAS L. BURROUGHS, JR.
R1
REEDSVILLE, OH. 45772

THOMAS L. BURROUGHS
BX. 157
TUPPERS PLN. OH. 45783

CLARENCE E. BURROUGHS
739 BROADWAY E.
LIMA, OH. 45804

CARL BURROUGHS
106 WALL ST. S.
VAN WERT, OH. 45891

CARROLL BURROUGHS
1201 WALNUT ST. E.
FRANKFORT, IN. 46041

NED J. BURROUGHS
511 EDGEWOOD DR.
LEBANON, IN. 46052

RALPH E. BURROUGHS
1104 MERIDIAN ST. N.
LEBANON, IN. 46052

JAMES R. BURROUGHS
113 GREGORY DR. R4
PENDLETON, IN. 46064

RONALD J. BURROUGHS
508 7TH ST. W.
SHERIDAN, IN. 46069

JERRY L. BURROUGHS
211 PARTHENIA AV.
BROWNSBURG, IN. 46112

OKEY BURROUGHS
JOHN TR CT. VIA
MORRISTOWN, IN. 46161

JON P. BURROUGHS
3846 MICHIGAN ST. E.
INDIANAPOLIS, IN. 46201

JON P. BURROUGHS
3848 MICHIGAN ST. E.
INDIANAPOLIS, IN. 46201

R. BURROUGHS
654 WEST DR.
INDIANAPOLIS, IN. 46201

LONNIE J. BURROUGHS
220 SUMMIT ST. N.
INDIANAPOLIS, IN. 46201

J. H. BURROUGHS
1219 10TH ST. E.
INDIANAPOLIS, IN. 46202

ROBERT J. BURROUGHS
621 RAYMOND ST. E.
INDIANAPOLIS, IN. 46203

GORDON A. BURROUGHS
3127 52ND ST. E. APT. E.
INDIANAPOLIS, IN. 46205

A. BURROUGHS
1312 LE MANS CT. APT. 11
INDIANAPOLIS, IN. 46205

JAMES E. BURROUGHS
870 BURDSAL PKWY.
INDIANAPOLIS, IN. 46208

MINNIE J. BURROUGHS
6158 COLONIAL AV.
INDIANAPOLIS, IN. 46208

STEVEN A. BURROUGHS
545 27TH ST. W.
INDIANAPOLIS, IN. 46208

DEBORAH A. BURROUGHS
537 UDELL ST.
INDIANAPOLIS, IN. 46208

CAROL S. BURROUGHS
2801 DEARBORN ST. N.
INDIANAPOLIS, IN. 46218

GEORGE W. BURROUGHS
2130 BOLTON AV. N.
INDIANAPOLIS, IN. 46218

WILLIAM L. BURROUGHS
2320 KITLEY AV. N.
INDIANAPOLIS, IN. 46219

WILLIAM BURROUGHS
5357 CARROLLTON AV.
INDIANAPOLIS, IN. 46220

WILLIAM H. BURROUGHS
637 NORTHVIEW AV.
INDIANAPOLIS, IN. 46220

HOWARD H. BURROUGHS
6233 WELHAM RD.
INDIANAPOLIS, IN. 46220

PHILLIP D. BURROUGHS
6487 PARK AV. N.
INDIANAPOLIS, IN. 46220

LINDA E. BURROUGHS
8 HELENA CT.
INDIANAPOLIS, IN. 46222

CARL L. BURROUGHS
3505 DUKANE WY. N.
INDIANAPOLIS, IN. 46224

LINDA E. BURROUGHS
4928 16TH ST. W.
INDIANAPOLIS, IN. 46224

D. I. BURROUGHS
2219 WHITE OAKS DR.
INDIANAPOLIS, IN. 46224

ALBERT L. BURROUGHS
3813 HAWTHORNE LN. N.
INDIANAPOLIS, IN. 46226

JANICE M. BURROUGHS
5925 MEADOWLARK DR.
INDIANAPOLIS, IN. 46226

DORIS I. BURROUGHS
4770 LONGWORTH AV. N.
INDIANAPOLIS, IN. 46226

ALVA L. BURROUGHS
3815 GLENCAIRN LN.
INDIANAPOLIS, IN. 46226

THOMAS E. BURROUGHS
4130 STONECREST CT. APT.
INDIANAPOLIS, IN. 46226

MICHAEL K. BURROUGHS
5619 LUNSFORD DR.
INDIANAPOLIS, IN. 46227

NORMAN BURROUGHS
316 BURKE ST. N.
INDIANAPOLIS, IN. 46234

J. M. BURROUGHS
7854 LANDINGS DR.
INDIANAPOLIS, IN. 46240

WILLIAM BURROUGHS
5432 WEST WIND LN.
INDIANAPOLIS, IN. 46250

JAMES B. BURROUGHS
7812 RED COACH DR.
INDIANAPOLIS, IN. 46250

FLOYD E. BURROUGHS
7865 WAWASEE DR.
INDIANAPOLIS, IN. 46250

JAMES BURROUGHS
2025 76TH ST. W.
INDIANAPOLIS, IN. 46260

ANDY BURROUGHS
7110 ROSEHILL DR.
INDIANAPOLIS, IN. 46260

KENNETH L. BURROUGHS
11317 151 AV. W.
CEDAR LAKE, IN. 46303

A. W. BURROUGHS
4012 DRUMMOND ST.
EAST CHICAGO, IN. 46312

AUDRIAN G. BURROUGHS
8124 JACKSON AV.
HAMMOND, IN. 46321

HARRY A. BURROUGHS
2614 JEWETT AV.
HAMMOND, IN. 46322

RUSSELL C. BURROUGHS
4905 173RD CT. W.
LOWELL, IN. 46356

ARTHUR L. BURROUGHS
117 1/2 JACKSON ST.
MICHIGAN CITY, IN. 46360

GEORGE BURROUGHS
9206 MORAINE HLS R2
MICHIGAN CITY, IN. 46360

MICHAEL W. BURROUGHS
416 SHOREWOOD CT.
VALPARAISO, IN. 46383

M. C. BURROUGHS
756 GOVERNOR RD.
VALPARAISO, IN. 46383

FRED BURROUGHS
1028 NEW JERSEY ST.
GARY, IN. 46403

RAY D. BURROUGHS
333 WALNUT ST. W.
ARGOS, IN. 46501

WILLIS BURROUGHS
335 WALNUT ST. W.
ARGOS, IN. 46501

HENRY W. BURROUGHS
71687 COUNTY RD. 9 R1
NAPPANEE, IN. 46550

WILLIAM T. BURROUGHS
1225 BISSELL ST.
SOUTH BEND, IN. 46617

JOHN F. BURROUGHS
266 CROOKED LAKE R5
ANGOLA, IN. 46703

LYNN BURROUGHS
300 STONY RIDGE DR.
ANGOLA, IN. 46703

EDITH C. BURROUGHS
932 MAIN N. APT. 6A-
BLUFFTON, IN. 46714

JOHN V. BURROUGHS
1032 MASTER DR.
DECATUR, IN. 46733

ROBERT G. BURROUGHS, JR.
411 MICHIGAN ST. E.
LAGRANGE, IN. 46761

GEORGIANNA BURROUGHS
614 HENDRICKS ST.
FORT WAYNE, IN. 46802

LOUELLA BURROUGHS
3412 SCHELE AV.
FORT WAYNE, IN. 46803

DON BURROUGHS
4720 DRUID HILLS DR. APT
FORT WAYNE, IN. 46815

RUSSELL L. BURROUGHS
6312 COOK RD. R3 W.
FORT WAYNE, IN. 46818

RICK E. BURROUGHS
1812 8TH ST. W.
MARION, IN. 46952

EDGAR G. BURROUGHS
R.R. 3
ROCHESTER, IN. 46975

LIBURN BURROUGHS
R.R. 1
STAR CITY, IN. 46985

WILBUR E. BURROUGHS, SR.
450 PARK AV.
AURORA, IN. 47001

CLARA F. BURROUGHS
210 MARKET ST. W.
VEVAY, IN. 47043

RICHARD S. BURROUGHS
725 ETTELS LN. APT. 10
JEFFERSONVL, IN. 47130

RICKY C. BURROUGHS
1813 TURPIN DR.
JEFFERSONVL, IN. 47130

DONALD BURROUGHS
6 WESTWOOD RD.
MUNCIE, IN. 47303

MICHAEL D. BURROUGHS
3568 TILLOTSON AV. N. AP
MUNCIE, IN. 47304

LOA E. BURROUGHS
RITTER RD.
EATON, IN. 47338

ANNA BURROUGHS
211 HIGH ST. W.
HAGERSTOWN, IN. 47346

ROBERT BURROUGHS
OLD ST. RD. 1 R. 2
HAGERSTOWN, IN. 47346

BERNARD BURROUGHS
BROAD
MOORELAND, IN. 47360

F. L. BURROUGHS
516 COLONIAL DR. W.
NEW CASTLE, IN. 47362

A. L. BURROUGHS
206 8TH ST. N.
RICHMOND, IN. 47374

JONATHAN BURROUGHS
215 1/2 14TH ST. N.
RICHMOND, IN. 47374

RUSSEL BURROUGHS
4705 NATIONL RD. WEST LO
RICHMOND, IN. 47374

E. BURROUGHS
ST. RD. 3
SPICELAND, IN. 47385

CODY BURROUGHS
BERGMAN RD.
CHRISNEY, IN. 47611

GEORGE BURROUGHS
CHRISNEY, IN. 47611

HOWARD BURROUGHS
RICHLAND, IN. 47634

GARY BURROUGHS
EBENEZER RD.
RICHLAND, IN. 47634

PERRY BURROUGHS
RICHLAND, IN. 47634

NOEL B. BURROUGHS
HIGHWAY 62 R1
EVANSVILLE, IN. 47712

MARGARET E. BURROUGHS
3629 POPLAR ST.
TERRE HAUTE, IN. 47803

P. BURROUGHS
2401 1/2 POPLAR ST.
TERRE HAUTE, IN. 47803

RAYMOND P. BURROUGHS
2216 FRUITRIDGE AV. S.
TERRE HAUTE, IN. 47803

HOWARD BURROUGHS
110 CHESTNUT ST. E.
BRAZIL, IN. 47834

BRENDA BURROUGHS
BIRCH
DANA, IN. 47847

KENNETH BURROUGHS
618 28TH ST. S.
LAFAYETTE, IN. 47904

RONALD E. BURROUGHS
2204 20TH ST. N.
LAFAYETTE, IN. 47904

T. E. BURROUGHS
1138 14TH ST. N. APT. 1
LAFAYETTE, IN. 47904

CHARLES W. BURROUGHS
3300 11TH ST. S.
LAFAYETTE, IN. 47905

JAMES E. BURROUGHS
4351 SOLDIERS HM RD.
LAFAYETTE, IN. 47906

WILLIAM BURROUGHS
R.R. 4
ATTICA, IN. 47918

CLAYTON BURROUGHS
BATTLE GROUND, IN. 47920

ROBERT H. BURROUGHS
11 GLENWOOD DR. R8
CRAWFORDSVL, IN. 47933

H. L. BURROUGHS
1401 MARKET ST. W.
CRAWFORDSVL, IN. 47933

CHARLES BURROUGHS
101 WESTWOOD DR.
CRAWFORDSVL, IN. 47933

SAM BURROUGHS
404 SPRUCE N.
MONON, IN. 47959

C. J. BURROUGHS
517 RACE N.
MONON, IN. 47959

NORMAN BURROUGHS
425 MARKET E.
NEWPORT, IN. 47966

RUBY BURROUGHS
440 MARKET W.
NEWPORT, IN. 47966

JACK D. BURROUGHS
605 MARKET
NEWPORT, IN. 47966

GEORGE BURROUGHS
MARKET E.
NEWPORT, IN. 47966

EDWARD T. BURROUGHS
335 HAMILTON RD.
BIRMINGHAM, MI. 48010

ROSWELL G. BURROUGHS
31905 CROSS BOW CT.
BIRMINGHAM, MI. 48010

VIRGINIA G. BURROUGHS
33333 MANOR DR. N. APT.
FARMINGTON, MI. 48024

JAMES M. BURROUGHS
33150 MANOR DR. S. APT.
FARMINGTON, MI. 48024

ROBERT J. BURROUGHS
37450 LAKE SHORE DR.
MOUNT CLEMENS, MI. 48045

KAY H. BURROUGHS
34764 JEFFERSON AV.
MOUNT CLEMENS, MI. 48045

VIRGINIA I. BURROUGHS
117 LYNDON CIR. R1
OXFORD, MI. 48051

HAZEL C. BURROUGHS
137 PALMER ST.
PONTIAC, MI. 48053

FLAVIS L. BURROUGHS
3665 NORTH RIVER RD.
PORT HURON, MI. 48060

ALBERT W. BURROUGHS
204 LANGLEY CIR.
SAINT CLAIR, MI. 48079

JOHN E. BURROUGHS
26521 CRYSTAL ST.
WARREN, MI. 48091

JESSE W. BURROUGHS
6311 DONALDSON ST.
TROY, MI. 48098

DANIEL L. BURROUGHS
1215 ARBOR VIEW BL
ANN ARBOR, MI. 48103

ROBERT E. BURROUGHS
1120 WAGNER RD. N.
ANN ARBOR, MI. 48103

EARL BURROUGHS
2155 HEMLOCK DR.
ANN ARBOR, MI. 48104

WILLIAM R. BURROUGHS
1419 MORTON AV.
ANN ARBOR, MI. 48104

ELDON T. BURROUGHS
3337 BURBANK DR.
ANN ARBOR, MI. 48105

M. J. BURROUGHS
4555 PLEASANT VLY R8
BRIGHTON, MI. 48116

SAMUEL A. BURROUGHS
18891 REED RD.
DEARBORN, MI. 48122

RONDA BURROUGHS
6056 NECKEL ST.
DEARBORN, MI. 48126

PAUL W. BURROUGHS
154 GEORGE ST.
GREGORY, MI. 48137

ROBERT BURROUGHS
3359 BAYHAM ST.
INKSTER, MI. 48141

HUEY BURROUGHS
29986 SPRING ARBOR DR.
INKSTER, MI. 48141

JAMES M. BURROUGHS
18229 UNIVERSITY PARK
LIVONIA, MI. 48152

JOHN J. BURROUGHS
360 COLE RD.
MONROE, MI. 48161

ROBERT J. BURROUGHS
507 TOLEDO AV.
MONROE, MI. 48161

GLENN H. BURROUGHS
6772 POLK ST.
TAYLOR, MI. 48180

S. L. BURROUGHS
2371 WINTHROP ST.
TRENTON, MI. 48183

STEPHEN W. BURROUGHS
7600 NANKIN CT. APT. 105
WESTLAND, MI. 48185

DENNIS M. BURROUGHS
32571 MERRITT DR.
WESTLAND, MI. 48185

WILLIAM H. BURROUGHS
8744 SHARI ST.
WESTLAND, MI. 48185

MARGARET L. BURROUGHS
17077 VALADE ST.
WYANDOTTE, MI. 48192

HAROLD J. BURROUGHS
14094 IRENE ST.
WYANDOTTE, MI. 48195

FRED W. BURROUGHS
1812 CRITTENDON AV.
YPSILANTI, MI. 48197

F. R. BURROUGHS
1705 FOREST AV. E.
YPSILANTI, MI. 48197

ALMA L. BURROUGHS
748 GRASSLAND ST.
YPSILANTI, MI. 48197

SYLVESTER H. BURROUGHS
860 DE SOTA AV.
YPSILANTI, MI. 48197

CUSIE BURROUGHS
2165 MARY CATHERINE
YPSILANTI, MI. 48197

JAMES W. BURROUGHS
2165 LAKEVIEW DR. APT. 5
YPSILANTI, MI. 48197

LURLEAN M. BURROUGHS
770 OSWEGO ST.
YPSILANTI, MI. 48197

MAUREEN M. BURROUGHS
4789 PINE BLUFF R5 3C
YPSILANTI, MI. 48197

N. BURROUGHS
501 PERRY ST.
YPSILANTI, MI. 48197

JAMES S. BURROUGHS
51 CHURCH AV.
DETROIT, MI. 48203

CHARLES W. BURROUGHS
8250 INDIANA ST.
DETROIT, MI. 48204

VALMA A. BURROUGHS
1 LAFAYETTE PLAIS APT. 6
DETROIT, MI. 48207

H. W. BURROUGHS
5320 ROOSEVELT ST.
DETROIT, MI. 48208

BEE BURROUGHS
614 SCHROEDER ST. S.
DETROIT, MI. 48209

BOB BURROUGHS
6451 CONCORD ST.
DETROIT, MI. 48211

BOB BURROUGHS
13881 MC DOUGALL ST.
DETROIT, MI. 48212

JERRY L. BURROUGHS
3827 BENITEAU ST.
DETROIT, MI. 48214

LEROY BURROUGHS
2837 BENITEAU ST.
DETROIT, MI. 48214

WYMAN BURROUGHS
4188 ASHLAND ST.
DETROIT, MI. 48215

RICHARD BURROUGHS
4114 LAKEVIEW ST.
DETROIT, MI. 48215

ROBERT H. BURROUGHS
1304 18TH ST.
DETROIT, MI. 48216

KENYON L. BURROUGHS
3546 ANNABELLE ST. S.
DETROIT, MI. 48217

JIMMIE B. BURROUGHS
3534 BEATRICE ST. S.
DETROIT, MI. 48217

JAMES C. BURROUGHS
20284 ASHTON AV.
DETROIT, MI. 48219

RONALD W. BURROUGHS
13939 BRAMELL ST.
DETROIT, MI. 48223

DOLORES A. BURROUGHS
14586 BLACKSTONE ST.
DETROIT, MI. 48223

BERTIN BURROUGHS
12750 RIAD ST.
DETROIT, MI. 48224

DAROLD BURROUGHS
14651 TERRY ST.
DETROIT, MI. 48227

LARRY BURROUGHS
9630 WHITCOMB ST.
DETROIT, MI. 48227

WYLEY B. BURROUGHS
9261 ARCHDALE ST.
DETROIT, MI. 48228

SHERMAN J. BURROUGHS
8580 TERRY ST.
DETROIT, MI. 48228

R. BURROUGHS
20479 CHEYENNE ST.
DETROIT, MI. 48235

GEORGE E. BURROUGHS
16613 STRATHMOOR ST.
DETROIT, MI. 48235

EDWARD P. BURROUGHS
5130 OUTER DR. W.
DETROIT, MI. 48235

J. E. BURROUGHS
13250 LAKESIDE LANDNG
FENTON, MI. 48430

EMMETT N. BURROUGHS
7188 JOHNSON RD. R4
FLUSHING, MI. 48433

SHIRLEY J. BURROUGHS
10343 COOLIDGE RD.
GOODRICH, MI. 48438

DANNY BURROUGHS
6161 KNOLLWOOD DR. APT.
GRAND BLANC, MI. 48439

GEORGE H. BURROUGHS
6165 KNOLLWOOD DR. APT.
GRAND BLANC, MI. 48439

HELEN S. BURROUGHS
2573 COOK RD. R8 E.
GRAND BLANC, MI. 48439

JOSEPH S. BURROUGHS
1214 KENSINGTON AV.
FLINT, MI. 48503

DEBRA BURROUGHS
406 WOOD ST. W.
FLINT, MI. 48503

JAMES R. BURROUGHS
3302 WESTWOOD PKWY.
FLINT, MI. 48503

LENNEX BURROUGHS
1118 SOMERSET LN.
FLINT, MI. 48503

KENNETH R. BURROUGHS
G3293 MOTT AV. W.
FLINT, MI. 48504

GWENDOLYN E. BURROUGHS
2602 NOLEN DR.
FLINT, MI. 48504

BASIL F. BURROUGHS, JR.
2535 WOLCOTT ST.
FLINT, MI. 48504

MACK BURROUGHS
4402 NORTH ST.
FLINT, MI. 48505

VALENTINE BURROUGHS
118 1/2 RIDGE ST.
FLINT, MI. 48506

THOMAS L. BURROUGHS
1626 MULBERRY LN.
FLINT, MI. 48507

DOUGLAS R. BURROUGHS
3834 RED ARROW RD.
FLINT, MI. 48507

GEORGE H. BURROUGHS
6165 EAST KNOLL BL APT.
FLINT, MI. 48507

STEVE L. BURROUGHS
751 WALDMAN AV.
FLINT, MI. 48507

J. P. BURROUGHS
3801 HOLLAND RD. R4 E.
SAGINAW, MI. 48601

EUGENE S. BURROUGHS
3816 FOUR SEAS ST. R1
GLADWIN, MI. 48624

JAMES R. BURROUGHS
5809 FLAXMOOR DR.
MIDLAND, MI. 48640

WILLIAM J. BURROUGHS
4211 PARTRIDGE LN.
MIDLAND, MI. 48640

NORMA A. BURROUGHS
GRAF.RD. R1
UNIONVILLE, MI. 48767

J. BURROUGHS
1259 GRAND RIVER AV. W.
EAST LANSING, MI. 48823

L. J. BURROUGHS
5209 CHILSON RD. R3
HOWELL, MI. 48843

GLADYS L. BURROUGHS
136 KIWANIS DR.
MASON, MI. 48854

JAMES D. BURROUGHS
GENEVA RD. R1
SHEPHERD, MI. 48883

ROBERT D. BURROUGHS
2018 HEATHER LN.
KALAMAZOO, MI. 49001

JAY A. BURROUGHS
7646 SPRINKLE RD.
KALAMAZOO, MI. 49001

KEITH D. BURROUGHS
748 DOUGLAS AV.
KALAMAZOO, MI. 49007

ROBERT C. BURROUGHS
1424 ORCHARD AV.
KALAMAZOO, MI. 49007

BILL A. BURROUGHS
736 DOUGLAS AV.
KALAMAZOO, MI. 49007

CLARENCE BURROUGHS
528 DENWAY CIR.
KALAMAZOO, MI. 49008

ELLA F. BURROUGHS
363 EEL ST.
BATTLE CREEK, MI. 49015

ALBERT M. BURROUGHS
7 DEBRA DR.
BATTLE CREEK, MI. 49017

JERRY R. BURROUGHS
13209 NORTH ST. R3 W.
BELLEVUE, MI. 49021

HAROLD BURROUGHS
BURROUGHS RD. R3
DELTON, MI. 49046

RALPH E. BURROUGHS
431 STATE RD. N.
HASTINGS, MI. 49058

ORRIN F. BURROUGHS, JR.
610 FAIR ST. S.
OTSEGO, MI. 49078

ORRIN F. BURROUGHS
1588 FRANK ST. R2
OTSEGO, MI. 49078

RICHARD D. BURROUGHS
621 MAIN ST. S.
PLAINWELL, MI. 49080

WANDA BURROUGHS
R2
QUINCY, MI. 49082

JOHN R. BURROUGHS
1400 ROLLING RDG R4
STURGIS, MI. 49091

EFFIE BURROUGHS
IVY CT.
EAU CLAIRE, MI. 49111

ELDON F. BURROUGHS
2529 YANKEE ST. R2
NILES, MI. 49120

WAYNE H. BURROUGHS
964 MAUMEE ST. W.
ADRIAN, MI. 49221

DONALD J. BURROUGHS
26612 DR. R2 E.
ALBION, MI. 49224

HELEN BURROUGHS
9275 28 MILE RD. R1
ALBION, MI. 49224

CYNTHIA A. BURROUGHS
26612 DR. NORTH E.
CONCORD, MI. 49237

MOLLY A. BURROUGHS
3591 COVERT RD.
LESLIE, MI. 49251

PATRICK R. BURROUGHS
340 CENTER ST.
MICHIGAN CTR, MI. 49254

MUSA BURROUGHS
402 NORTH ST.
MORENCI, MI. 49256

SHARON BURROUGHS
15338 COLEMAN ST.
GRAND HAVEN, MI. 49417

CHARLES BURROUGHS
13443 GREEN ST. R1
GRAND HAVEN, MI. 49417

VICKY BURROUGHS
1404 OAKLEA ST.
MUSKEGON, MI. 49442

W. H. BURROUGHS
2031 GETTY RD. R3 N.
MUSKEGON, MI. 49445

REX L. BURROUGHS
758 MORRIS N.
PENTWATER, MI. 49449

MARVIN BURROUGHS
14616 CROSSHELL
WEST OLIVE, MI. 49460

FRANK M. BURROUGHS
2437 BOULEVARD DR. S.W.
GRAND RAPIDS, MI. 49509

MILDRED BURROUGHS
2052 ROOS AV. S.W.
GRAND RAPIDS, MI. 49509

NANCY L. BURROUGHS
5606 OLDS MAPLE TRL
GRAWN, MI. 49637

RUTH M. BURROUGHS
BX. 162
GRAWN, MI. 49637

J. B. BURROUGHS
R1 BX. 8
HERSEY, MI. 49639

JESSE W. BURROUGHS
16 WHISPERING PINE
MANCELONA, MI. 49659

R. J. BURROUGHS
108 EDWARDS
MESICK, MI. 49668

GARRY M. BURROUGHS
R2
MESICK, MI. 49668

JAMES BURROUGHS
1497 VALY RD.
MACKINAW CITY, MI. 49701

CLIFFORD W. BURROUGHS
423 LAKESIDE DR.
MACKINAW CITY, MI. 49701

HARRY J. BURROUGHS
KILMER AV. SR.
CARP LAKE, MI. 49718

RICHARD J. BURROUGHS
501 1ST AV. S.
ESCANABA, MI. 49829

JANET M. BURROUGHS
1212 LAKE SHORE DR.
GLADSTONE, MI. 49837

JANE P. BURROUGHS
R1 BX. 37
BRUCE XING, MI. 49912

ROBERT G. BURROUGHS
700 14TH ST. E.
ATLANTIC, IA. 50022

CHARLES R. BURROUGHS
R1
COLUMBIA, IA. 50057

WALTER G. BURROUGHS
1307 SILOAM AV.
IOWA FALLS, IA. 50126

SALLY BURROUGHS
610 HENDERSON
IOWA FALLS, IA. 50126

ESTELLE BURROUGHS
134 MAIN ST. E. APT. 204
MARSHALLTOWN, IA. 50158

MICHAEL D. BURROUGHS
R1
MELBOURNE, IA. 50162

WILLARD H. BURROUGHS
728 4TH AV. E. S.
NEWTON, IA. 50208

E. D. BURROUGHS
203 ALPINE DR.
W. DES MOINES, IA. 50265

JOHN L. BURROUGHS
3420 8TH ST. S.W.
DES MOINES, IA. 50315

JOHN P. BURROUGHS
3214 28TH ST. S.W.
DES MOINES, IA. 50321

JOHN M. BURROUGHS
6408 HOLCOMB AV.
DES MOINES, IA. 50322

ANNA M. BURROUGHS
416 5TH ST. N.W.
MASON CITY, IA. 50401

PAUL R. BURROUGHS
R4
HAMPTON, IA. 50441

JOHN A. BURROUGHS
ALLISON, IA. 50602

CLAUDIA BURROUGHS
1939 COLLEGE ST. APT. 20
CEDAR FALLS, IA. 50613

CLIFFORD BURROUGHS
GREENE, IA. 50636

MARY V. BURROUGHS
GREENE, IA. 50636

HOWARD N. BURROUGHS
GREENE, IA. 50636

MONTE D. BURROUGHS
BX. 14
HANSELL, IA. 50640

DOROTHY M. BURROUGHS
704 CRESTVIEW DR.
TRAER, IA. 50675

PAUL S. BURROUGHS
401 LINN ST.
TRAER, IA. 50675

FLOYD H. BURROUGHS
137 HACKETT RD. S.
WATERLOO, IA. 50701

K. I. BURROUGHS
3115 KENNEDY LN. R4
WATERLOO, IA. 50701

HAROLD W. BURROUGHS
660 LUNAR LN.
WATERLOO, IA. 50701

RICHARD A. BURROUGHS
9030 DOUGLAS RD. R5
WATERLOO, IA. 50701

ALLEN H. BURROUGHS
201 MULBERRY ST.
WATERLOO, IA. 50703

LANCE J. BURROUGHS
125 WEMA AV.
WATERLOO, IA. 50707

GLEN R. BURROUGHS
610 POLLOCK BL R1
BEDFORD, IA. 50833

MARION BURROUGHS
R1
CORNING, IA. 50841

JANE L. BURROUGHS
R1
DANBURY, IA. 51019

J. BURROUGHS
R2
MAPLETON, IA. 51034

TONY J. BURROUGHS
R1
UTE, IA. 51060

FRANCIS L. BURROUGHS
UTE, IA. 51060

RAYMOND A. BURROUGHS
R1
UTE, IA. 51060

JOEL L. BURROUGHS
R3
DENISON, IA. 51442

STEVEN R. BURROUGHS
178 GRAHAM AV. W. AV. LO
COUNCIL BLFS, IA. 51501

HARRY E. BURROUGHS
17 AZTEC ST.
COUNCIL BLFS, IA. 51501

RALPH F. BURROUGHS
604 SOUTH OM BRG RD. W.
COUNCIL BLFS, IA. 51501

KAREN J. BURROUGHS
108 NAVAJO ST.
COUNCIL BLFS, IA. 51501

RICHARD O. BURROUGHS
2128 J. AV.
COUNCIL BLFS, IA. 515010

BENJAMIN R. BURROUGHS
R2
ESSEX, IA. 51638

RUSSELL D. BURROUGHS
R2
ESSEX, IA. 51638

CHARLES S. BURROUGHS
FARRAGUT, IA. 51639

JEROME P. BURROUGHS
169 1/2 MAIN ST.
DUBUQUE, IA. 52001

K. BURROUGHS
FARMERSBURG, IA. 52047

NANCY J. BURROUGHS
BX. 862
MAQUOKETA, IA. 52060

GARLAND J. BURROUGHS
R1
LANSING, IA. 52151

RAYMOND J. BURROUGHS
LANSING, IA. 52151

MICHAEL C. BURROUGHS
NEW ALBIN, IA. 52160

GARLAND G. BURROUGHS
R3
WAUKON, IA. 52172

ALFRED A. BURROUGHS
R1
WAUKON, IA. 52172

ROLAND E. BURROUGHS
102 5TH AV. R3 S.W.
WAUKON, IA. 52172

ERNEST A. BURROUGHS
507 ROSSVILLE RD.
WAUKON, IA. 52172

DAVID P. BURROUGHS
634 JOHNSON ST. S. APT.
IOWA CITY, IA. 52240

SAM BURROUGHS
630 JOHNSON ST. S. APT.
IOWA CITY, IA. 52240

ELIZABETH B. BURROUGHS
171 4TH ST. NORTH
SPRINGVILLE, IA. 52336

RONALD G. BURROUGHS
BX. 73
STANWOOD, IA. 52337

RONALD M. BURROUGHS
1115 E. AV.
VINTON, IA. 52349

MYRON BURROUGHS
LINN HLW TRL R2
WASHINGTON, IA. 52353

RICHARD L. BURROUGHS
201 3RD ST. E.
WASHINGTON, IA. 52353

VINCENT L. BURROUGHS
13TH ST.
WELLMAN, IA. 52356

JERRY L. BURROUGHS
907 REGENT ST. N.E.
CEDAR RAPIDS, IA. 52402

RICHARD J. BURROUGHS
1745 BEVER AV. S.E.
CEDAR RAPIDS, IA. 52403

EARL T. BURROUGHS
629 4TH ST. S.
BURLINGTON, IA. 52601

JOHN T. BURROUGHS
R3 BX. 201
BURLINGTON, IA. 52601

THOMAS L. BURROUGHS
IRISH RIDGE R3
BURLINGTON, IA. 52601

CLIFFORD P. BURROUGHS
108 BELLINGHAM ST. S.
BETTENDORF, IA. 52722

MARTY BURROUGHS
3795 CREEK HILL DR. APT.
BETTENDORF, IA. 52722

RICHARD L. BURROUGHS
BX. 633
BETTENDORF, IA. 52722

WILLIAM L. BURROUGHS
R2 BX. 154
COLUMBUS JCT, IA. 52738

M. BURROUGHS
1807 HOUSER ST.
MUSCATINE, IA. 52761

JULIA A. BURROUGHS
1819 SCHILLER ST.
MUSCATINE, IA. 52761

CHARLES W. BURROUGHS
R5
MUSCATINE, IA. 52761

JAMES E. BURROUGHS
527 WOODLAWN ST.
MUSCATINE, IA. 52761

CHARLES W. BURROUGHS
300 1/2 2ND ST. E.
MUSCATINE, IA. 52761

CHARLES BURROUGHS
R6
MUSCATINE, IA. 52761

DANIEL BURROUGHS
314 LOST GROVE RD.
PRINCETON, IA. 52768

RAYMOND E. BURROUGHS
220 LOST GROVE RD.
PRINCETON, IA. 52768

CLIFFORD E. BURROUGHS
R1
PRINCETON, IA. 52768

RONALD G. BURROUGHS
1015 CEDAR
TIPTON, IA. 52772

PEARLEY M. BURROUGHS
4141 ROCKINGHAM RD.
DAVENPORT, IA. 52802

ELIZA O. BURROUGHS
321 HAZELWOOD AV. S.
DAVENPORT, IA. 52802

PAUL J. BURROUGHS
1118 BRIDGE AV.
DAVENPORT, IA. 52803

JOHN BURROUGHS
1009 PERSHING AV. N.
DAVENPORT, IA. 52803

R. J. BURROUGHS
3510 PINE ST. N.
DAVENPORT, IA. 52806

REINOLD W. BURROUGHS
3518 PINE ST. N.
DAVENPORT, IA. 52806

RONNIE R. BURROUGHS
729 NORMANDY CIR.
HARTLAND, WI. 53029

CHARLES E. BURROUGHS
10937 HEDGEWOOD LN.
THIENSVILLE, WI. 53092

CHARLES H. BURROUGHS
1233 BALDWIN CT.
THIENSVILLE, WI. 53092

ROSETTA BURROUGHS
6119 13TH AV.
KENOSHA, WI. 53140

QUEENIE A. BURROUGHS
2561 8TH ST. N. APT. A.
MILWAUKEE, WI. 53206

HIAWATHA BURROUGHS
2870 24TH ST. N.
MILWAUKEE, WI. 53206

C. C. BURROUGHS
2502 23RD ST. N.
MILWAUKEE, WI. 53206

HUBERT BURROUGHS
3210 WELLS ST. W. APT. 3
MILWAUKEE, WI. 53208

BOBBY BURROUGHS
4533 36TH ST. N. APT. 10
MILWAUKEE, WI. 53209

HILDA L. BURROUGHS
2718 MEINECKE AV. W.
MILWAUKEE, WI. 53210

BENNY BURROUGHS
629 GARFIELD AV. W.
MILWAUKEE, WI. 53212

JULIUS BURROUGHS
3609 2ND ST. N.
MILWAUKEE, WI. 53212

MARIE BURROUGHS
3361 RUSKIN ST. W.
MILWAUKEE, WI. 53215

JAMES W. BURROUGHS
3108 29TH ST. N.
MILWAUKEE, WI. 53216

WILLIE R. BURROUGHS
4318 38TH ST. N.
MILWAUKEE, WI. 53216

GUY A. BURROUGHS
2327 81ST ST. S.
MILWAUKEE, WI. 53219

ANN M. BURROUGHS
185 90TH ST. N.
MILWAUKEE, WI. 53226

RONALD D. BURROUGHS
1503 JACKSON ST.
BELOIT, WI. 53511

CHARLES J. BURROUGHS
2813 ALEXANDRIA PL.
JANESVILLE, WI. 53545

MICHAEL D. BURROUGHS
1211 KING ST.
JANESVILLE, WI. 53545

DIANE K. BURROUGHS
538 MAIN ST. W.
MADISON, WI. 53703

KEN BURROUGHS
501 HENRY ST. N. APT. 60
MADISON, WI. 53703

D. H. BURROUGHS
3803 MONONA DR. APT. 111
MADISON, WI. 53714

MARY A. BURROUGHS
324 MILLS ST. S.
MADISON, WI. 53715

DELMER W. BURROUGHS
660 12TH ST.
BARABOO, WI. 53913

SUSAN M. BURROUGHS
BX. 121
NORTH FREEDOM, WI. 53951

ROGER R. BURROUGHS
251 CEDAR ST.
OCONTO FALLS, WI. 54154

RICHARD H. BURROUGHS
153 BROOKRIDGE ST.
GREEN BAY, WI. 54301

RODNEY L. BURROUGHS
R2 BX. 472
MOSINEE, WI. 54455

EDWARD BURROUGHS
R5 BX. 247
MOSINEE, WI. 54455

CEDRIC BURROUGHS
3270 HWY X. R2 N.
STEVENS POINT, WI. 54481

GARY A. BURROUGHS
1430 TOURN RD. R4 N.
STEVENS POINT, WI. 54481

RALPH G. BURROUGHS
R4
TOMAHAWK, WI. 54487

WILLIAM J. BURROUGHS
3011 25TH ST. S.
LA CROSSE, WI. 54601

JACK C. BURROUGHS
112 CRESTVIEW DR.
APPLETON, WI. 54911

MICHAEL R. BURROUGHS
222 AUBURN ST.
FOND DU LAC, WI. 54935

BRIAN D. BURROUGHS
300 MARQUETTE ST.
FOND DU LAC, WI. 54935

CARRIE R. BURROUGHS
284 LINDEN ST.
FOND DU LAC, WI. 54935

JUDITH A. BURROUGHS
2509 BROWN RD. R7
FOND DU LAC, WI. 54935

HOWARD E. BURROUGHS
1148 MANITOWOC RD.
MENASHA, WI. 54952

KENNETH BURROUGHS
1106 WOODLAND DR.
MENASHA, WI. 54952

DONALD BURROUGHS
808 HENRY ST.
NEENAH, WI. 54956

WILLIAM BURROUGHS
550 HALL ST.
RIPON, WI. 54971

OTTO T. BURROUGHS
1013 CENTRAL AV. W.
SAINT PAUL, MN. 55104

JOHN R. BURROUGHS
1606 HEWITT AV.
SAINT PAUL, MN. 55104

ARTHUR C. BURROUGHS
1193 6TH ST. E.
SAINT PAUL, MN. 55106

ROBERT R. BURROUGHS
2910 TORCHWOOD DR.
SAINT PAUL, MN. 55112

DONALD E. BURROUGHS
787 CLARK AV.
GIBBON, MN. 55335

I. M. BURROUGHS
787 CLRK AV.
GIBBON, MN. 55335

JAMES A. BURROUGHS
505 4TH AV. S.
PRINCETON, MN. 55371

STEVEN F. BURROUGHS
210 6TH AV. N.
PRINCETON, MN. 55371

DENNIS M. BURROUGHS
609 HAMILTON ST. APT. 30
SAVAGE, MN. 55378

CHARLES J. BURROUGHS
17210 11TH AV. N.
WAYZATA, MN. 55391

ELIZABETH A. BURROUGHS
2404 GARFIELD AV. S.
MINNEAPOLIS, MN. 55405

ANTHONY L. BURROUGHS
1400 27TH ST. E.
MINNEAPOLIS, MN. 55407

ESTHER F. BURROUGHS
701 8TH ST. S.E.
MINNEAPOLIS, MN. 55414

CATE A. BURROUGHS
6400 NICOLLET AV.
MINNEAPOLIS, MN. 55423

JENNE A. BURROUGHS
2727 RHODE ISLAND AV. S.
MINNEAPOLIS, MN. 55426

ALBERT C. BURROUGHS
R1 BX. 126
ASKOV, MN. 55704

YVONNE F. BURROUGHS
620 GRANT AV.
EVELETH, MN. 55734

HAROLD R. BURROUGHS
1207 3RD AV. N.H.
AUSTIN, MN. 55912

WILLIAM O. BURROUGHS
R5 BX. 45
AUSTIN, MN. 55912

DONALD J. BURROUGHS
R1
CALEDONIA, MN. 55921

ROBERT J. BURROUGHS
R2
CALEDONIA, MN. 55921

JESSE J. BURROUGHS
R3
CALEDONIA, MN. 55921

MILTON J. BURROUGHS
R2
CALEDONIA, MN. 55921

MILTON J. BURROUGHS
R3
CALEDONIA, MN. 55921

EVELYN S. BURROUGHS
R3 BX. 30
HOUSTON, MN. 55943

JEFFERY S. BURROUGHS
719 4TH ST. E.
REDWOOD FALLS, MN. 56283

STEVEN BURROUGHS
709 LAUREL APT. 1
BRAINERD, MN. 56401

MARY BURROUGHS
907 7TH ST.
BROOKINGS, S.D. 57006

EMMET BURROUGHS
BRIDGEWATER, S.D. 57319

MARVIN G. BURROUGHS
1001 PENNSYLVANIA ST. S.
ABERDEEN, S.D. 57401

RICHD M. BURROUGHS
1613 9TH AV. S.W. R5
ABERDEEN, S.D. 57401

RICHARD BURROUGHS
23 18TH AV. S.W.
ABERDEEN, S.D. 57401

CLARENCE BURROUGHS
130 MC ARTHUR ST.
RAPID CITY, S.D. 57701

LLOYD E. BURROUGHS
1327 STATE ST.
RAPID CITY, S.D. 57701

MICHAEL N. BURROUGHS
BX. 2582
GRAND FORKS, N.D. 58201

LEON W. BURROUGHS
FULLERTON, N.D. 58441

JOE BURROUGHS
R1 BX. 163
HARDIN, MT. 59034

DAN M. BURROUGHS
1018 30TH ST. N.
BILLINGS, MT. 59101

BENJAMIN J. BURROUGHS
BX. 483
COLSTRIP, MT. 59323

E. E. BURROUGHS
BX. 193
HINGHAM, MT. 59528

DAVID L. BURROUGHS
R4 BOX 49
BOZEMAN, MT. 59715

EDWARD R. BURROUGHS
2618 SPRINGCREEK DR.
BOZEMAN, MT. 59715

WALTER BURROUGHS
R1
ARLEE, MT. 59821

WILLIAM E. BURROUGHS
BX. 82
PLAINS, MT. 59859

MICHAEL N. BURROUGHS
R1 BX. 218B
ANTIOCH, IL. 60002

HARRY B. BURROUGHS
533 NORTH AV.
BARRINGTON, IL. 60010

JOHN D. BURROUGHS
824 SKYLINE DR.
BARRINGTON, IL. 60010

JOHN N. BURROUGHS
40 LLOYD ST.
CARY, IL. 60013

GERARD T. BURROUGHS
6915 MEADOW DR. R4
CRYSTAL LAKE, IL. 60014

ANTONIA M. BURROUGHS
1014 WASHINGTON AV. W.
LAKE BLUFF, IL. 60044

JAMES C. BURROUGHS
46 THOMAS PL.
LAKE FOREST, IL. 60045

STEVE BURROUGHS
221 GLENWOOD RD.
LAKE FOREST, IL. 60045

MARK A. BURROUGHS
215 MEADOWBROOK LN.
LAKE ZURICH, IL. 60047

JAMES E. BURROUGHS
707 PROSPECT MANOR
MT PROSPECT, IL. 60056

DIANE BURROUGHS
695 GROVE DR.
WHEELING, IL. 60090

ROBERT T. BURROUGHS
2808 ELIM AV.
ZION, IL. 60099

JAMES A. BURROUGHS
5890 BRADLEY CT.
BARTLETT, IL. 60103

ROY E. BURROUGHS
413 OLTENDORF RD. S.
BARTLETT, IL. 60103

ROBERT E. BURROUGHS
1155 GRACE ST. S.
LOMBARD, IL. 60148

RAYMOND R. BURROUGHS
4908 BUTTERFIELD RD.
MELROSE PARK, IL. 60162

WYMOND BURROUGHS
10107 PALMER AV.
MELROSE PARK, IL. 60164

PATSY BURROUGHS
R2 BX. 359
ROSELLE, IL. 60172

JAMES E. BURROUGHS
1489 CORNELL CT.
ROSELLE, IL. 60194

T. BURROUGHS
2099 DANBURY PL.
ROSELLE, IL. 60195

ALBERT D. BURROUGHS
2111 EMERSON ST.
EVANSTON, IL. 60201

WILLIAM BURROUGHS
2039 221ST ST.
CHICAGO HTS, IL. 60411

ROBERT O. BURROUGHS
819 VIOLETTA AV.
JOLIET, IL. 60432

ROBERT BURROUGHS
206 LOUIS RD.
JOLIET, IL. 60433

GAIL L. BURROUGHS
114 9TH ST. E. APT. 3
LOCKPORT, IL. 60441

TIMOTHY F. BURROUGHS
R6 BX. 373
LOCKPORT, IL. 60441

CLAUDIE F. BURROUGHS
410 LAUREL AV.
LOCKPORT, IL. 60441

WALLACE M. BURROUGHS
5850 SHABBONA RD. R5
MORRIS, IL. 60450

JAMES R. BURROUGHS
TABLER RD. R2
MORRIS, IL. 60450

CRAIG E. BURROUGHS
115 FRANCIS RD. E.
NEW LENOX, IL. 60451

ROBERT F. BURROUGHS
135 CENTRAL RD.
NEW LENOX, IL. 60451

SOL E. BURROUGHS
9141 FOREST DR.
OAK LAWN, IL. 60458

RUSS BURROUGHS
1500 SHEFFER RD. R2
AURORA, IL. 60504

MILBURN BURROUGHS
1500 SHEFFER RD.
AURORA, IL. 60505

SWINTON M. BURROUGHS, JR.
1960 LILAC LN. APT. B.
AURORA, IL. 60506

KENT D. BURROUGHS
239 WEST PARK AV.
AURORA, IL. 60506

JOSEPH M. BURROUGHS
5515 TENNESSEE AV.
CLARENDON HLS, IL. 60514

GEORGE H. BURROUGHS
219 CHARLES ST. W.
PLANO, IL. 60545

LEONA I. BURROUGHS
607 PRAIRIE ST. R3 E.
PLANO, IL. 60545

KENNETH L. BURROUGHS
17W514 CONCORD PL.
WESTMONT, IL. 60559

CRANSTON BURROUGHS
2723 JACKSON BL W.
CHICAGO, IL. 60612

FREEMAN BURROUGHS
8658 PHILLIPS AV. S.
CHICAGO, IL. 60617

JEANNE E. BURROUGHS
8831 PRAIRIE AV. S.
CHICAGO, IL. 60619

JOHN BURROUGHS
8952 EMERALD AV. S.
CHICAGO, IL. 60620

CLARENCE E. BURROUGHS
3725 FLOURNOY ST. W.
CHICAGO, IL. 60624

ASA M. BURROUGHS
10522 MARYLAND AV. S.
CHICAGO, IL. 60628

MICHAEL P. BURROUGHS
10215 LAFAYETTE AV. S.
CHICAGO, IL. 60628

MORRIS BURROUGHS
505 60TH ST. E.
CHICAGO, IL. 60637

MINNIE BURROUGHS
6350 KING DR.
CHICAGO, IL. 60637

JESSE E. BURROUGHS
5350 WOLCOTT AV. N.
CHICAGO, IL. 60640

ALVIN D. BURROUGHS
10118 CARPENTER ST. S.
CHICAGO, IL. 60643

TOMMIE L. BURROUGHS
337 LAVERGNE AV. S.
CHICAGO, IL. 60644

HENRY A. BURROUGHS
12415 BENCK DR. S. APT.
CHICAGO, IL. 60658

DEAN P. BURROUGHS
R3 BX. 115A
KANKAKEE, IL. 60901

CLIFFORD BURROUGHS
1151 NETTIE ST. APT. 601
BELVIDERE, IL. 61008

CHARLES BURROUGHS
417 WEBSTER ST.
BELVIDERE, IL. 61008

RICHARD BURROUGHS
R1
EAST DUBUQUE, IL. 61025

WILLIAM D. BURROUGHS
R1
EAST DUBUQUE, IL. 61025

KARL H. BURROUGHS
489 GREENWOOD ST.
EAST DUBUQUE, IL. 61025

TIMOTHY F. BURROUGHS
1105 2ND ST. W.
ROCK FALLS, IL. 61071

EUGENE F. BURROUGHS
142 FLINTRIDGE DR. APT.
ROCKFORD, IL. 61107

GEORGE W. BURROUGHS
4797 EASTLAWN DR.
ROCKFORD, IL. 61108

RONALD W. BURROUGHS
12126 92ND AV.
COAL VALLEY, IL. 61240

JOHN BURROUGHS
319 OLIVE ST. N.
TOLUCA, IL. 61369

JOHN H. BURROUGHS
TOLUCA, IL. 61369

RAPHAEL F. BURROUGHS
BX. 487
WENONA, IL. 61377

SHEILA BURROUGHS
770 HURST ST. W. APT. 72
BUSHNELL, IL. 61422

PHYLLIS E. BURROUGHS
BENSON, IL. 61516

BARRY G. BURROUGHS
R1
BENSON, IL. 61516

CHARLES Q. BURROUGHS
R4
CANTON, IL. 61520

DALE P. BURROUGHS
R1
MAPLETON, IL. 61547

CALVIN G. BURROUGHS
R1
MORTON, IL. 61550

JOHN C. BURROUGHS
R1
MORTON, IL. 61550

EDWARD H. BURROUGHS
2002 MARKET ST.
PEKIN, IL. 61554

EUNICE BURROUGHS
1514 HIGHWOOD AV.
PEKIN, IL. 61554

ROGER D. BURROUGHS
105 CLARK CT.
PEKIN, IL. 61554

DONALD BURROUGHS
1867 WASHINGTN RD. R1
WASHINGTON, IL. 61571

RALPH E. BURROUGHS
2237 LINNHILL LN. R3 E.
WASHINGTON, IL. 61571

JAMES BURROUGHS
205 VINE ST.
WASHINGTON, IL. 61571

PHILLIP G. BURROUGHS
1013 NORWOOD BL E.
PEORIA, IL. 61603

CLARENCE E. BURROUGHS
3429 GALE AV. N.
PEORIA, IL. 61604

STEPHEN M. BURROUGHS
1024 ELMWOOD AV. N.
PEORIA, IL. 61606

JOHN B. BURROUGHS
204 TIMBER LN. R6
PEORIA, IL. 61611

RICHARD F. BURROUGHS
500 ARNOLD RD.
PEORIA, IL. 61611

GRANT L. BURROUGHS
109 PATRICIA AV.
PEORIA, IL. 61611

EARL H. BURROUGHS
417 GLENDALE ST.
PEORIA, IL. 61611

STEVEN E. BURROUGHS
436 MAPLEWOOD ST.
PEORIA, IL. 61611

MABEL V. BURROUGHS
SPRING BY RD. R1
PEORIA, IL. 61611

ROBERT BURROUGHS
237 ATLANTIC AV.
PEORIA, IL. 61614

STEPHEN BURROUGHS
8500 DUNDEE RD. N.
PEORIA, IL. 61614

STEPHEN M. BURROUGHS
8500 DUNDEE RD. N.
PEORIA, IL. 61615

ROXANNA BURROUGHS
1830 OLIVE ST. N.
BLOOMINGTON, IL. 61701

WAYNE A. BURROUGHS
603 OAKLAND AV. W.
BLOOMINGTON, IL. 61701

WAYNE H. BURROUGHS
267 MAIN ST. W.
EL PASO, IL. 61738

WILLIAM E. BURROUGHS
99 ADAMS ST. N.
EL PASO, IL. 61738

KAY BURROUGHS
R2
EL PASO, IL. 61738

NORA L. BURROUGHS
377 MAIN ST. H.
EL PASO, IL. 61738

PERRY V. BURROUGHS
551 5TH ST. S.
FAIRBURY, IL. 61739

ARTHUR W. BURROUGHS
104 1ST
MACKINAW, IL. 61755

KENNETH E. BURROUGHS
203 AMBROSE WY.
NORMAL, IL. 61761

DAVID G. BURROUGHS
300 FELMLEY DR. R10
NORMAL, IL. 61761

DENNIS P. BURROUGHS
961 MAIN ST. N.
PONTIAC, IL. 61764

SUSAN L. BURROUGHS
2 APPLETREE ST. R1
URBANA, IL. 61801

HOLLY K. BURROUGHS
RFD
ALLERTON, IL. 61810

JAY W. BURROUGHS
608 DELLWOOD ST.
DANVILLE, IL. 61832

LUCY J. BURROUGHS
212 LINDENWOOD DR.
DANVILLE, IL. 61832

MILDRED BURROUGHS
107 HITHNER ST.
DANVILLE, IL. 61832

FRANK BURROUGHS
1808 VERMILION ST. N.
DANVILLE, IL. 61832

WILLIAM L. BURROUGHS
474 MACON DR.
MAHOMET, IL. 61853

STEPHEN W. BURROUGHS
BX. 417
POTOMAC, IL. 61865

STEPHEN W. BURROUGHS
R1
POTOMAC, IL. 61865

PAUL E. BURROUGHS
POTOMAC, IL. 61865

MARK A. BURROUGHS
BX. 675
RANTOUL, IL. 61866

JAMES L. BURROUGHS
R3
CHRISMAN, IL. 61924

CONNIE L. BURROUGHS
1409 SHELBY AV.
MATTOON, IL. 61938

WILLIAM A. BURROUGHS
2300 WESTERN AV.
MATTOON, IL. 61938

ROBERT E. BURROUGHS
141 CARDOT ST.
EAST ALTON, IL. 62024

A. F. BURROUGHS
R8 BX. 196
EDWARDSVILLE, IL. 62025

G. G. BURROUGHS
500 ST. LOUIS ST.
EDWARDSVILLE, IL. 62025

G. G. BURROUGHS
743 ST. LOUIS ST.
EDWARDSVILLE, IL. 62025

CORTLEY H. BURROUGHS
3300 MORKEL
GODFREY, IL. 62035

BILL BURROUGHS
R1 BX. 1314
GRANITE CITY, IL. 62040

RALPH BURROUGHS
3340 VILLAGE LN.
GRANITE CITY, IL. 62040

CHARLES E. BURROUGHS
526 CHESTNUT ST.
GREENFIELD, IL. 62044

WILLIAM D. BURROUGHS
R2 BX. 108
SORENTO, IL. 62086

MATTHEW C. BURROUGHS
200 EDWARDS ST.
STAUNTON, IL. 62088

PAULA J. BURROUGHS
698 6TH ST. N.
WOOD RIVER, IL. 62095

DARRELL BURROUGHS
1123 DAWN DR.
BELLEVILLE, IL. 62221

WILLIE E. BURROUGHS
200 ST. JOHN DR.
BELLEVILLE, IL. 62221

CARROLL BURROUGHS
22 HIGHVIEW CT. R4
BELLEVILLE, IL. 62221

LARRY D. BURROUGHS
128 BROOKSIDE DR.
CASEYVILLE, IL. 62232

MURIEL S. BURROUGHS
731 MAPLE ST.
COLLINSVILLE, IL. 62234

DON C. BURROUGHS
320 LOUISE DR.
COLLINSVILLE, IL. 62234

ROY E. BURROUGHS
211 BEVERLY LN.
COLLINSVILLE, IL. 62234

LEAH BURROUGHS
206 ST. LOUIS RD. APT. 3
COLLINSVILLE, IL. 62234

A. H. BURROUGHS
1331 ST. CLAIR AV.
COLLINSVILLE, IL. 62234

RAYMOND H. BURROUGHS
424 VANDALIA ST.
COLLINSVILLE, IL. 62234

RICHARD C. BURROUGHS
10 WILSON DR. R1
COLUMBIA, IL. 62236

ELISABETH H. BURROUGHS
1412 BROADWAY ST.
HIGHLAND, IL. 62249

DONALD E. BURROUGHS
513 W. ST. LOUIS
LEBANON, IL. 62254

DONALD E. BURROUGHS
513 ST. LOUIS ST. W.
LEBANON, IL. 62254

JOE D. BURROUGHS
R1 BX. 217
O. FALLON, IL. 62269

DANIEL R. BURROUGHS
1 EDWARDS ST. S.
ALTAMONT, IL. 62411

CHARLES F. BURROUGHS
BX. 121
HUTSONVILLE, IL. 62433

RONNIE BURROUGHS
R1
HAVANA, IL. 62644

STACY R. BURROUGHS
7 BOULDER PT DR.
SPRINGFIELD, IL. 62702

GERALD A. BURROUGHS
502 NEWTON S.
BUCKNER, IL. 62819

ARTHUR BURROUGHS
917 FACKNEY
CARMI, IL. 62821

GERTRUDE M. BURROUGHS
209 HERBERT AV.
CARMI, IL. 62821

BUENITA BURROUGHS
PARK LN. DR. R1
CARMI, IL. 62821

LARRY E. BURROUGHS
705 CHURCH ST. S.
CHRISTOPHER, IL. 62822

LESLIE R. BURROUGHS
R1
CISNE, IL. 62823

DANIEL BURROUGHS
COELLO, IL. 62825

DONALD C. BURROUGHS
R2
DU QUOIN, IL. 62832

WALTER W. BURROUGHS
613 WASHINGTON ST. N.
DU QUOIN, IL. 62832

LESLIE E. BURROUGHS
217 10TH ST. E.
FLORA, IL. 62839

MARLIN BURROUGHS
803 MAIN ST. N.
FLORA, IL. 62839

MARCIA K. BURROUGHS
232 7TH ST. E.
FLORA, IL. 62839

LOYAL D. BURROUGHS
R2
IUKA, IL. 62849

JIM BURROUGHS
R1
IUKA, IL. 62849

JERRY G. BURROUGHS
R2
IUKA, IL. 62849

MERVIN R. BURROUGHS
112 GREENVIEW DR. R3
MOUNT CARMEL, IL. 62863

M. BURROUGHS
R1
MOUNT CARMEL, IL. 62863

BILLY L. BURROUGHS
R1
ODIN, IL. 62870

TED BURROUGHS
530 MARION ST. S.
SALEM, IL. 62881

BOBBY L. BURROUGHS
R1
SALEM, IL. 62881

BOBBY L. BURROUGHS
R37S
SALEM, IL. 62881

ADRIAN L. BURROUGHS
BX. 215
XENIA, IL. 62899

JOHN BURROUGHS
R3
CARBONDALE, IL. 62901

PAUL L. BURROUGHS
R3
CARBONDALE, IL. 62901

GLEN A. BURROUGHS
608 BASINGER ST.
ELDORADO, IL. 62930

HARMON L. BURROUGHS
R1
ELKVILLE, IL. 62932

CHARLES D. BURROUGHS
R1
ELKVILLE, IL. 62932

JAMES R. BURROUGHS
303 SHERMAN S.
HARRISBURG, IL. 62946

ROGER A. BURROUGHS
1018 LILLY ST.
HARRISBURG, IL. 62946

RALPH W. BURROUGHS
910 WEBSTER ST. S.
HARRISBURG, IL. 62946

ROBERT B. BURROUGHS
1205 HENDRICKSON W.
MARION, IL. 62959

RAYMOND C. BURROUGHS
2215 DEWEY
MURPHYSBORO, IL. 62966

JANIS L. BURROUGHS
BX. 925
MURPHYSBORO, IL. 62966

EDGAR H. BURROUGHS
2305 STARLING AIRPRT
ARNOLD, MO. 63010

ILMER E. BURROUGHS
10 BRANSON ST. R2
ARNOLD, MO. 63010

JIM BURROUGHS
5 BELLA VISTA R6
ARNOLD, MO. 63010

THOMAS BURROUGHS
SUNRISE LAKE R3
DE SOTO, MO. 63020

EUGENE J. BURROUGHS
102 SHORT DR.
FENTON, MO. 63026

DANIEL BURROUGHS
1415 ASPEN DR.
FLORISSANT, MO. 63031

CHERYL BURROUGHS
2200 JENKEE AV.
FLORISSANT, MO. 63031

EUGENE H. BURROUGHS, JR.
2050 SHIRLEY DR.
FLORISSANT, MO. 63031

CLIFFORD BURROUGHS
1 LAS HEMBRA CT.
FLORISSANT, MO. 63033

GEORGE C. BURROUGHS
1530 BURNING TREE DR.
FLORISSANT, MO. 63033

LARRY D. BURROUGHS
3314 CROSS KEYS DR. APT.
FLORISSANT, MO. 63033

EDWARD J. BURROUGHS
2957 WESTMINSTER DR.
FLORISSANT, MO. 63033

VERA BURROUGHS
1045 WOODEN DR.
FLORISSANT, MO. 63033

CHARLES F. BURROUGHS
10166 CAMSHIRE CT. APT.
SAINT ANN, MO. 63074

ELDOR BURROUGHS
3554 DE HART PL. APT. 6
SAINT ANN, MO. 63074

JOHN L. BURROUGHS
7 GREEN GARDEN DR.
SAINT ANN, MO. 63074

I. B. BURROUGHS
47 TOPTON WY. APT. 1S
SAINT LOUIS, MO. 63105

ARTHUR L. BURROUGHS
18 KINGS HWY BL S. APT.
SAINT LOUIS, MO. 63108

C. M. BURROUGHS
4066 LINDELL BL APT. 710
SAINT LOUIS, MO. 63108

EARLINE BURROUGHS
5868 WABADA AV.
SAINT LOUIS, MO. 63112

LAWRENCE A. BURROUGHS
4533 GARFIELD AV.
SAINT LOUIS, MO. 63113

R. L. BURROUGHS
5050 RIDGE AV.
SAINT LOUIS, MO. 63113

VERNON S. BURROUGHS
3401 MARCUS AV.
SAINT LOUIS, MO. 63115

FRANK E. BURROUGHS
4932 PALM ST.
SAINT LOUIS, MO. 63115

ALFRED BURROUGHS
7905 HICKS AV.
SAINT LOUIS, MO. 63117

THOMAS N. BURROUGHS
6321 STRATFORD AV.
SAINT LOUIS, MO. 63120

ANTHONY BURROUGHS
6211 WESTERHOFF AV.
SAINT LOUIS, MO. 63121

RICHARD BURROUGHS
5607 HOLBORN DR.
SAINT LOUIS, MO. 63121

HAROLD E. BURROUGHS
4652 MEHL AV.
SAINT LOUIS, MO. 63129

WILLIAM H. BURROUGHS
7327 PERSHING AV.
SAINT LOUIS, MO. 63130

MORTIMER P. BURROUGHS, JR.
6617 PERSHING AV.
SAINT LOUIS, MO. 63130

KENNETH E. BURROUGHS
7823 GREENSFELDER LN.
SAINT LOUIS, MO. 63130

IDA BURROUGHS
322 ATWATER AV.
SAINT LOUIS, MO. 63135

DANIEL R. BURROUGHS
10129 WINKLER DR.
SAINT LOUIS, MO. 63136

JAMES E. BURROUGHS
408 LANARK RD.
SAINT LOUIS, MO. 63137

BEN M. BURROUGHS
1755 JUNE DR.
SAINT LOUIS, MO. 63138

THOMAS BURROUGHS
2168 ESTHER AV.
SAINT LOUIS, MO. 63139

C. BURROUGHS
6502 MARMADUKE AV.
SAINT LOUIS, MO. 63139

KIM BURROUGHS
2425 BELLEVUE AV.
SAINT LOUIS, MO. 63143

JEROME BURROUGHS
436 HUNTERS RIDGE
SAINT CHARLES, MO. 63301

ROBERT H. BURROUGHS
28 ROLLING MDWS R1
O. FALLON, MO. 63366

BOB BURROUGHS
183 ELDORADO
SAINT PETERS, MO. 63376

EDWIN J. BURROUGHS
5 DEBORAH DR.
SAINT PETERS, MO. 63376

WILLIAM BURROUGHS
R.R. 1
WINFIELD, MO. 63389

MAXINE BURROUGHS
417 ROCK ST.
HANNIBAL, MO. 63401

BILL J. BURROUGHS
1505 RUBY ST.
HANNIBAL, MO. 63401

GEORGE R. BURROUGHS
1408 WALNUT ST.
HANNIBAL, MO. 63401

ESTEL E. BURROUGHS
1113 VALLEY ST.
HANNIBAL, MO. 63401

DONALD L. BURROUGHS
3410 ELY RD. W.
HANNIBAL, MO. 63401

GEORGE BURROUGHS
3201 MOBERLY AV. R. 1
HANNIBAL, MO. 63401

CLAUDIE BURROUGHS
FRANKFORD, MO. 63441

RUFUS BURROUGHS
3995 LAKESHORE E.
BISMARCK, MO. 63624

PAUL BURROUGHS
CENTERVILLE, MO. 63633

PAUL BURROUGHS
LESTERVILLE, MO. 63654

DALE BURROUGHS
R.R. 1
FROHNA, MO. 63748

MARVIN BURROUGHS
FROHNA, MO. 63748

LESLIE BURROUGHS
FROHNA, MO. 63748

JERRY BURROUGHS
315 KATE ST.
JACKSON, MO. 63755

HAROLD W. BURROUGHS
314 MOULTON ST. S.
PERRYVILLE, MO. 63775

JERRY BURROUGHS
R.R. 4
PERRYVILLE, MO. 63775

ALBERT BURROUGHS
R.R. 2
PERRYVILLE, MO. 63775

GEORGE BURROUGHS
118 LASHMET ST.
SIKESTON, MO. 63801

H. N. BURROUGHS
604 MARION ST. N.
MALDEN, MO. 63863

LESLIE BURROUGHS
711 CEDAR ST.
BELTON, MO. 64012

JAMES BURROUGHS
801 CEDAR ST.
BELTON, MO. 64012

CHARLES K. BURROUGHS
14004 44TH ST. E. APT. B
INDEPENDENCE, MO. 64055

LARRY W. BURROUGHS
2500 WHITNEY RD. S.
INDEPENDENCE, MO. 64057

MYRA BURROUGHS
R.R. 1
PLEASANT HILL, MO. 64080

FREEMAN BURROUGHS
R.R. 4
PLEASANT HILL, MO. 64080

FRED W. BURROUGHS
100 SECOND ST.
SMITHVILLE, MO. 64089

JEWELL BURROUGHS
2737 GARFIELD AV.
KANSAS CITY, MO. 64109

LARRY BURROUGHS
3724 35TH ST. N.E.
KANSAS CITY, MO. 64117

GARY R. BURROUGHS
2000 68TH TER. N.E.
KANSAS CITY, MO. 64118

NATHAN D. BURROUGHS
4005 59TH TER. N.E.
KANSAS CITY, MO. 64119

GLENNIE M. BURROUGHS
3428 INDEPENDENCE AV. AP
KANSAS CITY, MO. 64124

WILLIE BURROUGHS
5413 BELLEFONTAINE
KANSAS CITY, MO. 64130

FAYE BURROUGHS
DARLINGTON, MO. 64438

WILLIAM BURROUGHS
1621 WASHINGTON ST. N.
NEVADA, MO. 64772

JOE F. BURROUGHS
R.D. 2
ASHLAND, MO. 65010

LYLE M. BURROUGHS
RT. P.
GRAVOIS MILLS, MO. 65037

JUDITH BURROUGHS
1301 BUSINSS LOOP 63 S.
COLUMBIA, MO. 65201

JAMES BURROUGHS
4300 ROCK QUARRY R4
COLUMBIA, MO. 65201

KENT BURROUGHS
816 RINGO ST.
MEXICO, MO. 65265

MINNIE E. BURROUGHS
410 WOODLAWN ST.
MEXICO, MO. 65265

DONALD W. BURROUGHS
R.R. 5
LEBANON, MO. 65536

ROGER BURROUGHS
R.R. 2
WAYNESVILLE, MO. 65583

MARY E. BURROUGHS
816 COLLEGE ST. E.
BOLIVAR, MO. 65613

NORMA BURROUGHS
108 JAY E.
OZARK, MO. 65721

M. J. BURROUGHS
LEBO SR.
WEST PLAINS, MO. 65775

ROSA L. BURROUGHS
SANDERS CR SR.
WEST PLAINS, MO. 65775

ROBERT F. BURROUGHS
2747 EAST AV. N.
SPRINGFIELD, MO. 65803

JAMES E. BURROUGHS
1841 MARSA DR. E. APT. 9
SPRINGFIELD, MO. 65804

O. K. BURROUGHS
R1
GARNETT, KS. 66032

REX BURROUGHS
R.R. 2
LAWRENCE, KS. 66044

ROGER L. BURROUGHS
R.R. 1
LEAVENWORTH, KS. 66048

DON K. BURROUGHS
1113 ELM ST. S.
OTTAWA, KS. 66067

MARY C. BURROUGHS
BX. 201
PLEASANTON, KS. 66075

BILLY E. BURROUGHS
BX. 301
RICHMOND, KS. 66080

H. F. BURROUGHS
R1
WILLIAMSBURG, KS. 66095

STANTON C. BURROUGHS
3131 PUCKETT RD.
KANSAS CITY, KS. 66103

LLOYD BURROUGHS
3352 55TH ST. N.
KANSAS CITY, KS. 66104

TOM BURROUGHS
1901 75TH TER. N.
KANSAS CITY, KS. 66112

E. D. BURROUGHS
R.R. 3
GRANTVILLE, KS. 66429

MARCIAL BURROUGHS
GRANTVILLE, KS. 66429

TED L. BURROUGHS
948 GRANT AV. R1 23
JUNCTION CITY, KS. 66441

ERNEST L. BURROUGHS
317 1 HOOD DR.
FORT RILEY, KS. 66442

ALBERT L. BURROUGHS
3031 WAYNE DR.
MANHATTAN, KS. 66502

LEO BURROUGHS
R.R. 1
MERIDEN, KS. 66512

ALBERT C. BURROUGHS
1915 OAKLEY AV.
TOPEKA, KS. 66604

RALPH B. BURROUGHS, JR.
1220 RANDOLPH AV.
TOPEKA, KS. 66604

DON D. BURROUGHS
1811 HIGHLAND ST. S.
CHANUTE, KS. 66720

STEVE BURROUGHS
214 CHEROKEE ST. N.
GIRARD, KS. 66743

KERMIT A. BURROUGHS
631 PRAIRIE ST.
EMPORIA, KS. 66801

JOHN D. BURROUGHS
10 LAWRENCE ST. S. LOT 2
EMPORIA, KS. 66801

LLOYD K. BURROUGHS
R3
CONCORDIA, KS. 66901

CRAIG BURROUGHS
223 COPELAND ST. E.
KINGMAN, KS. 67068

MARY J. BURROUGHS
328 CENTRAL ST. E. APT.
WICHITA, KS. 67202

B. J. BURROUGHS
2545 BURNS ST. N.
WICHITA, KS. 67204

KEN T. BURROUGHS
8520 LAKELAND CIR.
WICHITA, KS. 67207

EDWARD G. BURROUGHS
100 RIDGE RD. S. APT. 30
WICHITA, KS. 67209

HAROLD E. BURROUGHS
153 YOUNG ST. S.
WICHITA, KS. 67209

ROBERT L. BURROUGHS
1233 CLARA ST. N.
WICHITA, KS. 67212

CHARLES A. BURROUGHS
2018 51ST ST. SOUTH E.
WICHITA, KS. 67216

GLADYS M. BURROUGHS
4480 MERIDIAN ST. S. LOT
WICHITA, KS. 67217

BYRNARD W. BURROUGHS
4557 SYCAMORE ST. S.
WICHITA, KS. 67217

KIRBY W. BURROUGHS
2230 FOUNTAIN ST. S.
WICHITA, KS. 67218

ADAM J. BURROUGHS
6538 HYDRAULIC ST. N.
WICHITA, KS. 67219

CLARENCE R. BURROUGHS
606 MULBERRY ST.
INDEPENDENCE, KS. 67301

ELDON J. BURROUGHS
813 MOUNDVIEW ST.
SALINA, KS. 67401

DON BURROUGHS
TESCOTT, KS. 67484

DALE E. BURROUGHS
206 7TH ST. W.
ELLINWOOD, KS. 67526

MERLE BURROUGHS
309 GOETHE ST. N.
ELLINWOOD, KS. 67526

EVERETT BURROUGHS
803 10TH ST. R3
GREAT BEND, KS. 67530

DAVID W. BURROUGHS
715 MORTON ST.
GREAT BEND, KS. 67530

ANTHONY W. BURROUGHS
3805 PINTO CIR.
ELKHORN, NE. 68022

BRYSON A. BURROUGHS
32 CEDAR
YUTAN, NE. 68073

CLAIR G. BURROUGHS
1408 46TH AV. S.
OMAHA, NE. 68106

ALICE BURROUGHS
2047 FOWLER ST.
OMAHA, NE. 68110

BRYSON A. BURROUGHS, JR.
417 78TH ST. S. APT. 7
OMAHA, NE. 68114

GILBERT E. BURROUGHS
1207 COTTONWOOD CIR.
OMAHA, NE. 68128

HAZEL I. BURROUGHS
4114 CHARLES ST.
OMAHA, NE. 68131

RICHARD J. BURROUGHS
6760 CHARLES ST.
OMAHA, NE. 68132

DAVID A. BURROUGHS
9412 OHIO ST.
OMAHA, NE. 68134

HENRY H. BURROUGHS
6901 28TH ST. S.
OMAHA, NE. 68147

EDGAR S. BURROUGHS
R1
BEATRICE, NE. 68310

R. G. BURROUGHS
320 16TH ST. S.
BEATRICE, NE. 68310

MAX A. BURROUGHS
520 ELDON DR.
LINCOLN, NE. 68510

JANE E. BURROUGHS
5230 40TH ST. S. APT. 10
LINCOLN, NE. 68516

FRED M. BURROUGHS
2613 PROSPECT AV. W.
NORFOLK, NE. 68701

FRED M. BURROUGHS
BX. 411
NORFOLK, NE. 68701

MAX A. BURROUGHS
8 SIOUX LN.
KEARNEY, NE. 68847

BERTHA M. BURROUGHS
1527 9TH ST. W.
HASTINGS, NE. 68901

WALTER BURROUGHS
1910 N. ST.
GERING, NE. 69341

WILLIAM BURROUGHS
61 DERBES DR.
GRETNA, LA. 70053

MILLARD G. BURROUGHS, JR.
1507 CLAY ST.
KENNER, LA. 70062

MICHAEL A. BURROUGHS
2918 NAPOLEON AV. APT. 4
NEW ORLEANS, LA. 70115

ANGNETTA P. BURROUGHS
4547 WERNER DR.
NEW ORLEANS, LA. 70126

WILBURN BURROUGHS
4574 WERNER DR.
NEW ORLEANS, LA. 70126

ROBERT G. BURROUGHS
703 MAIN ST.
MADISONVILLE, LA. 70447

WILLIAM A. BURROUGHS
BX. 569
MADISONVILLE, LA. 70447

E. W. BURROUGHS
170 OAKWOOD DR.
MANDEVILLE, LA. 70448

PATRICK C. BURROUGHS
R1 BX. 700
PONCHATOULA, LA. 70454

VERA BURROUGHS
R2 BX. 158
PONCHATOULA, LA. 70454

MICHAEL P. BURROUGHS
292 CHARBONNET RD.
PONCHATOULA, LA. 70454

ROBERT P. BURROUGHS
112 COLUMBIA ST. R6
SLIDELL, LA. 70458

CLEMENT D. BURROUGHS
108 HIGHLAND DR. APT. A.
LAFAYETTE, LA. 70506

BONNIE BURROUGHS
304 PILLETTE DR. APT. 2
LAFAYETTE, LA. 70508

LOUISE K. BURROUGHS
602 CHARITY ST.
ABBEVILLE, LA. 70510

OLIVER BURROUGHS
BX. 563
CAMERON, LA. 70631

NANNIE E. BURROUGHS
10830 CANDLETREE R2
BAKER, LA. 70714

WILLIE BURROUGHS
R3 BX. 587
DENHAM SPG. LA. 70726

THOMAS BURROUGHS
2908 VINCENT DR. R7
DENHAM SPG. LA. 70726

RICHARD F. BURROUGHS
1163 CHEVELLE DR.
BATON ROUGE, LA. 70806

HAROLD R. BURROUGHS
5856 CHANDLER DR.
BATON ROUGE, LA. 70808

LAWRENCE BURROUGHS
4646 DRUSILLA DR.
BATON ROUGE, LA. 70809

JOHN L. BURROUGHS
6926 MODESTO AV.
BATON ROUGE, LA. 70811

ADRON BURROUGHS
3235 WOODBROOK DR.
BATON ROUGE, LA. 70816

H. C. BURROUGHS
BX. 143
GLOSTER, LA. 71030

EUNICE K. BURROUGHS
BX. 32
HAUGHTON, LA. 71037

RICHARD W. BURROUGHS
R1 BX. 719
HAUGHTON, LA. 71037

S. E. BURROUGHS
BX. 611
RINGGOLD, LA. 71068

RALPH B. BURROUGHS
R1 BX. 154B
RODESSA, LA. 71069

RUTHIE BURROUGHS
305 MERRICK ST. E.
SHREVEPORT, LA. 71104

FRANK H. BURROUGHS
160 SOUTHFIELD RD.
SHREVEPORT, LA. 71105

DAVID BURROUGHS
1705 CAPT SHREVE DR.
SHREVEPORT, LA. 71105

WILLIAM R. BURROUGHS
168 PRESTON AV.
SHREVEPORT, LA. 71105

J. R. BURROUGHS
229 BRUCE ST.
SHREVEPORT, LA. 71105

ROY BURROUGHS
5910 1/2 TULSA AV.
SHREVEPORT, LA. 71106

H. A. BURROUGHS
5439 OLD MOORNGPT R5
SHREVEPORT, LA. 71107

ROY D. BURROUGHS
9438 PITCH PINE DR.
SHREVEPORT, LA. 71108

HELEN BURROUGHS
3221 RED BUD LN.
SHREVEPORT, LA. 71108

ALLEN G. BURROUGHS
207 LA PLAZA DR.
BOSSIER CITY, LA. 71111

A. G. BURROUGHS
R1 BOX 607
BOSSIER CITY, LA. 71112

J. A. BURROUGHS
8601 JACKSON SQ. BL
SHREVEPORT, LA. 71115

NEILS J. BURROUGHS
9445 MC ADOO ST.
SHREVEPORT, LA. 71118

JOSEPH C. BURROUGHS
3440 GORTON RD.
SHREVEPORT, LA. 71119

BARRY BURROUGHS
1013 SPENCER AV.
MONROE, LA. 71201

GEORGE J. BURROUGHS
706 EASON PL.
MONROE, LA. 71201

THOMAS M. BURROUGHS
105 NEVADA DR.
MONROE, LA. 71202

FRANK L. BURROUGHS, JR.
710 CHERRY ST.
BERNICE, LA. 71222

F. L. BURROUGHS
R1 BOX 137B
BERNICE, LA. 71222

KENNETH N. BURROUGHS
R2 BX. 108
DELHI, LA. 71232

JOHNNIE R. BURROUGHS
R2 BX. 239D
DELHI, LA. 71232

J. T. BURROUGHS
1403 LOUISA ST. S.
RAYVILLE, LA. 71269

ROY B. BURROUGHS
R1 BX. 60
RAYVILLE, LA. 71269

GLENDA BURROUGHS
BX. 1095
TALLULAH, LA. 71282

VERNON BURROUGHS
6466 BOUEF TRACE ST.
ALEXANDRIA, LA. 71301

LINDA BURROUGHS
BX. 833
JENA, LA. 71342

RALPH BURROUGHS
1010 ALLEN DR.
PINEVILLE, LA. 71360

RONALD L. BURROUGHS
400 MAGNOLIA ST.
NEWLLANO, LA. 71461

AARON BURROUGHS
R1 BX. 172AA
OAKDALE, LA. 71463

STEVEN BURROUGHS
26 WOODLAND DR.
PINE BLUFF, AR. 71602

WILLIAM L. BURROUGHS, JR.
1300 36TH AV. W.
PINE BLUFF, AR. 71603

H. L. BURROUGHS, 3D
4005 FIR ST. S.
PINE BLUFF, AR. 71603

BILL J. BURROUGHS
241 ALLISON ST. S.E.
CAMDEN, AR. 71701

KENNETH BURROUGHS
111 HALEY AV.
CAMDEN, AR. 71701

C. BURROUGHS
1403 SCOTIA ST. S.W.
CAMDEN, AR. 71701

BILLY BURROUGHS
1304 8TH ST. W.
EL DORADO, AR. 71730

LEON BURROUGHS
JUNCTN CY RD. R2
EL DORADO, AR. 71730

WAYNE BURROUGHS
R.R. 1
MANNING, AR. 71757

DAVID E. BURROUGHS
1204 BROADWAY ST.
SMACKOVER, AR. 71762

OMA BURROUGHS
719 PARK DR.
HOPE, AR. 71801

KENNETH BURROUGHS
508 CLARK ST.
H. SPG NAT PK, AR. 71901

RANDY BURROUGHS
704 BURCHWOOD BAY RD.
H. SPG NAT PK, AR. 71901

J. R. BURROUGHS
129 BROWN DR.
H. SPG NAT PK, AR. 71901

JESSIE C. BURROUGHS
201 OLIVER ST.
H. SPG NAT PK, AR. 71901

TONYA BURROUGHS
129 MANOR PL. APT. 5
H. SPG NAT PK, AR. 71901

CALVIN C. BURROUGHS
210 RIVERS DR.
H. SPG NAT PK, AR. 71901

BRUCE M. BURROUGHS
304 LANGSTON AV.
H. SPG NAT PK, AR. 71901

CHARLES J. BURROUGHS
1006 HOBSON ST.
H. SPG NAT PK, AR. 71901

HAROLD BURROUGHS
5 MARBLE ST.
H. SPG NAT PK, AR. 71901

ODIE R. BURROUGHS
120 STARLITE BAY DR.
H. SPG NAT PK, AR. 71901

ELSTER A. BURROUGHS
415 OAKLAHN BL
H. SPG NAT PK, AR. 71901

MINNIE T. BURROUGHS
900 SUMMER ST.
H. SPG NAT PK, AR. 71901

HERSHEL G. BURROUGHS
171 RAVINE ST.
H. SPG NAT PK, AR. 71901

BETTY BURROUGHS
208 HONEYCUTT ST.
H. SPG NAT PK, AR. 71901

ODIS BURROUGHS
214 DAFFODIL LN.
H. SPG NAT PK, AR. 71901

LOIS B. BURROUGHS
607 6TH ST.
H. SPG NAT PK, AR. 71901

COY BURROUGHS
103 SYCAMORE DR. R. 8
H. SPG NAT PK, AR. 71901

TOMMY BURROUGHS
201 BROWNING DR. R9
H. SPG NAT PK, AR. 71901

D. J. BURROUGHS
SHADY GROVE RD.
H. SPG NAT PK, AR. 71901

J. C. BURROUGHS
HIGHWAY 290 R. 1
H. SPG NAT PK, AR. 71901

JAMES R. BURROUGHS
98 LK HAMLTN SH R4
H. SPG NAT PK, AR. 71901

HAROLD BURROUGHS
WOODED HILLS R9
H. SPG NAT PK, AR. 71901

EZRA BURROUGHS
306 LONG BCH DR. R. 1
H. SPG NAT PK, AR. 71901

MAX BURROUGHS
249 22ND N.
ARKADELPHIA, AR. 71923

FRED BURROUGHS
BISMARCK, AR. 71929

O. C. BURROUGHS
R.R. 1
BISMARCK, AR. 71929

GARY BURROUGHS
R.R. 1
BISMARCK, AR. 71929

DAVID BURROUGHS
R.R. 1
BISMARCK, AR. 71929

WILLIAM BURROUGHS
DELIGHT, AR. 71940

CLIFTON BURROUGHS
DONALDSON, AR. 71941

BILL BURROUGHS
MOUNTAIN PINE, AR. 71956

LARRY BURROUGHS
101 NORTE
PEARCY, AR. 71964

LESTER J. BURROUGHS
BEAR RD.
ROYAL, AR. 71968

O. L. BURROUGHS
ALEXANDER, AR. 72002

FARRIS BURROUGHS
HIGHWAY 64 SR3
BEEBE, AR. 72012

M. L. BURROUGHS
1019 CANDIS ST.
BENTON, AR. 72015

BURLIN BURROUGHS
204 ETHEL ST.
BRYANT, AR. 72022

ETTA BURROUGHS
R.R. 1
DAMASCUS, AR. 72039

RALPH BURROUGHS
R.R. 1
DAMASCUS, AR. 72039

J. E. BURROUGHS
R.R. 1
DAMASCUS, AR. 72039

W. H. BURROUGHS
R.R. 2
DAMASCUS, AR. 72039

O. T. BURROUGHS
R.R. 2
DAMASCUS, AR. 72039

GARY BURROUGHS
HONEYSUCKLE R.
HENSLEY, AR. 72065

RAY BURROUGHS
1625 GARLAND ST.
N LITTLE ROCK, AR. 72116

CARL D. BURROUGHS
R.R. 3
QUITMAN, AR. 72131

JAMES E. BURROUGHS
3319 7TH ST. W.
LITTLE ROCK, AR. 72205

SPENCER BURROUGHS
7201 KENTUCKY ST. APT. 3
LITTLE ROCK, AR. 72207

TOMMY L. BURROUGHS
323 DANNER AV. W.
WEST MEMPHIS, AR. 72301

ORREN BURROUGHS, 3D
561 BETHANY ST. R3
BLYTHEVILLE, AR. 72315

THOMAS BURROUGHS
TURRELL, AR. 72384

J. D. BURROUGHS
1205 ROYAL ST.
PARAGOULD, AR. 72450

BILL BURROUGHS
MOUNTAIN VIEW, AR. 72560

KERMIT BURROUGHS
R.R. 2
SILOAM SPG, AR. 72761

TERRY D. BURROUGHS
420 BEBEE ST.
JONES, OK. 73049

DOUGLAS BURROUGHS
916 EUFAULA ST. E.
NORMAN, OK. 73071

F. C. BURROUGHS
1045 27TH ST. S.W.
OKLAHOMA CITY, OK. 73109

GLENN A. BURROUGHS
3701 EDGEWATER DR.
OKLAHOMA CITY, OK. 73116

JIMMY BURROUGHS
2828 59TH ST. S.W. APT.
OKLAHOMA CITY, OK. 73119

SHELBY BURROUGHS
4611 NICKLAS ST. N. APT.
OKLAHOMA CITY, OK. 73132

DONALD G. BURROUGHS
6108 MC KINLEY AV. S.
OKLAHOMA CITY, OK. 73139

CLAUDE B. BURROUGHS
MANNSVILLE, OK. 73447

GEORGE BURROUGHS
R.R. 3
ALVA, OK. 73717

ROY E. BURROUGHS
4924 BIRCH ST. R6 S.
BROKEN ARROW, OK. 74012

DWIGHT BURROUGHS
7332 WHEELING AV. S. APT
TULSA, OK. 74136

JACK W. BURROUGHS
321 CYPRUS
COWETA, OK. 74429

PAULINE S. BURROUGHS
CADDO MILLS, TX. 75005

CARLTON BURROUGHS
4717 BUCKNELL DR.
GARLAND, TX. 75042

F. J. BURROUGHS
408 RIDGEVIEW DR.
RICHARDSON, TX. 75080

JANNIE M. BURROUGHS
503 J. AV.
DALLAS, TX. 75203

VIDA N. BURROUGHS
922 9TH ST. W. APT. 213
DALLAS, TX. 75208

STANLEY BURROUGHS
R.R. 2
DAMASCUS, AR. 72039

RICKY BURROUGHS
R.R. 2
DAMASCUS, AR. 72039

JAMES E. BURROUGHS
523 ORANGE ST. APT. 6
N LITTLE ROCK, AR. 72114

WALTER L. BURROUGHS
3901 MC CAIN PARK DR.
N LITTLE ROCK, AR. 72116

FISHER F. BURROUGHS
1418 14TH ST. W.
LITTLE ROCK, AR. 72202

CHARLIE BURROUGHS
4221 36TH ST. E.
LITTLE ROCK, AR. 72206

WILLIAM L. BURROUGHS
1832 BEECHWOOD AV.
LITTLE ROCK, AR. 72207

WILLIAM BURROUGHS
2306 GOODWIN AV. APT. 23
WEST MEMPHIS, AR. 72301

H. R. BURROUGHS
CHERRY VALLEY, AR. 72324

ELMIRA BURROUGHS
GAINSVILLE VIA
LAFE, AR. 72436

LEONARD BURROUGHS, SR.
305 14TH ST. S.
PARAGOULD, AR. 72450

MONNIE BURROUGHS
MOUNTAIN VIEW, AR. 72560

ROGER BURROUGHS
415 CENTER AV. W.
SPRINGDALE, AR. 72764

ALVA E. BURROUGHS
JONES, OK. 73049

C. D. BURROUGHS
8812 80TH ST. R1 N.W.
YUKON, OK. 73099

ESTIE P. BURROUGHS
2705 MC KINLEY AV. S.
OKLAHOMA CITY, OK. 73109

O. W. BURROUGHS
6527 AVONDALE DR.
OKLAHOMA CITY, OK. 73116

BEA BURROUGHS
2212 CHURCHILL WY.
OKLAHOMA CITY, OK. 73120

DEBBY BURROUGHS
6462 WILSHIRE BL N.W.
OKLAHOMA CITY, OK. 73132

LEWIS E. BURROUGHS
7905 HILLCREST DR. S.
OKLAHOMA CITY, OK. 73159

EARL T. BURROUGHS
614 JEFFERSON AV. S.W.
LAWTON, OK. 73501

M. BURROUGHS
423 PAWNEE
GARBER, OK. 73738

ALLEN P. BURROUGHS
3913 56TH ST. W.
TULSA, OK. 74107

MICHAEL BURROUGHS
CENTRALIA, OK. 74336

DOYLE BURROUGHS
FORT GIBSON O.
FORT GIBSON, OK. 74434

GRADY J. BURROUGHS
1916 B. AV.
DENISON, TX. 75020

DOUGLAS BURROUGHS
4561 CHAHA RD. APT. 190
GARLAND, TX. 75043

WAYNE BURROUGHS
512 CENTER ST. W.
SHERMAN, TX. 75090

MAUDE BURROUGHS
3904 WINDSOR AV.
DALLAS, TX. 75205

ROY M. BURROUGHS
4922 STANFORD ST.
DALLAS, TX. 75209

MEARL BURROUGHS
R.R. 1
DAMASCUS, AR. 72039

BUDDY BURROUGHS
DE VALLS BLF, AR. 72041

MAURICE F. BURROUGHS
902 KELLOGG RD.
N LITTLE ROCK, AR. 72116

LLOYD BURROUGHS
3700 CHANDLER ST.
N LITTLE ROCK, AR. 72118

SPENCER BURROUGHS
1100 FAIR PARK BL APT. 4
LITTLE ROCK, AR. 72204

CLAUDE BURROUGHS
1607 SCOTT ST. S. APT. C
LITTLE ROCK, AR. 72206

C. R. BURROUGHS
9715 WOODFORD DR.
LITTLE ROCK, AR. 72209

JIMMIE D. BURROUGHS
1702 BARTON AV. E.
WEST MEMPHIS, AR. 72301

FLORA M. BURROUGHS
HIWAY 75 N.
PARKIN, AR. 72373

ROY L. BURROUGHS
511 DIXIE N.
MANILA, AR. 72442

LEONARD B. BURROUGHS, JR.
307 14TH ST. S.
PARAGOULD, AR. 72450

JAMES BURROUGHS
SALADO, AR. 72575

RAY BURROUGHS
108 8TH ST. W.
RUSSELLVILLE, AR. 72801

T. M. BURROUGHS
2034 LONGVIEW DR. R1 W.
MUSTANG, OK. 73064

TOM L. BURROUGHS
1621 18TH ST. N.W.
OKLAHOMA CITY, OK. 73106

GERALD O. BURROUGHS
1328 92ND ST. N.W.
OKLAHOMA CITY, OK. 73114

BILLIE R. BURROUGHS
2324 34TH ST. S.W.
OKLAHOMA CITY, OK. 73119

TROY K. BURROUGHS
3500 FOREST PARK DR. N.
OKLAHOMA CITY, OK. 73121

STEVE BURROUGHS
8416 87TH ST. N.W.
OKLAHOMA CITY, OK. 73132

LOUIS BURROUGHS
2204 62ND ST. S.W.
OKLAHOMA CITY, OK. 73159

CHARLES E. BURROUGHS
7409 HUNTER RD. N.W.
LAWTON, OK. 73505

DENNIS BURROUGHS
411 PAWNEE
GARBER, OK. 73738

WILLIAM L. BURROUGHS
7112 ZION ST. E.
TULSA, OK. 74115

DARREL BURROUGHS
LANGLEY, OK. 74350

STEVE BURROUGHS
215 PLUM ST.
DURANT, OK. 74701

LAURA BURROUGHS
R4
DENISON, TX. 75020

ARVELLA BURROUGHS
228 THOMAS ST.
LEWISVILLE, TX. 75067

DAVID BURROUGHS
400 AVENUE C. R1
ENNIS, TX. 75119

GRADY W. BURROUGHS
5716 MARQUITA ST.
DALLAS, TX. 75206

C. M. BURROUGHS
2423 FT. WORTH AV. APT.
DALLAS, TX. 75211

W. E. BURROUGHS
DAMASCUS, AR. 72039

KEN BURROUGHS
R.R. 2
GREENBRIER, AR. 72058

WALTER L. BURROUGHS
801 MILLER RD.
N LITTLE ROCK, AR. 72116

JAMIE BURROUGHS
3305 SYCAMORE ST.
N LITTLE ROCK, AR. 72118

WOODROW W. BURROUGHS
3401 KATHRYN ST.
LITTLE ROCK, AR. 72204

COY BURROUGHS
ARCH ST. PKE. R4
LITTLE ROCK, AR. 72206

M. BURROUGHS
606 WEAVER DR.
WEST MEMPHIS, AR. 72301

CARL L. BURROUGHS
1802 CAPEHART HOUSNG
BLYTHEVILLE, AR. 72315

M. B. BURROUGHS
HWY 75 N.
PARKIN, AR. 72373

ROBE BURROUGHS
922 COURT ST. W.
PARAGOULD, AR. 72450

JOHN BURROUGHS
MOUNTAIN VIEW, AR. 72560

ELMER BURROUGHS
113 MC CULLOCH
PEA RIDGE, AR. 72751

VIRGINIA BURROUGHS
701 7TH ST. N.
FORT SMITH, AR. 72901

RICK BURROUGHS
1908 MELROSE DR.
NORMAN, OK. 73069

DONALD R. BURROUGHS
3804 OLIVER ST. N.W.
OKLAHOMA CITY, OK. 73107

GEORGE W. BURROUGHS
1113 79TH ST. N.W.
OKLAHOMA CITY, OK. 73114

JIMMY R. BURROUGHS
3317 51ST ST. S.W.
OKLAHOMA CITY, OK. 73119

CHARLES W. BURROUGHS
427 24TH ST. S.E.
OKLAHOMA CITY, OK. 73129

DAVE BURROUGHS
6312 WILSHIRE BL N.W.
OKLAHOMA CITY, OK. 73132

M. B. BURROUGHS
365 HIGHLAND PRK ST.
ARDMORE, OK. 73401

JESSE BURROUGHS
106 ELM ST. R1
ELK CITY, OK. 73644

CHARLES BURROUGHS
605 5TH ST. E.
HENNESSEY, OK. 73742

CHARLES F. BURROUGHS
7531 28TH ST. E.
TULSA, OK. 74129

PHILLIP E. BURROUGHS
901 9TH ST. N.
MIAMI, OK. 74354

CLEM BURROUGHS
PIKE RD. R1
HEAVENER, OK. 74937

EDWARD L. BURROUGHS
3122 PECAN LN.
GARLAND, TX. 75041

THOMAS H. BURROUGHS
628 NEWBERRY DR.
RICHARDSON, TX. 75080

R. BURROUGHS
12005 SEAGOVILLE RD.
MESQUITE, TX. 75180

TED BURROUGHS
5845 UNIVERSITY BL E. AP
DALLAS, TX. 75206

JAMES A. BURROUGHS
1234 TARPLEY ST.
DALLAS, TX. 75211

RAYMOND K. BURROUGHS
437 PALMER DR.
DALLAS, TX. 75211

CLENARTIS F. BURROUGHS
1308 AMOS ST.
DALLAS, TX. 75212

ROBERT BURROUGHS
6361 LANGE CIR.
DALLAS, TX. 75214

CHARLES O. BURROUGHS
6235 REIGER AV.
DALLAS, TX. 75214

FANNIE BURROUGHS
3505 CLEVELAND ST.
DALLAS, TX. 75215

CATHERINE BURROUGHS
2303 STONEMAN ST.
DALLAS, TX. 75215

ELBERT BURROUGHS
3031 HATCHER ST.
DALLAS, TX. 75215

PRINCE E. BURROUGHS
3216 LLEWELLYN ST. S.
DALLAS, TX. 75224

BIRL J. BURROUGHS
11107 DESDEMONA DR.
DALLAS, TX. 75228

BETTY BURROUGHS
11467 WOODMEADOW PKWY. A
DALLAS, TX. 75228

GLEN BURROUGHS
7167 BLACKWOOD ST.
DALLAS, TX. 75231

JAMES H. BURROUGHS
3112 SPRINGWOOD ST. APT.
DALLAS, TX. 75233

ROBERT J. BURROUGHS
2550 ENGLE ST.
DALLAS, TX. 75233

DAVID J. BURROUGHS
10123 CHESTERTON DR.
DALLAS, TX. 75238

GAIL BURROUGHS
9031 BOUNDBROOK ST.
DALLAS, TX. 75243

JOHNNIE BURROUGHS
4202 TEMPLETON ST.
GREENVILLE, TX. 75401

MARY S. BURROUGHS
1845 CLARKSVILLE ST.
PARIS, TX. 75460

GRADY BURROUGHS
R1
QUINLAN, TX. 75474

DOYLE E. BURROUGHS
700 ELM E.
WINNSBORO, TX. 75494

WILLIAM O. BURROUGHS
3701 CENTRAL ST.
TEXARKANA, AR. 75502

FORREST J. BURROUGHS, JR.
823 SYLVAN DR.
LONGVIEW, TX. 75602

JIMMY B. BURROUGHS
2804 AMBERWOOD ST.
LONGVIEW, TX. 75605

THERESA F. BURROUGHS
R1 BX. 113A
GLADEWATER, TX. 75647

W. M. BURROUGHS, JR.
910 BARBARA ST. E.
TYLER, TX. 75701

L. E. BURROUGHS
3631 NEW COPELAND RD.
TYLER, TX. 75701

J. C. BURROUGHS
1922 SPRING AV. N.
TYLER, TX. 75702

GENIA BURROUGHS
3631 NEW COPELAND R4
TYLER, TX. 75703

DOROTHY B. BURROUGHS
BX. 4246
TYLER, TX. 75712

JOHN R. BURROUGHS
R2
BIG SANDY, TX. 75755

RAYMON BURROUGHS
BX. 350
HAWKINS, TX. 75765

RAYMOND BURROUGHS
BX. 572
LINDALE, TX. 75771

SAM BURROUGHS
28 RAMBLING RD.
PALESTINE, TX. 75801

BOB BURROUGHS
1018 HILLTOP DR.
PALESTINE, TX. 75801

E. C. BURROUGHS
BX. 522
BUFFALO, TX. 75831

LOUISE BURROUGHS
BX. 126
CENTERVILLE, TX. 75833

G. S. BURROUGHS
R1 BX. 200A
JEWETT, TX. 75846

W. R. BURROUGHS
1412 SLEEPY HOLLW DR.
LUFKIN, TX. 75901

JON BURROUGHS
2216 PEARL ST. APT. A.
NACOGDOCHES, TX. 75961

E. M. BURROUGHS
BX. 356
WELLS, TX. 75976

M. L. BURROUGHS
BX. 37
WELLS, TX. 75976

A. M. BURROUGHS
BX. 452
WELLS, TX. 75976

SAM BURROUGHS
2228 JOEY LN.
ARLINGTON, TX. 76010

CLAUDE J. BURROUGHS
4602 WOODSTONE CT.
ARLINGTON, TX. 76016

JUDY A. BURROUGHS
282 WESTERN HLS HBR
GRANBURY, TX. 76048

FREDDIE BURROUGHS, JR.
1478 MORPHY ST. E.
FORT WORTH, TX. 76104

LINDA BURROUGHS
902 ARLINGTON ST. E.
FORT WORTH, TX. 76104

VAN C. BURROUGHS
3913 SANGUINET ST.
FORT WORTH, TX. 76107

VAN BURROUGHS
3825 ROSEDALE ST. W.
FORT WORTH, TX. 76107

LAWRENCE D. BURROUGHS
2905 CHENAULT ST.
FORT WORTH, TX. 76111

DAVID BURROUGHS
104 CHANDLER ST.
FORT WORTH, TX. 76111

JOHN W. BURROUGHS
2766 PRIMROSE ST.
FORT WORTH, TX. 76111

JOHN BURROUGHS
2525 BIRD ST.
FORT WORTH, TX. 76111

JACK E. BURROUGHS
2005 MILAM ST.
FORT WORTH, TX. 76112

SAM BURROUGHS
3076 LAS VEGAS TRL APT.
FORT WORTH, TX. 76116

D. D. BURROUGHS
3400 STALCUP RD.
FORT WORTH, TX. 76119

JOHN BURROUGHS
5313 SHACKELFORD ST.
FORT WORTH, TX. 76119

JOHN A. BURROUGHS
3733 LAWNDALE AV.
FORT WORTH, TX. 76133

PATRICIA A. BURROUGHS
6928 MARGARET ST.
FORT WORTH, TX. 76140

MICHAEL BURROUGHS
2138 AVENUE F.
WICHITA FALLS, TX. 76309

ROGER U. BURROUGHS
5101 INLET ST.
WICHITA FALLS, TX. 76310

RICKY G. BURROUGHS
807 MAIN ST. N.
ELECTRA, TX. 76360

BILLY H. BURROUGHS
404 HARRISON ST. E.
ELECTRA, TX. 76360

BRUCE G. BURROUGHS
310 COTTONWOOD DR.
COPPERAS COVE, TX. 76522

JOHN E. BURROUGHS
1304 W. S. YOUNG DR.
KILLEEN, TX. 76541

EDWIN BURROUGHS
1302 GRAY DR. N. APT. 16
KILLEEN, TX. 76541

ROBERT BURROUGHS
1304 YOUNG W. S. DR R5 N
KILLEEN, TX. 76541

FRANK BURROUGHS
1304 CAMERON ST. R2 E.
ROCKDALE, TX. 76567

B. B. BURROUGHS
124 BRENDA
HEWITT, TX. 76643

C. K. BURROUGHS
1011 HOPKINS ST. E.
MEXIA, TX. 76667

JAMES C. BURROUGHS
4617 ROBINWOOD DR.
WACO, TX. 76708

EDYTHE BURROUGHS
2515 AUSTIN AV.
BROWNWOOD, TX. 76801

GEORGE H. BURROUGHS
1200 15TH ST.
BROWNWOOD, TX. 76801

DOUGLAS BURROUGHS
R1
COLEMAN, TX. 76834

VAN H. BURROUGHS
2901 SUNSET DR. BLDG-27-
SAN ANGELO, TX. 76901

PHIL BURROUGHS
3805 HONEYSUCKLE LN.
SAN ANGELO, TX. 76901

VAN H. BURROUGHS
BX. 6896
SAN ANGELO, TX. 76903

FREDDIE BURROUGHS
1246 20TH ST. E.
SAN ANGELO, TX. 76903

JAMES BURROUGHS
3721 COBB ST.
HOUSTON, TX. 77004

JAMES L. BURROUGHS
5318 CHENEVERT ST.
HOUSTON, TX. 77004

JACK C. BURROUGHS
1414 CASTLE CT. APT. 5
HOUSTON, TX. 77006

JESSE B. BURROUGHS
7425 BIGWOOD ST.
HOUSTON, TX. 77016

B. H. BURROUGHS
10606 HIRSCH RD.
HOUSTON, TX. 77016

ROY C. BURROUGHS
1114 CHANTILLY LN.
HOUSTON, TX. 77018

DOROTHY BURROUGHS
878 SARAROSE ST.
HOUSTON, TX. 77018

VALERIE BURROUGHS
1831 LIBBEY DR.
HOUSTON, TX. 77018

GEORGE T. BURROUGHS
2208 HULDY ST.
HOUSTON, TX. 77019

HERMAN L. BURROUGHS
3925 CHARLESTON ST.
HOUSTON, TX. 77021

HERMAN L. BURROUGHS, JR.
3923 CHARLESTON ST.
HOUSTON, TX. 77021

MATTIE M. BURROUGHS
7002 TIERWESTER ST.
HOUSTON, TX. 77021

JAMES BURROUGHS
813 CAPERTON ST. APT. 13
HOUSTON, TX. 77022

CEBELL BURROUGHS
4412 HAYGOOD ST. APT. E.
HOUSTON, TX. 77022

T. S. BURROUGHS
3607 SONGWOOD ST.
HOUSTON, TX. 77023

RODERICK BURROUGHS
1801 HATWELL ST.
HOUSTON, TX. 77023

DONALD W. BURROUGHS
7617 CAROTHERS ST.
HOUSTON, TX. 77028

EVELYN BURROUGHS
BX. 23264
HOUSTON, TX. 77028

DONALD W. BURROUGHS
10430 NORVIC ST. !
HOUSTON, TX. 77029

BOBBYLENE L. BURROUGHS
1017 LYNDON ST. APT. I.
HOUSTON, TX. 77030

VIOLA L. BURROUGHS
5218 DOULTON DR.
HOUSTON, TX. 77033

H. D. BURROUGHS, SR.
418 CARBY ST. E.
HOUSTON, TX. 77037

DAVID BURROUGHS
7414 LUMBER JACK DR.
HOUSTON, TX. 77040

MIKE E. BURROUGHS
10726 WICKERSHAM LN.
HOUSTON, TX. 77042

GUY C. BURROUGHS
R5 BX. 490D
HOUSTON, TX. 77044

RICKEY C. BURROUGHS
R5 BX. 531A
HOUSTON, TX. 77044

NANCY K. BURROUGHS
12610 ENCHANTD PTH DR.
HOUSTON, TX. 77044

GALE BURROUGHS
8423 VERA LOU LN.
HOUSTON, TX. 77051

SHERMAN F. BURROUGHS
3110 BLOOMFIELD ST.
HOUSTON, TX. 77051

WILLIAM R. BURROUGHS
4877 RIDGE CRK DR. E.
HOUSTON, TX. 77053

E. G. BURROUGHS
1138 DANBURY RD.
HOUSTON, TX. 77055

WILLIAM T. BURROUGHS
6518 REMLAP AV.
HOUSTON, TX. 77055

MARILYN C. BURROUGHS
5856 SUGAR HILL DR.
HOUSTON, TX. 77057

MIKE A. BURROUGHS
279 CASA GRANDE DR.
HOUSTON, TX. 77060

JOHN E. BURROUGHS, JR.
7594 MORLEY ST.
HOUSTON, TX. 77061

J. W. BURROUGHS
11611 NEFF ST.
HOUSTON, TX. 77072

TERRY L. BURROUGHS
11539 BELLSPRING DR.
HOUSTON, TX. 77072

HOWARD D. BURROUGHS, JR.
22122 KENCHESTER DR.
HOUSTON, TX. 77073

RALPH P. BURROUGHS
222 TREASURE DR.
HOUSTON, TX. 77076

EVELYN BURROUGHS
9026 LEY RD.
HOUSTON, TX. 77078

GEORGE BURROUGHS
7353 KINGSWAY DR. APT. 3
HOUSTON, TX. 77087

BRUCE W. BURROUGHS
10530 SAGEBURROW ST.
HOUSTON, TX. 77089

BRUCE BURROUGHS
17914 WILD OAK DR.
HOUSTON, TX. 77090

BILLY R. BURROUGHS
2815 HURLINGHAM ST.
HOUSTON, TX. 77093

ESTER M. BURROUGHS
1831 HARTWICK RD.
HOUSTON, TX. 77093

HOYT BURROUGHS
2215 PARKER RD.
HOUSTON, TX. 77093

BILLY B. BURROUGHS
5322 RUTHERGLEN ST.
HOUSTON, TX. 77096

JANA R. BURROUGHS
BX. 2090
CONROE, TX. 77301

GLENN BURROUGHS
R1 BX. 739
CONROE, TX. 77301

H. C. BURROUGHS
R3 BX. 158
CONROE, TX. 77301

W. R. BURROUGHS
1822 CLOVER SPGS DR.
HUMBLE, TX. 77339

JAMES T. BURROUGHS
R1 BX. 3761
NEW CANEY, TX. 77357

RICHARD BURROUGHS
MAGNOLIA BOND
NEW CANEY, TX. 77357

N. M. BURROUGHS
306 MAGNOLIA BEND
NEW CANEY, TX. 77357

BYRON BURROUGHS
17926 DEEP BROOK DR.
SPRING, TX. 77373

KAROLYN G. BURROUGHS
6307 LOUETTA RD.
SPRING, TX. 77373

J. R. BURROUGHS
3510 LOUETTA RD.
SPRING, TX. 77373

BRYAN BURROUGHS
10548 SPELL RD.
TOMBALL, TX. 77375

CHARLES BURROUGHS
R4 BX. 565
BRAZORIA, TX. 77422

R. L. BURROUGHS, JR.
R1 BOX 301A
EL CAMPO, TX. 77437

R. T. BURROUGHS
15314 OHARA
MISSOURI CITY, TX. 77459

RONALD L. BURROUGHS, JR.
R2 BX. 176G
RICHMOND, TX. 77469

GARY BURROUGHS
705 LOBIT ST. E.
BAYTOWN, TX. 77520

GARY BURROUGHS
3404 COACHLIGHT LN.
BAYTOWN, TX. 77521

DON R. BURROUGHS
209 SHELDON RD.
CHANNELVIEW, TX. 77530

VINCENT B. BURROUGHS
16807 A. AV.
CHANNELVIEW, TX. 77530

DON R. BURROUGHS
R2 BX. 439
DAYTON, TX. 77535

GENE A. BURROUGHS, SR.
7002 JONES AV.
GALVESTON, TX. 77551

I. L. BURROUGHS
515 SHORE DR. W.
KEMAH, TX. 77565

RAYMOND BURROUGHS
1036 OLEANDER ST.
LAKE JACKSON, TX. 77566

STEVE BURROUGHS
R1 BX. 305
PEARLAND, TX. 77581

WILLIAM R. BURROUGHS
BX. 129
PEARLAND, TX. 77581

MIKE BURROUGHS
BX. 185
BUNA, TX. 77612

H. C. BURROUGHS
BX. K337
BUNA, TX. 77612

ELSIE M. BURROUGHS
BX. 74
GILCHRIST, TX. 77617

D. R. BURROUGHS
3048 ASH ST.
GROVES, TX. 77619

COOPER E. BURROUGHS
1312 17TH ST.
NEDERLAND, TX. 77627

COYA W. BURROUGHS
2703 MEMPHIS ST.
NEDERLAND, TX. 77627

CLYDE BURROUGHS
5108 4TH ST. E.
PORT ARTHUR, TX. 77640

CLYDE BURROUGHS
5036 9TH ST. E.
PORT ARTHUR, TX. 77640

TERRY L. BURROUGHS
1505 PINE LN. DR.
PORT NECHES, TX. 77651

CLAUDE E. BURROUGHS
1975 LEIGH ST.
VIDOR, TX. 77662

O. D. BURROUGHS
145 RAILROAD ST. E.
VIDOR, TX. 77662

JAMES W. BURROUGHS
895 NORWOOD DR.
BEAUMONT, TX. 77706

MICHAEL A. BURROUGHS
105 HASWELL DR. S.
BRYAN, TX. 77801

JOHN D. BURROUGHS
BX. 2794
COLLEGE STA, TX. 77840

KATHYN A. BURROUGHS
BX. 114
FLYNN, TX. 77855

C. A. BURROUGHS
21110 STATE HWY SOUTH
VON ORMY, TX. 78073

FRANCIS M. BURROUGHS, JR.
BX. 6
GERONIMO, TX. 78115

REVA BURROUGHS
621 PINE ST. S.
SAN ANTONIO, TX. 78203

JOEL J. BURROUGHS
235 SAYERS AV. W.
SAN ANTONIO, TX. 78214

BOB R. BURROUGHS
9514 NONA KAY ST.
SAN ANTONIO, TX. 78217

JANIS L. BURROUGHS
8702 VILLAGE DR. APT. 12
SAN ANTONIO, TX. 78217

RICHARD H. BURROUGHS
5911 LAKE NACOMA ST.
SAN ANTONIO, TX. 78222

ROBERT H. BURROUGHS
4351 SHALLOW WATER
SAN ANTONIO, TX. 78233

DONALD R. BURROUGHS
6022 WINDING RDGE DR.
SAN ANTONIO, TX. 78239

RONALD E. BURROUGHS
8430 CREEK BEND DR.
SAN ANTONIO, TX. 78242

MICHAEL BURROUGHS
5530 KNOLL KREST ST.
SAN ANTONIO, TX. 78242

ELAINE S. BURROUGHS
7614 MEADOW GREEN ST.
SAN ANTONIO, TX. 78251

M. W. BURROUGHS
BX. 1203
SAN ANTONIO, TX. 78294

OTIS W. BURROUGHS
BX. 159
BANQUETE, TX. 78339

LOUIS L. BURROUGHS
BOX 808
INGLESIDE, TX. 78362

FRANCIS M. BURROUGHS
R1 BX. 33E
RIVIERA, TX. 78379

KATHLEEN C. BURROUGHS
621 MC CALL ST.
CORPUS CHRSTI, TX. 78404

ROSE M. BURROUGHS
MASON SR.
FREDERICKSBG, TX. 78624

KEN BURROUGHS
3208 CHURCHILL DR.
AUSTIN, TX. 78703

GREGORY N. BURROUGHS
7215 RUNNING ROPE ST.
AUSTIN, TX. 78731

MARTIN M. BURROUGHS
BX. 393
MC LEAN, TX. 79057

JESSIE L. BURROUGHS
3417 10TH ST. W.
AMARILLO, TX. 79106

PAUL W. BURROUGHS
5208 CORNELL ST.
AMARILLO, TX. 79109

WILLIAM I. BURROUGHS
2010 JACKSON ST. S.
AMARILLO, TX. 79109

GREG BURROUGHS
1516 43RD ST.
LUBBOCK, TX. 79412

LYNN BURROUGHS
3313 36TH ST.
LUBBOCK, TX. 79413

HOMER N. BURROUGHS
4515 40TH ST.
LUBBOCK, TX. 79414

ROBERT BURROUGHS
1845 LOCUST ST.
COLORADO CITY, TX. 79512

JOE BURROUGHS
BX. 48
NOVICE, TX. 79538

CHARLES R. BURROUGHS
1204 12TH PL. N.W.
ANDREWS, TX. 79714

WADE BURROUGHS
4044 VICKY ST.
BIG SPRING, TX. 79720

WALTER G. BURROUGHS, JR.
3139 EISENHOWER RD.
ODESSA, TX. 79762

JOE B. BURROUGHS
409 45TH ST. E.
ODESSA, TX. 79762

DON BURROUGHS
610 STANTON ST. N. APT.
EL PASO, TX. 79901

BEULAH R. BURROUGHS
4741 TETONS DR.
EL PASO, TX. 79904

JONNIE C. BURROUGHS
9213 MC FALL DR.
EL PASO, TX. 79925

AARON H. BURROUGHS
12852 MEXICO AV. E.
AURORA, CO. 80012

EARL BURROUGHS
982 POTOMAC WY. S.
AURORA, CO. 80012

NEIL W. BURROUGHS
15939 UNION AV. E.
AURORA, CO. 80015

ALFRIEDA BURROUGHS
7150 32ND AV.
WHEAT RIDGE, CO. 80033

DONALD E. BURROUGHS
546 LAKE AV. W.
LITTLETON, CO. 80120

KATHLEEN M. BURROUGHS
6978 KNOLLS WY. S.
LITTLETON, CO. 80122

CHARLES J. BURROUGHS
6628 ARBOR DR. W.
LITTLETON, CO. 80123

HAROLD W. BURROUGHS
4513 PONDS CIR. W.
LITTLETON, CO. 80123

M. E. BURROUGHS
R1 BX. 138
STRASBURG, CO. 80136

HENRIETTA BURROUGHS
809 30TH ST.
DENVER, CO. 80205

T. N. BURROUGHS
1015 JOSEPHINE ST. S.
DENVER, CO. 80209

JOHN BURROUGHS
4152 KING ST.
DENVER, CO. 80211

MARY E. BURROUGHS
2627 26TH AV. W.
DENVER, CO. 80211

RONALD G. BURROUGHS
1965 INGALLS ST.
DENVER, CO. 80214

FRITZIE BURROUGHS
1940 DUDLEY ST.
DENVER, CO. 80215

WILLIE E. BURROUGHS
1629 NIAGARA ST.
DENVER, CO. 80220

MARTHA E. BURROUGHS
769 GLENCOE ST.
DENVER, CO. 80220

DANIEL K. BURROUGHS
1620 EUDORA ST.
DENVER, CO. 80220

ROBERT J. BURROUGHS
1226 EATON ST. S.
DENVER, CO. 80226

JOHN R. BURROUGHS
911 PIERSON WY. S.
DENVER, CO. 80226

GARY BURROUGHS
2132 HARLAN ST. S.
DENVER, CO. 80227

RAYMOND BURROUGHS
4496 VRAIN ST. S.
DENVER, CO. 80236

HARRY BURROUGHS
2703 TENNYSON WY. S.
DENVER, CO. 80236

GREGORY N. BURROUGHS
314 PINE NEEDLE RD.
BOULDER, CO. 80302

KELLY BURROUGHS
340 GOLDCO CIR.
GOLDEN, CO. 80401

RONALD G. BURROUGHS
18856 62ND AV. W.
GOLDEN, CO. 80401

GARVIN L. BURROUGHS
R6 BX. 29
GOLDEN, CO. 80401

ALFREDA BURROUGHS
5400 MC INTYRE ST. R1
GOLDEN, CO. 80401

MICHAEL L. BURROUGHS
1745 COVE CT.
LONGMONT, CO. 80501

STEVEN L. BURROUGHS
228 22ND ST. S.E.
LOVELAND, CO. 80537

EARL R. BURROUGHS
BX. 617
LYONS, CO. 80540

LESLIE W. BURROUGHS
275 3RD AV. S.
BRIGHTON, CO. 80601

LEAH BURROUGHS
250 4TH AV. S.
BRIGHTON, CO. 80601

J. H. BURROUGHS
BX. 579
AULT, CO. 80610

JOHN H. BURROUGHS
BX. 459
AULT, CO. 80610

GAYLE L. BURROUGHS
1123 SIMPSON ST.
FORT MORGAN, CO. 80701

JUDITH M. BURROUGHS
R2 BX. 21
RUSH, CO. 80833

JAMES M. BURROUGHS
1223 CHELTON RD. N.
COLORADO SPG, CO. 80909

LACEL BURROUGHS
R1 BX. 10A
WETMORE, CO. 81253

GEORGE O. BURROUGHS
BX. 264
EL JEBEL, CO. 81628

JEAN K. BURROUGHS
BX. 3154
VAIL, CO. 81657

ANCIL R. BURROUGHS
2717 11TH ST. E.
CHEYENNE, WY. 82001

B. J. BURROUGHS
109 5 S.
BASIN, WY. 82410

THOMAS G. BURROUGHS
251 JEFFERSON ST.
BLACKFOOT, ID. 83221

ROBERT R. BURROUGHS
648 ADAMS ST. S.
BLACKFOOT, ID. 83221

ROBERT T. BURROUGHS
645 ADAMS ST. S.
BLACKFOOT, ID. 83221

DARLS BURROUGHS
R1 BX. 396
FIRTH, ID. 83236

JOHN H. BURROUGHS
R1 BX. 141B
FIRTH, ID. 83236

TOM L. BURROUGHS
2145 BALBOA ST.
IDAHO FALLS, ID. 83401

T. BURROUGHS
215 BALBOA DR.
IDAHO FALLS, ID. 83401

PAUL W. BURROUGHS
441 6TH ST. N.
PAYETTE, ID. 83661

A. H. BURROUGHS, 3D
BX. 1676
BOISE, ID. 83701

BLAIR B. BURROUGHS
920 WASHINGTON ST. W.
BOISE, ID. 83702

AMBROSE H. BURROUGHS, 3D
1617 CLAREMONT DR.
BOISE, ID. 83702

BERTHA K. BURROUGHS
3120 CRESCENT RIM DR. AP
BOISE, ID. 83704

TIMOTHY W. BURROUGHS
1693 CURTIS RD. S.
BOISE, ID. 83705

GRACE M. BURROUGHS
923 6TH ST. N.
COEUR D ALENE, ID. 83814

D. R. BURROUGHS
465 ADAMS ST. N.
MOSCOW, ID. 83843

PHANCES J. BURROUGHS
BX. 173
RATHDRUM, ID. 83858

ALFRED S. BURROUGHS
BX. 371
SANDPOINT, ID. 83864

CHARLES L. BURROUGHS
2113 400 WEST ST. N.
CLEARFIELD, UT. 84015

MICHL S. BURROUGHS
5547 3000 WEST ST. R1 S.
ROY, UT. 84067

LETTA V. BURROUGHS
364 DOWNINGTON AV.
SALT LAKE CY, UT. 84115

EUGENE BURROUGHS
N. A.
DELTA, UT. 84624

RUTH L. BURROUGHS
3056 32ND ST. N. APT. 35
PHOENIX, AZ. 85018

JOHN M. BURROUGHS
7535 22ND PL. N.
PHOENIX, AZ. 85020

EUGENE L. BURROUGHS
7024 BARBADOS PL. N.
PHOENIX, AZ. 85021

JOHN R. BURROUGHS
3842 YUCCA ST. N.
PHOENIX, AZ. 85029

BEN F. BURROUGHS
5417 HIGHLAND AV. H.
PHOENIX, AZ. 85031

DONALD BURROUGHS
2622 65TH AV. N.
PHOENIX, AZ. 85035

JAMES BURROUGHS
3120 87TH AV. N.
PHOENIX, AZ. 85037

JEFF BURROUGHS
1135 2ND ST. H.
MESA, AZ. 85201

STEPHEN D. BURROUGHS
2121 PAMPA AV. W.
MESA, AZ. 85202

LARRY E. BURROUGHS
603 DIANE CIR. N.
MESA, AZ. 85203

ELDEN E. BURROUGHS
1637 GREENWAY ST. E.
MESA, AZ. 85203

WILLIAM D. BURROUGHS
453 WILLIAMS ST. N. APT.
MESA, AZ. 85203

WILLIAM H. BURROUGHS
1406 CASA GRANDE AV. N.
CASA GRANDE, AZ. 85222

HELEN D. BURROUGHS
7830 PALM LN. E.
SCOTTSDALE, AZ. 85257

ROBERT E. BURROUGHS
1243 SUSAN LN.
TEMPE, AZ. 85281

RONALD D. BURROUGHS
1506 BROADMOOR DR.
TEMPE, AZ. 85282

MARY A. BURROUGHS
1727 GAYLON DR.
TEMPE, AZ. 85282

GEORGE W. BURROUGHS
4711 ECHO LN.
GLENDALE, AZ. 85302

JAMES C. BURROUGHS
10245 DESERT HILLS DR. W
SUN CITY, AZ. 85351

G. G. BURROUGHS
17635 LINDGREN AV. N.
SUN CITY, AZ. 85373

RICHARD N. BURROUGHS
910 CATALINA DR.
SIERRA VISTA, AZ. 85635

ROBERT C. BURROUGHS
5810 WILLIAMS DR. N.
TUCSON, AZ. 85704

WILBER G. BURROUGHS, JR.
4535 FAIRVIEW RD. N.
TUCSON, AZ. 85705

LEROY W. BURROUGHS
1135 PRINCE RD. W. LOT 2
TUCSON, AZ. 85705

ROBERT J. BURROUGHS
1110 FORDHAM DR. S.
TUCSON, AZ. 85710

MARTIN E. BURROUGHS
1709 WOODLAND AV. S.
TUCSON, AZ. 85711

L. R. BURROUGHS
1910 POPLAR DR.
LK HAVASU CY, AZ. 86403

ROBERT BURROUGHS
1195 BASELINE
RIVIERA, AZ. 86442

G. BURROUGHS
BX. 99
TIJERAS, N.M. 87059

MARVIN BURROUGHS
403 1/2 15TH ST. N.W.
ALBUQUERQUE, N.M. 87104

CLYDAS R. BURROUGHS
9964 MENAUL BL N.E.
ALBUQUERQUE, N.M. 87112

ROBERT B. BURROUGHS
100 JUNIPR HL PL. N.E.
ALBUQUERQUE, N.M. 87122

JACK D. BURROUGHS
1507 KILMER DR.
LAS CRUCES, N.M. 88001

GLEN BURROUGHS
1530 MARETH PL.
CLOVIS, N.M. 88101

JOHN H. BURROUGHS
1505 ABILENE S.
PORTALES, N.M. 88130

F. R. BURROUGHS
LA LUZ, N.M. 88337

ROLLIE BURROUGHS
303 KANSAS AV.
HENDERSON, NV. 89015

SCOTT BURROUGHS
2512 BROOKS AV. E.
N. LAS VEGAS, NV. 89030

S. R. BURROUGHS
3008 BASSLER ST.
N. LAS VEGAS, NV. 89030

STEVE E. BURROUGHS
1630 JAMES ST. E.
N. LAS VEGAS, NV. 89030

DONALD BURROUGHS
1603 MAYFAIR CIR.
LAS VEGAS, NV. 89101

LEONARD E. BURROUGHS
4870 MAR VISTA HY.
LAS VEGAS, NV. 89121

F. BURROUGHS
FERNLEY, NV. 89408

CHARLES H. BURROUGHS
5589 SIDEHILL DR.
SPARKS, NV. 89431

PRESTON BURROUGHS
852 YORK HY. E.
SPARKS, NV. 89431

KENT BURROUGHS
556 CAPITOL HILL AV.
RENO, NV. 89502

JUDY BURROUGHS
700 PECKHAM LN. E. APT.
RENO, NV. 89502

JOHN R. BURROUGHS
4280 NEIL RD.
RENO, NV. 89502

LINDEE BURROUGHS
825 PENNSYLVANIA DR.
RENO, NV. 89503

M. BURROUGHS
241 CALIENTE ST.
RENO, NV. 89509

JESSE BURROUGHS
1239 PATRICK AV.
RENO, NV. 89509

WAYNE BURROUGHS
13101 VIRGINIA ST. R9 S.
RENO, NV. 89511

WAYNE BURROUGHS
10310 OLD VIRGINA RD.
RENO, NV. 89511

H. W. BURROUGHS
10310 OLD VIRGINIA R7
RENO, NV. 89511

H. W. BURROUGHS
13101 VIRGINIA ST. R4 S.
RENO, NV. 89511

ELMER BURROUGHS
419 CORBETT ST.
CARSON CITY, NV. 89701

LEONARD BURROUGHS
540 HUMBOLDT S.
BATTLE MTN, NV. 89820

ANDRE L. BURROUGHS
247 82ND ST. E.
LOS ANGELES, CA. 90003

HENRY A. BURROUGHS
1107 42ND PL. E.
LOS ANGELES, CA. 90011

TIMOTHY J. BURROUGHS
5582 VILLAGE GRN ST.
LOS ANGELES, CA. 90016

PATSY J. BURROUGHS
1481 37TH ST. W.
LOS ANGELES, CA. 90018

DAVID S. BURROUGHS
3656 VAN NESS AV. S.
LOS ANGELES, CA. 90018

ALICE W. BURROUGHS
348 BLACKSHEAR AV.
LOS ANGELES, CA. 90022

HAROLD A. BURROUGHS
10577 KINNARD AV.
LOS ANGELES, CA. 90024

ROBERT S. BURROUGHS
2366 ROSCOMARE RD.
LOS ANGELES, CA. 90024

JANE C. BURROUGHS
551 MIDVALE AV.
LOS ANGELES, CA. 90024

WILLIAM BURROUGHS
1521 MURRAY CIR.
LOS ANGELES, CA. 90026

SARAH A. BURROUGHS
630 41ST PL. W.
LOS ANGELES, CA. 90037

HAROLD E. BURROUGHS
BX. 38387
LOS ANGELES, CA. 90038

PAULINE BURROUGHS
6563 VICTORIA AV. S.
LOS ANGELES, CA. 90043

JOHN J. BURROUGHS
831 62ND ST. H.
LOS ANGELES, CA. 90044

JAMES E. BURROUGHS
1122 71ST ST. H.
LOS ANGELES, CA. 90044

BILLY A. BURROUGHS
7250 MC COOL AV.
LOS ANGELES, CA. 90045

CAROL F. BURROUGHS
621 BARRINGTON AV. S. AP
LOS ANGELES, CA. 90049

RICHARD J. BURROUGHS
3280 INGLEWOOD BL
LOS ANGELES, CA. 90066

MIKE BURROUGHS
3625 ASHWOOD AV.
LOS ANGELES, CA. 90066

CHRISTINA C. BURROUGHS
159 ELM DR. S.
BEVERLY HILLS, CA. 90212

CLAUDE L. BURROUGHS
422 MAYO ST. S.
COMPTON, CA. 90221

NEAL H. BURROUGHS, JR.
12531 OLD RIVER RD.
DOWNEY, CA. 90242

WILLIE L. BURROUGHS
2919 141ST PL. W. APT. 2
GARDENA, CA. 90249

ASA BURROUGHS
4201 CORTLAND AV.
LYNWOOD, CA. 90262

DIANE M. BURROUGHS
33522 PACFC CST HY R2
MALIBU, CA. 90265

WILLIAM W. BURROUGHS
1601 PINE AV.
MANHATTAN BCH, CA. 90266

TOM E. BURROUGHS
863 TOULON DR.
PCFIC PALSADS, CA. 90272

NANCY J. BURROUGHS
2006 179TH ST. H.
TORRANCE, CA. 90504

ARTHUR T. BURROUGHS
22615 GAYCREST AV. S.
TORRANCE, CA. 90505

JOSEPH P. BURROUGHS
5421 JONESBORO HY.
BUENA PARK, CA. 90621

CHARLEY D. BURROUGHS
4360 CASA GRANDE CIR. AP
CYPRESS, CA. 90630

JACK A. BURROUGHS
11615 JAVA ST.
CYPRESS, CA. 90630

JOHN J. BURROUGHS
6129 EGLISE AV.
PICO RIVERA, CA. 90660

CHARLES W. BURROUGHS
12341 GLENCREEK RD.
ARTESIA, CA. 90701

SAM K. BURROUGHS
4950 CASTANA AV. APT. 13
LAKEWOOD, CA. 90712

JOHN M. BURROUGHS
6303 EDGEFIELD ST.
LAKEWOOD, CA. 90713

ROBERT H. BURROUGHS
635 5TH ST. W.
LONG BEACH, CA. 90802

CECIL BURROUGHS
2830 DE FOREST AV.
LONG BEACH, CA. 90806

ESTHER A. BURROUGHS
1990 PASADENA AV.
LONG BEACH, CA. 90806

RICHARD F. BURROUGHS
1720 SILVA ST. E.
LONG BEACH, CA. 90807

JACK A. BURROUGHS
1165 CARSON ST. E.
LONG BEACH, CA. 90807

PHILLIP H. BURROUGHS
3363 FANWOOD AV.
LONG BEACH, CA. 90808

RAY H. BURROUGHS
430 GRAND AV. N.
MONROVIA, CA. 91016

WILLIAM I. BURROUGHS
8237 CORA ST.
SUNLAND, CA. 91040

DORIS C. BURROUGHS
2620 SAN PASQUAL ST.
PASADENA, CA. 91107

DAVID S. BURROUGHS
1801 GLENWOOD RD.
GLENDALE, CA. 91201

DEWEY C. BURROUGHS
819 GLENVIEW RD.
GLENDALE, CA. 91202

FRANK S. BURROUGHS, JR.
241 SLEEPY HLW TER.
GLENDALE, CA. 91206

DEWEY C. BURROUGHS, JR.
1112 HOWARD ST. N.
GLENDALE, CA. 91207

FRANK S. BURROUGHS
1234 ETHEL ST.
GLENDALE, CA. 91207

JOHN R. BURROUGHS
BX. 12
AGOURA, CA. 91301

THOMAS J. BURROUGHS
6023 LAKE NADINE PL.
AGOURA, CA. 91301

ROBERT L. BURROUGHS
30421 SANDTRAP DR.
AGOURA, CA. 91301

WILLIAM M. BURROUGHS
7735 JORDAN AV.
CANOGA PARK, CA. 91304

RODNEY K. BURROUGHS
18916 SYLVAN ST.
RESEDA, CA. 91335

WILLIAM L. BURROUGHS
1236 SAN FERNANDO RD.
SAN FERNANDO, CA. 91340

MARK F. BURROUGHS
28428 ALDER PEAK AV.
CANYON CNTRY, CA. 91351

JOHN E. BURROUGHS
11320 SATICOY ST.
SUN VALLEY, CA. 91352

RALPH H. BURROUGHS
23035 GARZOTA DR.
VALENCIA, CA. 91355

HULBERT BURROUGHS
BX. 277
TARZANA, CA. 91356

DANTON BURROUGHS
18341 TARZANA DR.
TARZANA, CA. 91356

ELAINE D. BURROUGHS
1422 CALLE COLINA
THOUSAND OAKS, CA. 91360

G. T. BURROUGHS
3916 FRESHWIND CIR.
THOUSAND OAKS, CA. 91361

CLARK K. BURROUGHS
5167 LLANO DR.
WOODLAND HLS, CA. 91364

JEAN L. BURROUGHS
5841 FULTON AV.
VAN NUYS, CA. 91401

WILLIAM D. BURROUGHS, 3D
14832 HART ST.
VAN NUYS, CA. 91405

RICHARD W. BURROUGHS
532 HAMPTON RD.
BURBANK, CA. 91504

EDWARD N. BURROUGHS
1041 SCREENLAND DR. N.
BURBANK, CA. 91505

JERRY L. BURROUGHS
448 FREDERIC ST. N.
BURBANK, CA. 91505

HENRY C. BURROUGHS
11441 KITTRIDGE ST.
N. HOLLYWOOD, CA. 91606

MICHAEL J. BURROUGHS
5305 1/2 VANTAGE AV.
N. HOLLYWOOD, CA. 91607

ISAAC P. BURROUGHS
8867 RANCHO RD.
CUCAMONGA, CA. 91701

KENNETH W. BURROUGHS
6710 AMBERWOOD DR.
CUCAMONGA, CA. 91701

JILL I. BURROUGHS
6399 ELENA ST.
CHINO, CA. 91710

ARTHUR L. BURROUGHS
2375 AVNIDA DEL VSTA
CORONA, CA. 91720

JOHN S. BURROUGHS
314 BELLBROOK ST. E.
COVINA, CA. 91722

GARY R. BURROUGHS
279 TUDOR ST. W.
COVINA, CA. 91722

RICHARD L. BURROUGHS
1421 ADAMS PARK DR. E.
COVINA, CA. 91724

MARGARET C. BURROUGHS
11412 CHERRYLEE DR.
EL MONTE, CA. 91732

RONALD M. BURROUGHS
3340 EDWARDS AV.
EL MONTE, CA. 91733

ELEANOR I. BURROUGHS
2650 SEAMAN AV.
EL MONTE, CA. 91733

ROBERT A. BURROUGHS
843 NORTHRIDGE AV. E.
GLENDORA, CA. 91740

SIGNID H. BURROUGHS
5101 LIVE OAK CYN RD.
LA VERNE, CA. 91750

ROLLA T. BURROUGHS
934 BONNIE BRAE CT. W.
ONTARIO, CA. 91762

THOMAS E. BURROUGHS
5640 ORCHARD ST.
MONTCLAIR, CA. 91763

JOHN H. BURROUGHS
1512 5TH ST. E. APT. 24
ONTARIO, CA. 91764

MARY N. BURROUGHS
932 CATARACT AV. N.
SAN DIMAS, CA. 91773

CLARENCE G. BURROUGHS
5508 DEL LOMA AV. N.
SAN GABRIEL, CA. 91776

THELSTAN H. BURROUGHS
1395 SAN ANTONIO AV. N.
UPLAND, CA. 91786

JOHN E. BURROUGHS
2653 ALTAMIRA DR.
WEST COVINA, CA. 91792

BEVERLY BURROUGHS
1071 WOODLAKE DR.
CARDIF BY SEA, CA. 92007

SANDRA K. BURROUGHS
931 GRAND AV.
CARLSBAD, CA. 92008

GEORGE W. BURROUGHS, JR.
3100 OCEAN ST. APT. D.
CARLSBAD, CA. 92008

ROGER L. BURROUGHS
132 MITSCHER ST.
CHULA VISTA, CA. 92010

MOLLY D. BURROUGHS
1646 VIA ELISA
EL CAJON, CA. 92021

EDWARD N. BURROUGHS
1507 SUNDIAL TER.
EL CAJON, CA. 92021

ROBERT W. BURROUGHS
955 HOWARD AV. APT. 100
ESCONDIDO, CA. 92025

JOHN M. BURROUGHS
4703 SN JCNTO TER. R3
FALLBROOK, CA. 92028

VERNA E. BURROUGHS
12103 ORANGE CREST CT. A
LAKESIDE, CA. 92040

ROBERT BURROUGHS
9108 CLEAR LAKE WY.
LAKESIDE, CA. 92040

WENDY C. BURROUGHS
6187 SEVERIN DR.
LA MESA, CA. 92041

DARLENE BURROUGHS
4529 NORMANDIE PL.
LA MESA, CA. 92041

NADINE C. BURROUGHS
4088 LAKE BL
OCEANSIDE, CA. 92054

CARROLL A. BURROUGHS
BX. 967
SAN MARCOS, CA. 92069

JOHN H. BURROUGHS
1445 LA LOMA DR.
SAN MARCOS, CA. 92069

HEDWIG M. BURROUGHS
1620 BAYVIEW HTS. DR. AP
SAN DIEGO, CA. 92105

PAULETTA M. BURROUGHS
3613 CHAMOUNE AV.
SAN DIEGO, CA. 92105

GEORGE F. BURROUGHS
1307 CAMINITO GABLDN APT
SAN DIEGO, CA. 92108

HAROLD O. BURROUGHS
2859 GRANDVIEW ST.
SAN DIEGO, CA. 92110

RICHARD BURROUGHS
1054 MARJORIE DR.
SAN DIEGO, CA. 92114

PAMELA M. BURROUGHS
4415 HAMILTON ST. APT. 2
SAN DIEGO, CA. 92116

DOUGLAS A. BURROUGHS
2522 CLAIREMONT DR. APT.
SAN DIEGO, CA. 92117

SHERMAN E. BURROUGHS
810 GLORIETTA BL
SAN DIEGO, CA. 92118

JEANETTE C. BURROUGHS
521 C. AV.
SAN DIEGO, CA. 92118

JOSEPH G. BURROUGHS
8171 EL BANQUERO CT.
SAN DIEGO, CA. 92119

ROBERT L. BURROUGHS
6405 LAKE KATHLEN AV.
SAN DIEGO, CA. 92119

FRANK E. BURROUGHS
9592 LARRABEE AV.
SAN DIEGO, CA. 92123

ALFRED B. BURROUGHS
4404 TERRENO CT.
SAN DIEGO, CA. 92124

HOWARD A. BURROUGHS
17329 GRANDEE PL.
SAN DIEGO, CA. 92128

WILLIAM BURROUGHS
43 022 BURR ST.
INDIO, CA. 92201

CLARENCE M. BURROUGHS
363 AVENIDA ANDORRA
CATHEDRAL CY, CA. 92234

S. J. BURROUGHS
18035 CORONADO
LA QUINTA, CA. 92253

STANLEY J. BURROUGHS
78035 CORONADOS CIR.
LA QUINTA, CA. 92253

LUELLA L. BURROUGHS
1080 INDIAN AV. N.
PALM SPRINGS, CA. 92262

MURLIN L. BURROUGHS
25107 HILLMER ST.
HEMET, CA. 92343

EUGENE W. BURROUGHS, JR.
26665 CHESTNUT DR.
HEMET, CA. 92343

TIMOTHY E. BURROUGHS
6265 SPRING MEADW LN.
HIGHLAND, CA. 92346

JOSEPH BURROUGHS
415 ACOMA ST.
NEEDLES, CA. 92363

LESLIE T. BURROUGHS
1765 SAPPHIRE ST.
PERRIS, CA. 92370

GLENN A. BURROUGHS
416 3RD ST. W.
RIALTO, CA. 92376

GLENN R. BURROUGHS
27581 GROSSE POINT DR.
SUN CITY, CA. 92381

DARLENE L. BURROUGHS
SPRING VLY HSR BX. 1277
VICTORVILLE, CA. 92392

D. L. BURROUGHS
SPRING VLY HSR
VICTORVILLE, CA. 92392

STEVEN R. BURROUGHS
2732 G. ST. N.
SN BERNARDINO, CA. 92405

DORIS Y. BURROUGHS
2667 2ND ST. W.
SN BERNARDINO, CA. 92410

JEANETTE E. BURROUGHS
6638 GERANIUM PL.
RIVERSIDE, CA. 92503

JOSEPH M. BURROUGHS
1740 PRINCE ALBRT DR.
RIVERSIDE, CA. 92507

PETER BURROUGHS
3120 SEAVIEW AV.
CRONA DEL MAR, CA. 92625

EDRIS L. BURROUGHS
2107 WESTMINSTER AV.
COSTA MESA, CA. 92627

ROBERT E. BURROUGHS
24872 ROLLINGWOOD RD.
EL TORO, CA. 92630

J. M. BURROUGHS
1519 ROYER AV. S.
FULLERTON, CA. 92633

CAROLE BURROUGHS
2910 PINEWOOD CT.
FULLERTON, CA. 92635

DAN W. BURROUGHS
12371 DELTA ST.
GARDEN GROVE, CA. 92640

KENNETH O. BURROUGHS
13291 SIEMON AV.
GARDEN GROVE, CA. 92643

DIANA L. BURROUGHS
9672 MADISON CIR.
GARDEN GROVE, CA. 92644

DIANA L. BURROUGHS
9432 DAKOTA AV.
GARDEN GROVE, CA. 92644

ROBERT L. BURROUGHS
20552 COHASSET LN.
HUNTINGTN BCH, CA. 92646

DEBORAH K. BURROUGHS
19132 HUNTINGTON AV. APT
HUNTINGTN BCH, CA. 92648

WALTER BURROUGHS
511 CLIFF DR.
NEWPORT BEACH, CA. 92663

VAN L. BURROUGHS
3539 LA QUINTA
SAN CLEMENTE, CA. 92672

VAN L. BURROUGHS
902 CAUE GOMERO
SAN CLEMENTE, CA. 92672

DICK H. BURROUGHS
23842 CASSANDRA BAY
LAGUNA BEACH, CA. 92677

LINDA R. BURROUGHS
BX. 2397
SN JUN CPSTRN, CA. 92690

RALPH W. BURROUGHS
2327 POINSETTIA ST.
SANTA ANA, CA. 92706

GILBERT W. BURROUGHS
1302 SYCAMORE ST. S.
SANTA ANA, CA. 92707

LAWRENCE W. BURROUGHS
4092 SALACIA DR.
SANTA ANA, CA. 92714

JESS W. BURROUGHS
1807 BROADWAY ST. W.
ANAHEIM, CA. 92804

ROY L. BURROUGHS
3224 STONYBROOK DR. W.
ANAHEIM, CA. 92804

PHIL I. BURROUGHS
61 LOYOLA AV.
VENTURA, CA. 93003

LESTER M. BURROUGHS
BX. 54
FILLMORE, CA. 93015

BONNIE J. BURROUGHS
474 ARNAZ AV. R3 LT N. S
OJAI, CA. 93023

BEN H. BURROUGHS
1925 H. ST. N. APT. 60
OXNARD, CA. 93030

GERALDINE A. BURROUGHS
4940 TULSA ST.
OXNARD, CA. 93030

STEVEN C. BURROUGHS
2269 ROCKDALE AV.
SIMI VALLEY, CA. 93063

JOHN R. BURROUGHS
2225 DAY CT.
SIMI VALLEY, CA. 93065

JANE R. BURROUGHS
1925 BATH ST.
SANTA BARBARA, CA. 93101

JESSICA H. BURROUGHS
2023 CHAPALA ST. APT. B.
SANTA BARBARA, CA. 93105

FREDDIE M. BURROUGHS
107 PRINCETON AV.
COALINGA, CA. 93210

JULIA D. BURROUGHS
15970 CITRUS AV.
IVANHOE, CA. 93235

ROGER BURROUGHS
767 TERRACE PARK DR.
TULARE, CA. 93274

COLLEEN A. BURROUGHS
525 DEMAREE RD. S. APT.
VISALIA, CA. 93277

S. BURROUGHS
32099 ROAD 122 R8 9
VISALIA, CA. 93277

JOHN F. BURROUGHS, JR.
33376 ROAD 140 R5
VISALIA, CA. 93277

GLENN R. BURROUGHS
1811 20TH ST.
BAKERSFIELD, CA. 93301

DONALD R. BURROUGHS
4620 QUARTER AV.
BAKERSFIELD, CA. 93309

WILLIAM C. BURROUGHS
805 BOYSEN AV. APT. 13
SN LUIS OBSPO, CA. 93401

ROBERT BURROUGHS
204 CALIFORNIA BL APT. 1
SN LUIS OBSPO, CA. 93401

EMZY BURROUGHS
214 PATRICIA DR.
SN LUIS OBSPO, CA. 93401

WILLIAM E. BURROUGHS
BX. 167
ATASCADERO, CA. 93422

GEORGE W. BURROUGHS
521 G. ST. S.
LOMPOC, CA. 93436

HUBERT H. BURROUGHS
1038 PEG ST.
RIDGECREST, CA. 93555

DIANE BURROUGHS
232 VALERIA ST. N. APT.
FRESNO, CA. 93701

JOHN F. BURROUGHS, JR.
3616 LAMONA AV. E.
FRESNO, CA. 93703

ROBERT BURROUGHS
1729 TEILMAN AV. N.
FRESNO, CA. 93705

JOHN BURROUGHS
1150 HERNDON AV. E. APT.
FRESNO, CA. 93710

KEVIN M. BURROUGHS
24820 TORRES AV.
CARMEL, CA. 93921

CLAUDE E. BURROUGHS
250 CARMEL AV.
MARINA, CA. 93933

HERBERT D. BURROUGHS
89 PARKROSE ST.
DALY CITY, CA. 94015

RICHARD P. BURROUGHS
431 WAVE AV.
HALF MOON BAY, CA. 94019

MARGARET E. BURROUGHS
1555 MIDDLEFIELD RD. W.
MOUNTAIN VIEW, CA. 94043

WILLIAM B. BURROUGHS
1686 HOLLY AV.
SAN BRUNO, CA. 94066

FRANKLIN E. BURROUGHS
430 LIQUID AMBAR HY.
SUNNYVALE, CA. 94086

CARLTON M. BURROUGHS
1193 BERNARDO AV.
SUNNYVALE, CA. 94087

LORRAINE BURROUGHS
1222 EGBERT AV.
SAN FRANCISCO, CA. 94124

G. C. BURROUGHS
559 TERESITA BL
SAN FRANCISCO, CA. 94127

EDWARD BURROUGHS
5337 DIAMOND HTS. BL APT
SAN FRANCISCO, CA. 94131

GEORGE H. BURROUGHS
201 SARGENT ST.
SAN FRANCISCO, CA. 94132

JAY D. BURROUGHS
383 VERNON ST.
SAN FRANCISCO, CA. 94132

LARRY S. BURROUGHS
870 GARLAND DR.
PALO ALTO, CA. 94303

BILLY B. BURROUGHS
2356 OAKWOOD DR.
PALO ALTO, CA. 94303

HOWARD A. BURROUGHS
749 NEVADA AV.
SAN MATEO, CA. 94402

FRANKLIN S. BURROUGHS
160 LA SERENA AV.
ALAMO, CA. 94507

RODNEY M. BURROUGHS
5550 PLAZA ERMITA
CONCORD, CA. 94521

ROBERT E. BURROUGHS
21 ST. JOAN CT.
DANVILLE, CA. 94526

BRUCE A. BURROUGHS
720 EL CAPITAN DR.
DANVILLE, CA. 94526

JOHN W. BURROUGHS
1663 ST. HELENA DR.
DANVILLE, CA. 94526

RANDALL M. BURROUGHS
34626 GREENSTONE CMN
FREMONT, CA. 94536

WILLIAM B. BURROUGHS
37536 GLENMOOR DR.
FREMONT, CA. 94536

BOBBY G. BURROUGHS
21812 WESTFIELD AV.
HAYWARD, CA. 94541

ERWIN S. BURROUGHS
24978 2ND ST.
HAYWARD, CA. 94541

BRUCE K. BURROUGHS
1647 SUNNY PL.
HAYWARD, CA. 94545

DAVID A. BURROUGHS
3187 ROHRER DR.
LAFAYETTE, CA. 94549

ROBERT B. BURROUGHS, JR.
3195 LUCAS CIR.
LAFAYETTE, CA. 94549

HERBERT E. BURROUGHS
1067 LAUREL DR.
LAFAYETTE, CA. 94549

ROBERT C. BURROUGHS
4605 TAHOE DR.
MARTINEZ, CA. 94553

ROBERT C. BURROUGHS
BX. 963
MARTINEZ, CA. 94553

STEPHEN BURROUGHS
2926 SOSCOL AV. APT. 27
NAPA, CA. 94558

ERNEST C. BURROUGHS
R2 BX. 477
OAKLEY, CA. 94561

BERTHA M. BURROUGHS
831 EL PUEBLO AV.
PITTSBURG, CA. 94565

WALTER C. BURROUGHS
153 MAUREEN CIR.
PITTSBURG, CA. 94565

DARYL F. BURROUGHS
1584 164TH AV. APT. 3
SAN LEANDRO, CA. 94578

ROBERT E. BURROUGHS
650 LA VISTA RD.
WALNUT CREEK, CA. 94598

DEBORA R. BURROUGHS
1808 90TH AV.
OAKLAND, CA. 94603

WILLIAM J. BURROUGHS
7022 LACEY AV.
OAKLAND, CA. 94605

BISHOP R. BURROUGHS
6606 WHITNEY ST.
OAKLAND, CA. 94609

HENRY BURROUGHS
5362 HILLEN DR.
OAKLAND, CA. 94619

THOMAS BURROUGHS
5254 BAYVIEW AV.
RICHMOND, CA. 94804

ALLEN I. BURROUGHS
769 HUMBOLDT ST. APT. A.
RICHMOND, CA. 94805

GEORGE F. BURROUGHS
3919 CLINTON AV.
RICHMOND, CA. 94805

J. D. BURROUGHS
30 BUCK POINT RD.
INVERNESS, CA. 94937

RANDALL J. BURROUGHS
1008 PALMETTO WY.
PETALUMA, CA. 94952

RICHARD S. BURROUGHS
920 ALDERWOOD CT.
PETALUMA, CA. 94952

ROGER M. BURROUGHS
523 B. ST.
PETALUMA, CA. 94952

DOROTHY M. BURROUGHS
907 CAPITOLA AV.
CAPITOLA, CA. 95010

O. S. BURROUGHS
BX. GP
LOS GATOS, CA. 95030

CARROL G. BURROUGHS
BX. 2428
SANTA CLARA, CA. 95051

PAMELA BURROUGHS
BX. 1121
SANTA CRUZ, CA. 95061

DEAN O. BURROUGHS
251 CAMINO AL MAR
WATSONVILLE, CA. 95076

AILIAN D. BURROUGHS
380 26TH ST. N. APT. 9
SAN JOSE, CA. 95116

ROBERT A. BURROUGHS
265 18TH ST. S.
SAN JOSE, CA. 95116

MARVETTE J. BURROUGHS
1450 REVERE AV.
SAN JOSE, CA. 95118

FREDERICK J. BURROUGHS, JR.
5926 FISHBURNE AV.
SAN JOSE, CA. 95123

LARRY D. BURROUGHS
2191 LITTLE ORCHARD
SAN JOSE, CA. 95125

ADELLE M. BURROUGHS
1691 MONTEMAR WY.
SAN JOSE, CA. 95125

LARRY BURROUGHS
1886 KIRKLAND AV.
SAN JOSE, CA. 95125

GARY E. BURROUGHS
1201 LANCELOT LN.
SAN JOSE, CA. 95127

CARLTON H. BURROUGHS
1433 SPRUANCE ST.
SAN JOSE, CA. 95128

MELVIN B. BURROUGHS
1636 RAMSTREE DR.
SAN JOSE, CA. 95131

BOBBY D. BURROUGHS
4625 COLUMBIA RVR CT.
SAN JOSE, CA. 95136

ELAINE BURROUGHS
443 GLENDORA AV. APT. 22
STOCKTON, CA. 95207

BENJAMIN R. BURROUGHS
6123 WILLIAMSBURG PL.
STOCKTON, CA. 95207

JOSEPH R. BURROUGHS
2236 SWAIN RD. W.
STOCKTON, CA. 95207

ROBERT W. BURROUGHS
4546 QUASCHNICK RD.
STOCKTON, CA. 95212

ROBERT W. BURROUGHS
2132 GATEWAY CIR.
LODI, CA. 95240

WARD N. BURROUGHS
22329 MONTE VISTA E.
DENAIR, CA. 95316

JAY W. BURROUGHS
1330 DENT ST.
ESCALON, CA. 95320

RACHEL R. BURROUGHS
BX. 313
ESCALON, CA. 95320

CRAIG R. BURROUGHS
732 ELM AV.
GUSTINE, CA. 95322

NORMA D. BURROUGHS
243 LOVELL HY.
MANTECA, CA. 95336

ADISON D. BURROUGHS, 3D
290 23RD ST. E.
MERCED, CA. 95340

DOUGLAS M. BURROUGHS
3633 GANADO WY.
MODESTO, CA. 95350

C. L. BURROUGHS
1116 FAUSTINA AV.
MODESTO, CA. 95351

JOE V. BURROUGHS
1604 SEATTLE ST.
MODESTO, CA. 95351

ALVEY C. BURROUGHS
1624 SAILFISH ST. R6
MODESTO, CA. 95355

WILLIAM D. BURROUGHS
1725 J. ST. W.
OAKDALE, CA. 95361

EUGENE BURROUGHS
433 2ND AV. S.
OAKDALE, CA. 95361

JAMES F. BURROUGHS
6725 ESTELLE AV.
RIVERBANK, CA. 95367

JOHN W. BURROUGHS
17874 LARK DR.
TWAIN HARTE, CA. 95383

JACK W. BURROUGHS
3507 DEER TRAIL RD.
SANTA ROSA, CA. 95404

DENNIS E. BURROUGHS
725 HILMA DR.
EUREKA, CA. 95501

ELEANOR BURROUGHS
2920 ALBEE ST.
EUREKA, CA. 95501

JEAN M. BURROUGHS
1412 B. ST.
EUREKA, CA. 95501

ROBERT C. BURROUGHS
68 12TH ST. E.
ARCATA, CA. 95521

ERVIN J. BURROUGHS
BX. 152
WILLOW CREEK, CA. 95573

STEVE BURROUGHS
7756 CLAYPOOL HY.
CITRUS HTS, CA. 95610

RUTH D. BURROUGHS
6631 GRAHAM CIR.
CITRUS HTS, CA. 95610

JAMES M. BURROUGHS
6117 MERLINDALE DR.
CITRUS HTS, CA. 95610

WILLIS F. BURROUGHS
6225 RUMFORD AV.
CITRUS HTS, CA. 95610

ERNEST BURROUGHS
R1 BX. 23A
CLARKSBURG, CA. 95612

RUTH M. BURROUGHS
660 D. ST. W.
DIXON, CA. 95620

ROBERT D. BURROUGHS
BOX 597
DIXON, CA. 95620

S. A. BURROUGHS
1100 BURRO WY.
PLACERVILLE, CA. 95667

HARRY J. BURROUGHS
10433 MILLS TOWER DR.
RNCH CORDOVA, CA. 95670

WILLIS F. BURROUGHS, JR.
3480 ARGONAUT AV.
ROCKLIN, CA. 95677

MICHAEL L. BURROUGHS
R2 BX. 1212T
SHINGLE SPG, CA. 95682

HAZEL BURROUGHS
2320 P. ST. APT. 304
SACRAMENTO, CA. 95816

LINDA L. BURROUGHS
2390 MARCONI AV.
SACRAMENTO, CA. 95821

JON BURROUGHS
1530 FULTON AV. APT. 128
SACRAMENTO, CA. 95825

CALVIN L. BURROUGHS
8932 ROSEWOOD DR.
SACRAMENTO, CA. 95826

LYNN R. BURROUGHS
9190 TUOLUMNE DR. APT. 3
SACRAMENTO, CA. 95826

GEOFFREY BURROUGHS
310 CRUISE WY.
SACRAMENTO, CA. 95831

B. M. BURROUGHS
5213 CALISTOGA WY.
SACRAMENTO, CA. 95841

WILLIAM E. BURROUGHS
233 JOHNSON AV.
MARYSVILLE, CA. 95901

RICHARD D. BURROUGHS
BX. 431
DOWNIEVILLE, CA. 95936

OSCAR N. BURROUGHS
R2 BX. 177A
ORLAND, CA. 95963

MARION R. BURROUGHS
6695 SHAY LN. R6
PARADISE, CA. 95969

EDDIE L. BURROUGHS
2295 ST. FRANCS WY. R4
YUBA CITY, CA. 95991

BOYD BURROUGHS
3276 ALEXANDER DR. APT.
REDDING, CA. 96001

LINDA L. BURROUGHS
2358 WALDON ST.
REDDING, CA. 96001

EARL BURROUGHS
8117 RIVERLAND DR.
REDDING, CA. 96001

D. E. BURROUGHS
BX. 1571
REDDING, CA. 96001

BOYD M. BURROUGHS
BOX 2581
REDDING, CA. 96001

DARRELL E. BURROUGHS
BX. 156
CENTRAL VLY, CA. 96019

CLYDE E. BURROUGHS
BX. 518
CHESTER, CA. 96020

PHILIP L. BURROUGHS
R1 BX. 248F
CORNING, CA. 96021

STUART E. BURROUGHS
R5 BX. 312
PAYNES CREEK, CA. 96075

RAYMOND H. BURROUGHS
4741 EKAHI WY. W.
EWA BEACH, HI. 96706

T. J. BURROUGHS
91740 POHAKUPUNA RD.
EWA BEACH, HI. 96706

THOMAS BURROUGHS
129 KALUAMOO ST.
KAILUA, HI. 96734

STANLEY BURROUGHS
888 AKIU PL.
KAILUA, HI. 96734

F. S. BURROUGHS
46105 OHALA ST.
KANEOHE, HI. 96744

LARRY BURROUGHS
760 KIHOI RD. S.
KIHEI, HI. 96753

MICHAEL BURROUGHS
R. 1
PAPAIKOU, HI. 96781

MICHAEL N. BURROUGHS
1334 7TH AV.
HONOLULU, HI. 96816

JOHN N. BURROUGHS
7026 KALANIANAOLE
HONOLULU, HI. 96825

CATHY A. BURROUGHS
FURGUESON RD. R1
BEAVERCREEK, OR. 97004

ROLAND R. BURROUGHS
685 MEADOW DR. S.W.
BEAVERTON, OR. 97005

JERRY M. BURROUGHS
5750 TARALYNN ST. S.W.
BEAVERTON, OR. 97005

GARY BURROUGHS
9025 PARKVIEW LP S.W.
BEAVERTON, OR. 97005

ROBERT B. BURROUGHS
5555 142ND AV. S.W.
BEAVERTON, OR. 97005

TERRY BURROUGHS
28660 CHURCH S.E.
BORING, OR. 97009

CHARLES W. BURROUGHS
110 MAPLE ST. R4 N.
CANBY, OR. 97013

MICHAEL H. BURROUGHS
R1 BOX 205
MOLALLA, OR. 97038

CHARLES W. BURROUGHS
2009 12TH ST.
OREGON CITY, OR. 97045

DEBRA R. BURROUGHS
542 EDWARDS DR. S.E.
DUNDEE, OR. 97115

RAY BURROUGHS
BX. 51
NEWBERG, OR. 97132

MATHEW C. BURROUGHS
BOX 5 RT. 3
NEWBERG, OR. 97132

RODNEY BURROUGHS
SR. BOX 1848B
TIMBER, OR. 97144

DUANE A. BURROUGHS
2743 RUTLAND TER. S.W.
PORTLAND, OR. 97201

JANICE R. BURROUGHS
4207 DIVISION ST. S.E.
PORTLAND, OR. 97206

DANIEL F. BURROUGHS
2615 35TH PL. N.E.
PORTLAND, OR. 97212

CHARLES D. BURROUGHS
1904 ELLIOT AV. S.E.
PORTLAND, OR. 97214

LYDIA W. BURROUGHS
1225 FREEMAN ST. S.W.
PORTLAND, OR. 97219

RODNEY BURROUGHS
1822 MOSS ST. S.W.
PORTLAND, OR. 97219

EVA M. BURROUGHS
12415 64TH AV. S.W.
PORTLAND, OR. 97219

CLARENCE M. BURROUGHS
15351 MC LOUGHLIN BL SE
PORTLAND, OR. 97222

JOSEPH A. BURROUGHS
12680 FOOTHILL DR. S.W.
PORTLAND, OR. 97225

EDWARD L. BURROUGHS
13625 STARK ST. S.E. APT
PORTLAND, OR. 97233

BILL BURROUGHS
3815 122ND AV. S.E. APT.
PORTLAND, OR. 97236

MARIE BURROUGHS
12115 FOSTER PL. S.E.
PORTLAND, OR. 97266

VIOLA G. BURROUGHS
9353 SUN CREST DR. S.E.
PORTLAND, OR. 97266

EDWARD E. BURROUGHS
9638 CRYSTAL VIEW DR. SE
PORTLAND, OR. 97266

DELLA M. BURROUGHS
575 WILLOW ST. N.E.
SALEM, OR. 97301

MARGARET E. BURROUGHS
555 18TH ST. N.E.
SALEM, OR. 97301

DEAN BURROUGHS
835 CHEMAWA RD. N.
SALEM, OR. 97303

ROBERT L. BURROUGHS
638 32ND AV. N.E.
ALBANY, OR. 97321

RICHARD D. BURROUGHS
470 ROSE ST. W.
LEBANON, OR. 97355

WILLIAM H. BURROUGHS
1805 CRESTVIEW PL. N.E.
NEWPORT, OR. 97365

CONNIE BURROUGHS
892 LOCUST ST. W.
STAYTON, OR. 97383

VAN C. BURROUGHS
9233 CASCADE HWY
SUBLIMITY, OR. 97385

E. L. BURROUGHS
R1 BX. 286
WILLAMINA, OR. 97396

JULIA R. BURROUGHS
755 LAWRENCE ST. S.
EUGENE, OR. 97401

ROBERT D. BURROUGHS
345 LASSEN ST.
EUGENE, OR. 97402

WILLIAM B. BURROUGHS
317 LIMERICK AV.
EUGENE, OR. 97404

RICHARD E. BURROUGHS
2210 JEFFERSON ST.
EUGENE, OR. 97405

L. E. BURROUGHS
28182 BRIGGS HILL RD.
EUGENE, OR. 97405

ELVIN G. BURROUGHS
BX. 660
BANDON, OR. 97411

LARRY A. BURROUGHS
R3 BX. 61
COOS BAY, OR. 97420

ALTA L. BURROUGHS
3510 2ND AV.
COOS BAY, OR. 97420

ED R. BURROUGHS
BX. 629
COOS BAY, OR. 97420

LINDA J. BURROUGHS
32028 EL CAMAS
CRESWELL, OR. 97426

DENNIS L. BURROUGHS
81650 LOST CREEK RD.
DEXTER, OR. 97431

RONALD E. BURROUGHS
39264 LOWELL JASPER R.
LOWELL, OR. 97452

FREDERICK H. BURROUGHS, JR.
1012 CENTENNIAL BL
SPRINGFIELD, OR. 97477

DONALD D. BURROUGHS
955 LONGRIDGE DR. R1
SPRINGFIELD, OR. 97477

ELVIN G. BURROUGHS
BX. 128
WINSTON, OR. 97496

WILLIAM H. BURROUGHS
SR. BX. 1014
WINSTON, OR. 97496

JUDY A. BURROUGHS
100 LINCOLN ST.
ASHLAND, OR. 97520

NANCY M. BURROUGHS
BX. 993
GRANTS PASS, OR. 97526

EVELYN M. BURROUGHS
WILLAM HWY SR.
GRANTS PASS, OR. 97526

ROYAL L. BURROUGHS
2325 HIGHLAND AV. APT. 4
GRANTS PASS, OR. 97526

BARBARA J. BURROUGHS
834 DOTY ST.
KLAMATH FALLS, OR. 97601

ROGER G. BURROUGHS
7746 REEDER RD.
KLAMATH FALLS, OR. 97601

ALMA H. BURROUGHS
BX. 192
CONDON, OR. 97823

PHILIP D. BURROUGHS
30200 26TH PL. S.  !
AUBURN, WA. 98003

WILLIAM D. BURROUGHS
3317 EVERGREEN PT RD.
BELLEVUE, WA. 98004

E. R. BURROUGHS
16240 14TH ST. N.E. APT.
BELLEVUE, WA. 98008

WILLIAM BURROUGHS
540 MAPLE ST.
EDMONDS, WA. 98020

B. J. BURROUGHS
12103 150TH ST. N.E.
KIRKLAND, WA. 98033

D. K. BURROUGHS
9421 112TH AV. N.E.
KIRKLAND, WA. 98033

WM. D. BURROUGHS
22520 218TH ST. S.E.
MAPLE VALLEY, WA. 98038

WM. D. BURROUGHS
3317 EVERGREEN PT
MEDINA, WA. 98039

RILEY A. BURROUGHS
3101 6TH ST. S.E.
RENTON, WA. 98055

CAROLA BURROUGHS
310 43RD ST. N.
SEATTLE, WA. 98103

JOHN BURROUGHS
2011 RAVENNA BL N.E.
SEATTLE, WA. 98105

ROBERT B. BURROUGHS, JR.
2735 46TH AV. S.
SEATTLE, WA. 98116

ROBERT L. BURROUGHS
3809 TRENTON ST. S.
SEATTLE, WA. 98118

J. W. BURROUGHS
1934 10TH AV. W.
SEATTLE, WA. 98119

HORACE F. BURROUGHS
2700 125TH ST. N.E. APT.
SEATTLE, WA. 98125

JAMES L. BURROUGHS
8115 31ST AV. S.W.
SEATTLE, WA. 98126

KENNETH BURROUGHS
4252 148TH ST. S.
SEATTLE, WA. 98168

JOHN D. BURROUGHS
10468 FOREST AV. S.
SEATTLE, WA. 98178

PAUL BURROUGHS
6059 FAZON RD. R3
BELLINGHAM, WA. 98225

WILLIAM R. BURROUGHS
1618 PETERSON RD.
BURLINGTON, WA. 98233

DEAN BURROUGHS
2114 THORNTON ST.
FERNDALE, WA. 98248

LONNIE L. BURROUGHS
1712 HOUSTON AV.
BREMERTON, WA. 98310

M. BURROUGHS
10236 KITSAP WY.
BREMERTON, WA. 98310

DWIGHT M. BURROUGHS
2300 10TH ST.
BREMERTON, WA. 98310

RUTH E. BURROUGHS
1248 7TH ST.
BREMERTON, WA. 98310

LLOYD E. BURROUGHS
241 TRACY ST.
BREMERTON, WA. 98310

JOHN BURROUGHS
3222 8TH ST. N.
TACOMA, WA. 98406

JOHN J. BURROUGHS
5314 119TH ST. S.W.
TACOMA, WA. 98499

MARK BURROUGHS
9521 16TH ST. N.E.
VANCOUVER, WA. 98661

WILLIAM J. BURROUGHS, SR.
163 LAHTI RD.
WOODLAND, WA. 98674

ROBERT W. BURROUGHS
2220 JEFFERSON ST. S.
SPOKANE, WA. 99203

DEAN BURROUGHS
1822 3RD AV. R3 E.
KENNEWICK, WA. 99336
ROBERT M. BURROUGHS
3204 OREGON DR.
3204 OREGON DR.
ANCHORAGE, AK. 99503

BRETT BURROUGHS
17356 HALLMAN RD. N.W.
POULSBO, WA. 98370

L. A. BURROUGHS
3320 THOMPSON AV. S.
TACOMA, WA. 98408

DON BURROUGHS
13313 REEDER RD. R4 S.W.
OLYMPIA, WA. 98502

MILTON M. BURROUGHS
8808 33RD ST. N.E.
VANCOUVER, WA. 98662

DAVID L. BURROUGHS
CHEWELAH, WA. 99109

TED W. BURROUGHS
13318 MILL RD. R5 N.
SPOKANE, WA. 99208

JAMES A. BURROUGHS
1304 SACRAMENTO BL
RICHLAND, WA. 99352
EDWARD E. BURROUGHS
GULKANA CIR.
GULKANA CIR.
EAGLE RIVER, AK. 99577

ERIC BURROUGHS
POULSBO, WA. 98370

CHARLES F. BURROUGHS
6810 WAPATO ST. S.
TACOMA, WA. 98409

MILO D. BURROUGHS
7702 288 S.
ROY, WA. 98580

JERRY W. BURROUGHS
2108 108TH ST. N.W.
VANCOUVER, WA. 98665

LEE E. BURROUGHS
201 7TH AV. E.
RITZVILLE, WA. 99169

RUSSELL M. BURROUGHS
12321 27TH AV. E.
SPOKANE, WA. 99216

JOHN B. BURROUGHS
1906 DELMONT ST.
WALLA WALLA, WA. 99362
W. L. BURROUGHS
PEEDE RD.        S
PEEDE RD.
FAIRBANKS, AK. 99705

ROBERT K. BURROUGHS
R.R. 5 BX. 5180
POULSBO, WA. 98370

LESLIE C. BURROUGHS
805 BROOKDALE RD. E.
TACOMA, WA. 98445

WAYNE O. BURROUGHS
6507 EVERGREEN HWY S.E.
VANCOUVER, WA. 98661

GEORGE W. BURROUGHS
909 OVERLOOK DR.
VANCOUVER, WA. 98665

JOHN T. BURROUGHS
118 7 E.
USK, WA. 99180

DEAN R. BURROUGHS
1707 19TH AV. N.
PASCO, WA. 99301

BILL BURROUGHS
413 4TH AV. N.
WALLA WALLA, WA. 99362

| STATE | COUNT | STATE | COUNT | STATE | COUNT |
|-------|-------|-------|-------|-------|-------|
| AL | 309 | ME | 17 | OR | 59 |
| AK | 3 | MD | 115 | PA | 83 |
| AZ | 28 | MA | 63 | RI | 14 |
| AR | 104 | MI | 140 | SC | 168 |
| CA | 306 | MN | 27 | SD | 7 |
| CO | 41 | MS | 61 | TN | 108 |
| CT | 32 | MO | 92 | TX | 219 |
| DE | 14 | NE | 19 | UT | 4 |
| FL | 267 | NV | 21 | VT | 31 |
| GA | 152 | MT | 8 | VA | 181 |
| HI | 9 | NH | 29 | WA | 53 |
| ID | 17 | NJ | 119 | WV | 31 |
| IL | 179 | NM | 8 | WI | 43 |
| IN | 111 | NY | 188 | WY | 2 |
| IA | 86 | NC | 237 | GU | |
| KS | 42 | ND | 2 | DC | 27 |
| KY | 23 | OH | 226 | PR | |
| LA | 58 | OK | 48 | CZ | |
| ?? | | | | | |

TOTAL BURROUGHS FAMILIES     4,231